C000043850

The Channel Tunnel

and its

High Speed Links

by
Nicholas Comfort

THE OAKWOOD PRESS

© Oakwood Press & Nicholas Comfort 2006

British Library Cataloguing in Publication Data
A Record for this book is available from the British Library
ISBN 0 85361 644 2

Typeset by Oakwood Graphics.
Repro by PKmediaworks, Cranborne, Dorset.
Printed by Cambrian Printers, Aberystwyth, Ceredigion.

For other books by Nicholas Comfort, visit www.nicholascomfort.com

The 1212 Paris-Waterloo International Eurostar passes Wandsworth Road station on 4th February, 1995, formed of class '373' half-sets, No. 3017 leading No. 3018. *Brian Morrison*

Title page: Nos. 3003 and 3004 have just arrived at Brussels-Midi with the 1023 from Waterloo on 25th Otober, 1994. *Brian Morrison*
Front cover: A Eurostar enters the French portal of the Channel Tunnel. *Bob Sweet*
Rear cover, centre: North Pole depot at night. *Eurostar*
Rear cover, bottom: Waterloo International at night, showing Nicholas Grimshaw's design to best advantage. *Eurostar*

Published by The Oakwood Press (Usk), P.O. Box 13, Usk, Mon., NP15 1YS.
E-mail: sales@oakwoodpress.co.uk
Website: www.oakwoodpress.co.uk

Contents

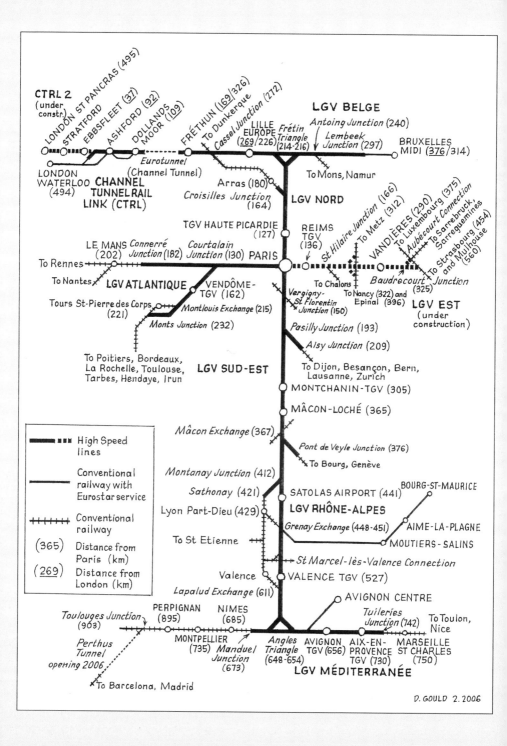

CTRL 2 (under constr.)

LONDON ST PANCRAS (495)
STRATFORD
EBBSFLEET (37)
ASHFORD (92)
DOLLANDS MOOR (109)
FRÉTHUN (169/326)
To Dunkerque
Cassel Junction (272)

LILLE EUROPE (269/226)
Frétin Triangle (214-216)

LGV BELGE
Antoing Junction (240)
Lembeek Junction (297)
BRUXELLES MIDI (376/314)

LONDON WATERLOO (494)
CHANNEL TUNNEL RAIL LINK (CTRL)
Eurotunnel (Channel Tunnel)

To Mons, Namur

Arras (180)
Croisilles Junction (164)
LGV NORD

REIMS TGV (136)
St Hilaire Junction (166)
To Metz (312)
VANDIÈRES (290)
To Luxembourg (375)
Aubécourt Connection
To Sarrebruck, Sarreguemines (454)
To Strasbourg and Mulhouse (560)

TGV HAUTE PICARDIE (127)

LE MANS (202)
Connerré Junction (182)
Courtalain Junction (130)
PARIS

To Rennes
To Nantes
LGV ATLANTIQUE
VENDÔME-TGV (162)
To Chalons
Vergigny-St Florentin Junction (150)
To Nancy (322) and Epinal (396)
Baudrecourt Junction (325)
LGV EST (under construction)

Tours St-Pierre des Corps (221)
Montlouis Exchange (215)
Monts Junction (232)

To Poitiers, Bordeaux, La Rochelle, Toulouse, Tarbes, Hendaye, Irun

LGV SUD-EST

Pasilly Junction (193)
Aisy Junction (209)
To Dijon, Besançon, Bern, Lausanne, Zurich
MONTCHANIN-TGV (305)

MÂCON-LOCHÉ (365)

Mâcon Exchange (367)
Pont de Veyle Junction (376)
To Bourg, Genève

Montanay Junction (412)
Sathonay (421)
SATOLAS AIRPORT (441)
BOURG-ST-MAURICE

Lyon Part-Dieu (429)
LGV RHÔNE-ALPES
Grenay Exchange (448-451)
AIME-LA-PLAGNE
MOUTIERS-SALINS

To St Etienne
St Marcel-lès-Valence Connection
Valence
VALENCE TGV (527)

Lapalud Exchange (611)
AVIGNON CENTRE

PERPIGNAN (895)
NIMES (685)
Tuileries Junction (742)
To Toulon, Nice

Toulouges Junction (903)
MONTPELLIER (735)
Manduel Junction (673)
Angles Triangle (648-654)
AVIGNON TGV (656)
AIX-EN-PROVENCE TGV (730)
MARSEILLE ST CHARLES (750)

Perthus Tunnel opening 2006
To Barcelona, Madrid
LGV MÉDITERRANÉE

Legend:
■■■ High Speed lines
— Conventional railway with Eurostar service
++++ Conventional railway
(365) Distance from Paris (km)
(269) Distance from London (km)

D. GOULD 2.2006

Foreword

The Channel Tunnel and the high-speed railways now connecting to it in Britain, France and Belgium between them represent the most formidable civil engineering achievement of the 20th and early 21st centuries. The tunnel has provided a long-overdue connection between Continental Europe and its principal offshore island, and has already proved its value, if not always quite in the way its promoters intended. It is now established as an essential means of conveying lorry traffic between Britain and the Continent, and has proved relatively successful in generating rail passenger traffic and rather disappointing in encouraging rail freight, which it was assumed would become more competitive than the rail ferries that preceded the tunnel. Promoters of a tunnel over the centuries had envisaged it having a geopolitical impact, but they could not have foreseen its role as a route to Britain for asylum-seekers and illegal immigrants as a great movement of populations began out of eastern Europe, the Middle East and Asia at the close of the second millennium. The story has turned out to be far more complex and diverse than when I first started researching it.

The concept of a Channel Tunnel, and its implications for Britain and its railways, has fascinated me for almost as long as I can remember, and I am fortunate that at various stages in my life I have been close to the project. At school I shared a desk with the son of Deryck Abel, one of the leading campaigners for a tunnel during the 1950s. As a Lobby correspondent with the *Daily Telegraph* I monitored the political manoeuvrings that led to the adoption of the Eurotunnel scheme, and the detailed Parliamentary examination of the Channel Tunnel Bill. As a co-author with Bronwen Jones - to whom special thanks are due - of the book *The Tunnel: The Channel and Beyond* I visited the tunnel construction sites just as work was beginning. Again wearing my journalist's hat, I followed closely the construction of the tunnel, being on the first press trip through it in March 1991 and on another occasion sharing a helicopter with Sir Alastair Morton, who despite his fearsome reputation could be one of the nicest of men. I was on the first Eurostar to Paris in October 1994 as a guest of European Passenger Services, and have in various guises - including a spell as a lobbyist for London & Continental Railways (LCR) - kept a close eye on the promotion of the Channel Tunnel Rail Link. As consultant on European presentation to the Department of Trade and Industry, I became a frequent - and satisfied - Eurostar traveller to Brussels. And as special adviser to the Secretary of State for Scotland, I was closely involved in efforts to end the disruption of tunnel freight traffic by asylum-seekers, because of its disastrous effect on Scotch whisky exports.

Despite my own fascination and involvement with the project, this book could not have been written without an immense amount of help over the years from many people who found time to explain things, show me round and answer highly complicated questions. If I have failed to understand the answers and errors have crept into this text, the fault is mine alone. I have also been fortunate that a number of dedicated fellow-enthusiasts have been prepared to lend me their much-prized records.

At the top of the list of credits must come everyone from Eurotunnel who has helped with this project, and the journalistic work that led up to it, in particular Sir Alastair Morton, Tony Guterbock (Lord Berkeley), John Weaver, Annabel Salmon, Alison Porter (chaperone of the 1991 first press transit), Simon Storer, Sarah Griffiths, Jane Bowles, Jeremy Close and especially Camille Newall. During and since my time with LCR, I have had particular help from Theo Steel - who kindly read an early draft of the manuscript and suggested important alterations - Jeremy Candfield, Bernard Gambrill, Peter Kendall, and from Eurostar Debra Aspin, Jim

Rowe, Jeremy d'Souza, Roger Harrison and Gareth Headon. Maureen Tomison lobbied me relentlessly for the Arup route of the Channel Tunnel Rail Link (CTRL), BR's Gil Howarth in the very early days explained the alternative routeings, Alistair Dick helped me understand the economics of the tunnel and the services using it, and Bob Smalley and Jeanette Owens were enthusiastic in promoting the Kings Cross terminal project to me; more recently Pascale Jessel has helped me greatly with the technicalities of the CTRL. Pen Kent gave me insights into the tunnel's financing, Adrian Shooter took time off from running Chiltern Railways to give me a masterclass on Automatic Train Protection (ATP), and Sue Evans and Graham Meiklejohn of English, Welsh & Scottish Railway (EWS) plied me with information - and a remarkable video - on the disruption caused at Fréthun by asylum-seekers. Andy Lickfold of EWS, Lyn Harvey of Railtrack and several of the Railtrack/Network Rail press office team ran me through how the tunnel has impacted on Britain's domestic rail system. And the section on the tunnel's construction railways could not have been written without the generous assistance of the Industrial Railway Society, Bob Darvill, Ian Bendall and Keith Clingan.

For my written sources, I have relied heavily on the *Railway Magazine*, *Modern Railways*, *RAIL*, *entrain*, *Today's Railways*, *Railway Gazette International*, *Le Train*, *Rail et Transports* and *La Vie du Rail*. Each does its job supremely well. Eurotunnel's annual reports have been essential reading, and the library staff of the *Daily Telegraph* have been superb in locating cuttings. For the saga of the Sangatte refugee centre, *Le Figaro's* coverage has been most informative. As for books, the following have proved invaluable:

The Channel Tunnel and Ferry, J.L. Harrington, Oakwood Press, 1949.
Chunnel, C.A. Pequinot, CR Books, 1965.
Channels and Tunnels, Nicholas Henderson, Weidenfeld, 1987.
The Tunnel: The Channel and Beyond, ed. Bronwen Jones, Ellis Horwood, 1988.
Industrial Railway Record 131, Industrial Railway Society, 1992.
Eurotunnel: The Illustrated Journey, Jeremy Wilson & Jerome Spick, Harper Collins, 1994.
Channel Tunnel Trains, Peter Semmens & Yves Machefert-Tassin, Eurotunnel, 1994.
The Channel Tunnel: Aspects of Health and Safety During Construction, Health and Safety Executive, 1996.
Eurostar, Simon Pielow, Ian Allan, 1997.
Railway Track Diagrams: 5. England South and London Underground, Quail Map Co., 2002.
'Le TGV Nord Europe', *La Vie du Rail*, 1993.
'Le Tunnel Sous La Manche', *La Vie du Rail*, 1994.
'De Paris a Londres a bord d'Eurostar', *La Vie du Rail*, 1995.
'Le TGV: La Genèse, les prototypes, les lignes' Olivier Constant, *Le Train*, 1998.

I have to thank Jane Kennedy of Oakwood Press for asking me to write this book in the first place, and for putting the Oakwood archives at my disposal. I could not have had a better publisher.

But this book can only be dedicated to Sir Alastair Morton, for without his leadership and determination there is every likelihood that the tunnel would not have been brought to fruition. For any man, that is quite a monument.

Chapter One

A Century of False Starts
. . . and eventual approval

Man's dream of connecting England and France at their closest points was born the moment a North Sea swollen by the melting of the Ice Age's great glaciers broke through to create the Channel some 10,000 years ago. Travellers had to take their chances across a stretch of water whose narrowness was no guarantee of a safe crossing; the sight of land fore and aft made the need for what became a voyage of at least 21 miles all the more frustrating. Yet such dreams had no point to them until modern technology made some man-made connection possible, and even once the means existed to avoid a sea crossing, politicians and financiers questioned whether such a link was desirable or viable. Some, indeed, still have to be convinced, for even now the tunnel has been open for a decade, it has proved a technical achievement rather than a bonanza for its promoters, and there have been unexpected disadvantages.

A link was first advocated by the reputedly insane Roman emperor Caligula. He proposed spanning the Channel by a bridge of ships, interspersed with rest houses and watering places, and even commissioned a two-mile trial pontoon jutting out from the Italian coast before other eccentricities took over. His aim was to secure Rome's hold on Britain - finally achieved by Claudius in 43 AD, two years after Caligula died - by assuring the legions a safe crossing.

The idea did not resurface until 1751, when Nicholas Desmaret, a French farmer, advanced the opinion that England and France had once been linked by a 'communication d'origine divine' as wolves then nearing extinction in Britain must have originated on the Continent. He proposed restoring the connection through a bridge, tunnel or causeway.

The first serious proposal dates from 1802 when, during a lull in hostilities between Britain and France, Albert Mathieu-Favier, a French mining engineer, suggested to Napoleon Bonaparte, then First Consul, that a tunnel would be a fitting symbol of peace. He proposed a bore for horse-drawn traffic, illuminated by candles and ventilated by flues reaching above the sea. It would be in two sections, punctuated by an 'island city' on the Varne bank to change horses and give passengers on the five-hour journey relief from the twin odours of horse manure and burning tallow. Napoleon was impressed enough to discuss the idea with the Whig statesman Charles James Fox, who declared: 'This is one of the great enterprises we can now undertake together'. Interest in a link heightened, with Mottray, an Englishman, proposing a submerged-tube tunnel, way beyond the capabilities of the age, and the Montgolfier brothers, a shade less impractically, a shuttle service of hot air balloons each carrying 3,000 passengers. But the Napoleonic wars resumed soon after, and the vision - save for the Emperor's dream of one-way traffic - went into abeyance for a quarter of a century until the dawn of the railway age gave it a new impetus and credibility.

From 1833 Aimé Thome de Gamond, a doctor, lawyer and civil engineer, proposed in turn a brick-lined submerged tube, a submerged arch that would take 30 years to build, four plans for bridges, two for causeways punctuated by shipping channels, and finally, in 1856, two submerged tubes spiralling upward to surface at the Varne, where he envisaged a star-shaped harbour. This was the first scheme formally considered by the French and British Governments; Napoleon III was enthusiastic and so was Prince Albert, mindful of Queen Victoria's seasickness, but Palmerston scorned the idea, declaring that France was quite close enough already. The French proposed spending

£20,000 on exploratory works for the tunnel, but de Gamond was by now suggesting a bridge and an attempt in 1858 to assassinate the Emperor with a bomb apparently made in Britain killed the project. De Gamond's research was meticulous: he surveyed the seabed in person, weighing himself down with bags of flints and using inflated pigs' bladders to regain the surface; on one dive to 30 m. he was attacked by conger eels. His preferred route began inland of Dover, running parallel to the coast before swerving south-east at Shakespeare Cliff on a direct course to Cap Gris Nez, halfway between Sangatte and Boulogne and the nearest point in France. His tunnel would continue inland for a further 10 km before surfacing to split into a line to Boulogne, for Paris, and one linking with the main Nord route to Calais 8 km inland, for traffic to Belgium and Germany.

By now a steady stream of engineers and pipe-dreamers were proposing schemes, though without political or financial support. The initial favourite was the submerged tube, advocated in 1842 by a Mr Pearse, in 1848 by a M. de la Haye, and in 1851 by Hector Horeau whose tube, costed at £87 million, involved glass panels in the roof to provide illumination, ventilation shafts topped by gothic turrets and trains propelled by a combination of gravity and pneumatic pressure. A Dr Lacomme went even further, proposing a submarine railway without a tunnel.

By the end of the 1860s the classic boat train routes between London and Dover and Paris and Calais were complete, and enthusiasm for some means of making the entire journey by rail intensified.

In 1867 de Gamond produced a scheme for parallel rail tunnels, such as would eventually be constructed, with the noted British engineers Brunlees and William Low who favoured a route between St Margaret's Bay and Sangatte. It won the support of the Emperor and the Grosvenor Committee of British and French scientists, but the Franco-Prussian War halted its momentum and by de Gamond's death in 1876 a rival scheme from Sir John Hawkshaw, with whom Low had once collaborated, was running ahead.

Hawkshaw's plan for a single-bore double-track steam railway tunnel was less technically sophisticated (or feasible) than that of de Gamond and Low, who favoured compressed air traction, but he had powerful backers. In 1872 they formed the Channel Tunnel Company, which two years later adopted Hawkshaw's scheme against bitter objections from Low.

On 2nd August, 1875 the British and French Parliaments passed Bills empowering the tunnel company and a parallel French consortium to construct pilot tunnels, and on 30th May, 1876 the two Governments agreed a protocol for construction of the tunnel and a 99-year franchise for its promoters. Trial boring by Hawkshaw near the London, Chatham and Dover Railway (LCDR) at St Margaret's Bay, began that year. By 1878 French engineers had completed test borings and begun digging at Sangatte, but the British company had run out of funds.

Low now secured the backing of Sir Edward Watkin, Chairman of the LCDR's arch-rival the South Eastern Railway and the Manchester, Sheffield and Lincolnshire (later the Great Central). Watkin envisaged connecting the latter system with the Continent to operate through trains between Manchester and Paris via Baker Street and the East London Line, and with the South Eastern's route from London to Dover running from Folkestone below the cliffs, he was eager for the tunnel to start there - so eager that in 1880 he excavated an 800 metre bore from Abbot's Cliff without Parliamentary authority. The following year the South Eastern obtained powers for Low to start a pilot tunnel beneath Shakespeare Cliff, in concert with the French company which was still hard at work. Before long nearly a mile had been dug at this latter site by the Submarine Continental Railway Company which had taken over the project using Col Frederick Beaumont's revolutionary compressed air boring machine, and Watkin entertained his City friends in the tunnel by electric light. The resulting publicity in the *Illustrated London News* and maybe lobbying by the LCDR alarmed the military that a completed tunnel might tempt the French general staff to plan an invasion, and with public opinion turning hostile vigorous lobbying by Watkin could not save the project.

In April 1882 the Board of Trade ordered a halt, claiming the strata beneath Britain's territorial waters (then extending three miles out) as Crown property. Watkin dug for a further three months until halted by a Court order, narrowly escaping prosecution for contempt when the Board's inspector, Col Yolland, reported that between his visits the bore had mysteriously lengthened by 20 metres. He had by then tunnelled out nearly 2,000 m, slightly further than the French who kept going until March 1883, when a Lords/Commons committee rejected any idea of a tunnel because it could not be easily blown up should a foreign power attempt to invade through it. Lord Wolseley, the Adjutant-General, told the committee that if a force of 6,000 men came through the tunnel to Dover, they could fan out and overcome every military objective in the town before an alarm could be given. In 1886 the determined Watkin's tunnelling subsidiary acquired the dormant Channel Tunnel Company of Hawkshaw, who by now had the added credential of completing the Severn Tunnel after the inundation of the original workings. However MPs were still cool about the Channel Tunnel project, and rejected a Bill to authorise it by 76 votes. Three further Bills in as many years were defeated, and in 1890 Watkin finally gave up. His Great Central main line would, nevertheless, be constructed to Continental loading gauge but would not survive to carry tunnel traffic.

The adverse political climate in Britain doomed a proposal in 1889 from two engineers from the Le Creusot steel company, Hersant and Schneider, for a sturdy metal bridge, and one three years later for a transporter running on rails 15 metres below the surface of the sea, carrying trains in batches of four. It would take the *Entente Cordiale* of 1904 to provide a serious stimulus: Albert Sartiaux, chief civil engineer of the Chemin de Fer du Nord and Sir Francis Fox, engineer for the dormant British tunnel company, proposed a scheme remarkably similar to that eventually constructed: twin tunnels for electric trains connected by cross-passages to assist ventilation, with a pilot construction tunnel which Sartiaux and Fox earmarked for drainage. Loops leaving both the Folkestone and Canterbury lines from London (now under combined South Eastern and Chatham management) as they approached Dover would curve west to merge at a terminal station, then loop southward in tunnel under the shore below Shakespeare Cliff. The French company's tunnel approach provided, as in its earlier scheme, for a loop of track on an offshore viaduct south of Sangatte so that if relations deteriorated, a naval bombardment could sever the link. The Liberal Prime Minister Sir Henry Campbell-Bannerman was intrigued, but strategic objections proved too strong even to a connection that could be broken and he was forced to concede that 'there would exist throughout the country a feeling of insecurity'. The Labour pioneer Keir Hardie dismissed the military opposition as based on 'neurotic foolishness', a fair comment as the French general staff reckoned it would take 15 days to get a force through the tunnel, and then only with 'full co-operation of the British authorities'. Intriguingly, the German Field Marshal Moltke had observed some years previously that the capacity of a tunnel to ferry troops and materiel from Britain would prove 'fatal to Germany in case of a conflict'. And in 1995, with the tunnel finally open, the Commons Defence Select Committee reported that in the event of a future war in

Europe, the Army would need to send troops and equipment through the tunnel as the British merchant fleet was now too small to be operationally useful. An early transit by armoured cars bound for Bosnia demonstrated the tunnel's potential, though the bar imposed by the Inter-Governmental Safety Commission on ammunition and explosives also showed its limitations.

In 1912 the Sartiaux/Fox scheme was revived, an all-party committee of nearly 90 MPs chaired by Sir Arthur Fell urging Campbell-Bannerman's successor Herbert Asquith to support it. By now the Army chief of staff, Sir John French, and the First Sea Lord Prince Louis of Battenberg could see no strategic argument against a tunnel, but when Asquith referred the matter to the Committee of Imperial Defence the old guard in the Admiralty and the War Office ensured a hostile report, issued just three weeks before the outbreak of war.

If anything, World War I demonstrated that Moltke had been right, and that a tunnel would have helped the Allies break the deadlock in the trenches of Flanders; Marshal Foch observed that had it been built, the carnage might have been over in half the time. After the war, with encouragement from Lloyd George, the British tunnel company commissioned from Whitaker of Leicester a new tunnel boring machine of a type used to undermine enemy trenches and capable of advancing at 1.3 metres an hour, and in 1921 trial borings began in the cliff near Folkestone. Sadly the machine did not live up to its advance billing, not least because if the cutting heads became embedded in the chalk the entire machine rotated at high speed; after advancing erratically for 140 metres it was left to rust until 1990, when it was dug out minus several of its components and put on show, first at Eurotunnel's Folkestone exhibition centre and later at the Science Museum in London.

When Labour first came to power in 1924, the tunnel promoters appealed to Ramsay MacDonald for support. He consulted the Committee of Imperial Defence, whose membership included four former Prime Ministers; they were hostile and MacDonald rejected the project, citing the poor state of the economy. Winston Churchill denounced MacDonald for lack of vision, and as unemployment soared on both sides of the Channel after the Great Crash of 1929, some form of link gained support as a job-creating public work. The tunnel companies revived the Sartiaux/Fox scheme in that year, minus the collapsible viaduct; the Committee of Imperial Defence remained opposed, but a Royal Commission set up by Stanley Baldwin reported that the tunnel 'could be built and would be of economic value'. Schemes considered along the way included a Brunel-style 7 ft gauge railway from London to Paris, a bridge carrying a four-lane road and two-track railway (costed at £75 million), a submerged tube and a cross-Channel canal with a causeway on either side. The plan finally put forward was for a 57 km rail tunnel, two-thirds of it under the sea, joined to the national network by a 5 km link from Sandling Junction and a 8 km connection from Sangatte to Marquise Rinxent, on the line between Calais and Boulogne. The Channel Tunnel Company, undertaking that no taxpayers' money would be needed for an economically benefical scheme, promoted a Bill with high hopes, only to see it defeated by seven votes in the Commons.

As plans for a tunnel became more sophisticated, the nature of the problems changed. The replacement of steam by electric traction made the challenge of ventilating the tunnel less of a headache, though the Victorians had been prepared to put up with a degree of smuts and smoke. But consulting engineers building on the work of Sartiaux and Fox now raised the concern that the chalky stratum might not continue right under the Channel. They thus suggested boring a 12 ft pilot tunnel, with a 7 ft drainage tunnel running parallel, along the entire distance to prove the stratum before starting work on the running tunnels.

In the meantime the railway companies were developing mass cross-Channel travel using the ferries they had been operating since the previous century. In 1929 the Southern and Nord railways jointly introduced the daily 'Golden Arrow' service between Victoria and the Gare du Nord via Dover and Calais, which would survive after wartime interruption until 1971 when the French Railways (SNCF) unilaterally abandoned its leg of the service; and in 1936 the Southern gave up waiting for a tunnel and introduced a train ferry between Dover and a special newly-constructed enclosed dock at Dunkerque. Train ferries operating from Dover had come close to fruition as early as 1855, but the first such route serving Britain had not begun until 1924, between Harwich and Zeebrugge using equipment left over from World War I when large quantities of rolling stock had to be transferred to the Continent by sea. The 'Night Ferry' through sleeper from Victoria to Paris and Brussels would run until 1980, with freight traffic continuing to use the ferries until the opening of the tunnel.

Just after the outbreak of war in 1939, the French tried to interest Neville Chamberlain in a tunnel on strategic grounds, but he cold-shouldered them. Once Germany invaded France in 1940, the tunnelling site at Sangatte was taken over by the Wehrmacht; British intelligence kept a special watch for excavations until it was pointed out that the spoil would be obvious if work resumed. Throughout the four-year German occupation British guns shelled the Sangatte site, and its moonscape of shell-holes punctuated by German blockhouses was only smoothed when the Fond Pignon sludge pool was spread over it during construction of the tunnel. In advance of D-Day the idea of the Allies invading France by tunnel was toyed with, the decisive factor against being the eight years it would take to complete.

The first post-war proposal came from the French engineer André Basdevant, who in 1947 advocated a single bore taking a four-lane highway and two railway tracks. This initial airing of an idea that would resurface in the 1980s prompted doubts over whether road and rail traffic could coexist, and whether petrol and diesel fumes could be dispelled from so long a tunnel. More significant in the long term was the formation in 1948 after a meeting between British and French legislators of a Channel Tunnel Study Group at Westminster; though lacking any official status, it did much to prepare the ground. As late as 1949 the Foreign Office warned that a tunnel would undermine 'that unquestioning sense of superiority over the peoples of the Continent which forms an essential element in British self-confidence'. Yet short of an actual Government commitment to a tunnel, the most important political advance came on 16th February, 1953, when Harold Macmillan, then Defence Minister, conceded that there was no longer an overriding strategic objection; future wars would be decided in the air.

The Channel Tunnel Study Group was relaunched in 1957 at the urging of the SNCF president Louis Armand to advance the project and technical studies were undertaken, but there was no response from Government. Then, in 1963, Macmillan as Prime Minister was spurned by President de Gaulle when he attempted to lead Britain into what was then known as the 'Common Market'. Support for a Channel Tunnel became a ready barometer of enthusiasm for 'Europe', and Euro-scepticism in Britain became as powerful a drag on the momentum for a link as did suspicion of *l'Albion perfide* in France.

Nevertheless in the mid-1960s a head of steam began to build, principally because of the mistaken belief that rocketing cross-Channel traffic, both passenger and freight, would soon overwhelm ferry capacity. In 1966 for the first time the British and French Prime Ministers, Harold Wilson and Georges Pompidou, declared their support for a link and the following year Barbara Castle, the Labour Transport Secretary, was envisaging a start on work in 1970 despite a new *froideur* in relations with France. When Edward Heath's Conservatives took office committed both to Europe and such grandiose projects as Concorde and the stillborn Maplin Airport in the Thames Estuary, the time seemed ripe for the Channel Tunnel at last.

In consultation with British Rail (BR), the Channel Tunnel Company and the French, the Heath Government swiftly refined a scheme for twin large-bore rail tunnels linking roll-on/roll-off terminals at Cheriton, on the landward side of Folkestone, and Fréthun, south of Calais: 51.5 km, of which 38 km would be beneath the sea. A White Paper in September 1973 put a £468 million price on the tunnel, with a further £120 million needed for a high-speed link to a London rail terminal at White City on the West London line. Hourly passenger trains from London to both Paris and Brussels were contemplated, with some starting back from Manchester or Birmingham and others running on from Brussels to Amsterdam or Cologne. Sleeper, Motorail (as far as Munich and Narbonne) and holiday charter services would also operate. Freight traffic would comprise fast Freightliner services, and trainloads of bulk commodities and fruit and vegetables; wagonload freight was barely mentioned.

On 15th November, 1973 the Governments signed an agreement initiating the first boring operations; this the French regarded as the point of no return. Preparations proceeded at a cracking pace, and on 5th February, 1974 BR published its plans for the high-speed link. Bypassing Ashford to the south, it followed the existing main line to Tonbridge, continuing due west on the Redhill route to a point west of Edenbridge where it forked north on new track to parallel (on a more easterly alignment) the Oxted line from Woldingham almost to Clapham Junction; two sections, including a six-mile stretch from South Croydon to Streatham Hill, would be in tunnel. From Clapham Junction trains would take the West London line to White City, with empty stock continuing to Old Oak Common and inter-regional traffic joining the West Coast Main Line at Willesden Junction or the Great Western at Acton.

The chosen route sparked fury in east Surrey, where the prospects of disruptive construction work and the noise of high-speed trains were considerable vote-losers. Moreover BR soon realised it had seriously underestimated the cost of the link, 40 km of which would be on an entirely new alignment, and jitters over this began to translate into renewed public opposition to the tunnel itself. Even now, Britain's defence chiefs were worried that the tunnel might be used by an invading Soviet army, and took steps to prevent this happening. The Chiefs of Staff commissioned a study which proposed building into the tunnel a nuclear device to be triggered if hostile forces appeared; the idea was dropped because the French would have to be told about the chamber where it would be lodged and, more seriously, because the MoD advised in February 1974 that the device would turn the tunnel into a giant mortar and devastate the area of Kent directly in line with it. Other means of blockage including conventional high explosive concealed in the roof of the tunnel and the installation of two valves to flood the centre section were also mooted, with the Chiefs of Staff stipulating that the tunnel could be restored to use in a matter of months, but the exercise was overtaken by events.

The furore over the route for the high speed link coincided with the snap election of February 1974 which brought to power a Labour Government sceptical about Europe, dubious about the economics of the tunnel and facing a financial crisis. That September, with a second election looming, Anthony Crosland, the Environment Secretary, shelved the high-speed link, whose cost had tripled in little over a year, just after the French Government had unveiled its own plans for a high-speed route from Paris to the tunnel and Brussels; meanwhile the Channel Tunnel Bill was proceeding through Parliament, but too slowly to meet the 1st January, 1975 deadline for ratifying the tunnel Treaty. On 25th January, 1975, Harold Wilson's Government unilaterally withdrew from the project, confirming every French prejudice about the British. Cost was the main concern, with Crosland sceptical that the tunnel could be constructed to budget at a time when UK inflation was nudging 20 per cent. He had in fact asked the British and French tunnel companies to agree a 12-month standstill while economies were considered, particularly on construction of the high-speed link; they refused, unaware that BR was about to present a far cheaper option largely involving the use of existing tracks, but with a tunnel from East Croydon to White City. Ironically Crosland, by then Foreign Secretary, confided to the author shortly before his death two years later: 'I wish I could have done something for the railways'. The dream seemed further from fruition than ever.

At the moment of cancellation the British tunnellers were ready to start on the pilot tunnel with the boring machine in place, and the Government authorised a 350 yard experimental bore before sealing the machine's head in concrete; it would prove hard to remove when work resumed 12 years later. Only a forlorn-looking marshalling area for supplies at the foot of Shakespeare Cliff, and a heap of concrete tunnel segments, gave visible evidence that work had so nearly begun in earnest.

*   *   *   *   *

In the atmosphere of despair and mistrust after the cancellation of the 1974 tunnel, it seemed inconceivable that the link could materialise within a generation. Yet BR and SNCF refused to be beaten, and each, mindful of the rickety state of public finances after the hyper-inflation of the mid-1970s and of opposition in England to any high-speed connection, quietly began devising the most economical and least controversial scheme possible.

In September 1978 the BR chairman Sir Peter Parker and his SNCF opposite number simultaneously proposed a slimmed-down project comprising a single-track rail tunnel 5.6 m in diameter, compared with the 7.6 m of today's running tunnels, and with no provision for carrying cars or HGVs. Immediately nicknamed 'The Mousehole', the project was worked up and presented to both Governments in February 1979. It provided for batches of trains in each direction transiting in alternating 'flights'; a pilot tunnel alongside would provide for service and escape. The 'Mousehole's' cost, £752 million, was greater than for the grander, cancelled, scheme because of intervening inflation and a more realistic assessment of the task.

This time, though, there would be no high-speed link. BR's Southern Region, which had previously argued that it could not accommodate international services on its saturated commuter lines, was now told bluntly by its parent Board that it would have to. Nor would there be a shuttle terminal on the sensitive site at Cheriton; this time only through passenger and freight trains would use the tunnel, hence the tighter loading gauge.

Despite the unpromising political and economic climate - and the discontinuance from the night of 31st October, 1980 of the 'Night Ferry' sleeper between Victoria and Paris and Brussels - the 'Mousehole' attracted interest from banks and contractors. The French Government, despite having got its fingers burned, remained committed in principle, but a change in Britain weeks after publication of the scheme raised few hopes; Margaret Thatcher, the incoming Conservative prime minister, disliked railways, was eager to curb public spending and was sceptical about Europe. Yet her Transport Minister, Norman Fowler, had the scheme examined in detail, and on 19th March, 1980 invited bids to build a tunnel; he declared himself 'enthusiastically in favour' should a link prove viable, but warned that it would have to be privately funded as the Government 'cannot contemplate finding expenditure on this scale from public funds'. The Commons Transport Select Commitee examined several options, among them the forerunners of both the Eurotunnel scheme and the rival EuroRoute comprising a bridge-tunnel-bridge link for both rail and road traffic. Its report favoured a single-track rail tunnel, but with a 6.85 m bore to accommodate vehicle-carrying shuttle trains; it costed this at £806 million.

Eight would-be promoters contacted Mr Fowler, among them an Anglo Channel Tunnel Group* chaired by Sir Raymond Pennock, chairman of the Confederation of British Industry, and backed by British Insulated Callender's Cables, the contractors Balfour Beatty, Edmund Nuttall and Taylor Woodrow and the merchant bankers Morgan Grenfell; this consortium, which did not include the still-extant British tunnel company, was the embryo of Eurotunnel. Feeling threatened, the ferry companies rushed out a report asserting that they could handle all conceivable traffic and that any link would prove a commercial disaster. Their concern heightened in September 1981 with the launch of EuroRoute, headed by the British Steel chairman Ian MacGregor, proposing a tunnel and bridge combination for road traffic with vehicles spiralling underground from artificial islands, and a separate rail tunnel. This ambitious project was priced even then at £3.8 billion.

The French felt that this time the British might be serious. That September their Transport Minister Charles Fiterman broached the subject with Mr Fowler, and a week later the newly-installed President Mitterrand and Mrs Thatcher committed themselves to agree a scheme, with work beginning by 1984. Why was a mystery: the political and financial risks were considerable, one wanted public finance and the other private, and each had in mind a different kind of link. Mrs Thatcher was attracted by a drive-through tunnel, reckoning shuttle trains no better than ferries, and her counterpart, the driving force behind so many grandiose schemes, by a bridge. But each saw a completed connection as a worthy monument to their period in office. M. Mitterrand was also keen to stimulate the depressed Pas de Calais region; Mrs Thatcher believed a cross-Channel link would benefit the whole of Britain. She did not consider it a threat to national sovereignty, but there were worried private questions from the Prince of Wales.

In April 1982 three large buckets of cold water were emptied over the project. Sir Alec Cairncross, who had advised on the previous scheme, reported to Mr Fowler that there was 'no overwhelming case for a fixed link' and that the ferries offered a better return. An Oxford University report commissioned by the ferry companies predicted that a tunnel would lose £144 million over the first 25 years, while a bridge might just break even. And the Anglo-French working party charged with deciding the form of the link rejected anything as limited as the 'Mousehole', but also concluded that doing nothing at all was an option. That option seemed set to prevail when the Cabinet discussed a paper on the tunnel project on the very day during the Falklands war that HMS *Sheffield* was sunk by a French-made Exocet missile.

Mr Fowler's replacement David Howell did announce in June that a group of British and French banks would conduct a further study, but with an election in sight the project seemed off the boil; indeed when lobbied by ferry operators in Dover during the 1983 campaign, Mrs Thatcher said as much. The truth was that would-be promoters and her Government were deadlocked over whether it should underwrite the project; in May 1984 another Transport Secretary, Nicholas Ridley, ruled out even a 'minimum guarantee' against political cancellation of a tunnel under construction which the banks saw as essential. With M. Fiterman wanting a decision within weeks, the outlook seemed bleak.

* Anglo was soon dropped from the group's title, it became known as the Channel Tunnel Group (CTG).

Yet behind the scenes momentum was building. The CTG, now with Sir Nicholas Henderson, the former UK ambassador to France, in the chair, reworked its sums and told Mr Ridley construction could be cut from six years to four and a half through new boring techniques and round-the-clock working, raising costs by 10 per cent but shortening the time before investors saw a dividend. Mr Ridley relented and on 29th November, 1984 Mrs Thatcher and M. Mitterrand reaffirmed their agreement, though the Prime Minister - who began highly cautious and came round to a very bullish position - warned that it would be a 'very, very long time' before a tunnel was built. For eight weeks British and French officials worked round the clock to prepare specifications for a link: it should be safe from terrorist attack, last for at least 120 years, have a minimum speed of 80 kph and be capable of evacuation within 90 minutes; the French later added a caveat over rabies. On 21st March, 1985 promoters were given five months to submit detailed schemes, for a decision three months later, and shortly afterward the two Governments issued a 64-page 'invitation to promoters'. On 2nd July that year twin consortia to advance the project were formed: Balfour Beatty Construction, Taylor Woodrow Construction, Costain UK, Tarmac Construction, George Wimpey International, National Westminster bank and Midland Bank in the UK and in France Bouygues, Dumez, the Société Auxiliaire d'Entreprises, the Société Générale d'Entreprises Sainrapt et Brice, Spie Batignolles, Banque Nationale de Paris, Crédit Lyonnais and the Banque Indosuez.

The prospect of a link actually being built revived the debate over the desirability of any connection at all. The antis in Parliament were more vocal despite their small numbers, with a minority in both main parties vociferously opposed. But the greatest hostility came from 'Flexilink', launched in April 1985 by Sealink British Ferries which had been acquired by the Sea Containers group headed by the mercurial American James Sherwood . . . later the operators of Great North Eastern Railway (GNER) and of debranded Eurostar trains. Flexilink united all ferry interests to argue that they could cope and that a tunnel would create misery all round. It went for the jugular, urging the Government to block all the schemes submitted, fighting the project in the courts, trying to sabotage the raising of capital and rallying opposition with a poster campaign depicting rats, juggernauts and garlic-breathing Frenchmen swarming from the tunnel. Within months, Flexilink turned a Gallup poll majority of 50-37 for a link into a 51-36 margin against.

With rival groups fine-tuning their bids and competing for political and financial support, Sherwood now threw a spanner in the works with a scheme of his own: Channel Expressway. At first this was to be a road tunnel with rails set in the floor, 'swept' of traffic every so often to allow trains through; within weeks he proposed separate road and rail tunnels. By the simple expedient of claiming to have influential support, Sherwood started to attract it and by the 31st October deadline he was a serious contender.

Nine schemes were submitted, including one from the Boothroyd Airship Company for a suspension bridge held in place by heavy-lift airships. This and four bridge, tunnel or barrage projects were ruled out as lacking credible financial backing, leaving four contenders: Channel Expressway's twin-bore tunnels (at this stage still taking both road and rail traffic); the Channel Tunnel Group's twin-bore rail tunnel; the combined 21 km tunnel and two bridges for road and rail proposed by EuroRoute, now headed by Sir Nigel Broackes of Trafalgar House; and Eurobridge, a suspension bridge with 4.5 km spans supporting a motorway enclosed in a tube, rated the outsider.

The Transport Select Committee endorsed the CTG's project on its chairman's casting vote, with the proviso that if the Government felt a road link was essential it should embrace EuroRoute. But Mr Ridley was tempted by Channel Expressway, and stood his ground with his French counterpart Jean Auroux, who was under domestic pressure to go for EuroRoute. The CTG's tunnel was hardly mentioned, but re-entered the frame after the consortium - which relaunched itself as Eurotunnel on 18th December, 1985 - offered to build a separate road tunnel later and the French construction magnate Francis Bouygues gave his support. Finally M. Mitterrand informed Mr Ridley he would back the tunnel option if Britain pulled the plug on Mr Sherwood, who had no French business backing. The CTG had by now lined up heavy financing in the City by predicting that its link would cost £5 billion to build, be worth £20 billion when open, generate £474 million of revenue in 1993 and in the worst case give an 18.8 per cent return on investors' capital.

On 20th January, 1986 Mrs Thatcher and M. Mitterrand announced at Lille town hall that the CTG and its partner France-Manche (by now subsidiaries of Eurotunnel) had won the concession (at that stage for 55 years to 2042) to construct twin rail tunnels capable of carrying through trains and drive-on 'shuttles', with plans for a drive-through link to follow by 2000. An Inter-Governmental Commission would supervise construction, and a Safety Authority would enforce the safe operation of the completed tunnel. The French President stated tellingly: 'There will be no going back on this'. The Commons backed the choice by 268 votes to 107, and rejected by a tighter margin a Labour call for a public inquiry instead of a Parliamentary Bill. On 12th February, 1986, the agreement was enshrined in a Treaty signed in the Chapter House of Canterbury Cathedral by the Foreign Secretary, Sir Geoffrey Howe, and his counterpart Roland Dumas.

Sir Nicholas Henderson stepped down as UK co-chairman of Eurotunnel soon after the announcement, and the now Lord Pennock returned as the challenge shifted to raising funds, finalising plans and trying to buy off or otherwise satisfy objectors to the revived plan for a Cheriton terminal. Eurotunnel became a commissioning company, standing between the Governments on one hand and the contractors, who had created it, on the other; the contractors' final act was to write the contract under which they would build the tunnel, setting a balance of risk that Eurotunnel's subsequent chiefs were to rue.

Eurotunnel now became a truly Anglo-French company with staff of both nationalities on either side of the Channel, but separate subsidiaries remained in being because of the different requirements of British and French company law; every share in Eurotunnel in fact comprises one equal share in both the British and the French companies. The first share issue, Equity 1, raised £46 million from the 10 construction companies and five banks in the Eurotunnel consortium. Equity 2 raised £206 million from financial institutions while the Bill authorising the tunnel was on its way through Parliament, though only after a struggle - during which the muscle of the Bank of England proved decisive - which gave opponents of the project new hope. And Equity 3, the public offering of £770 million in shares to enable work to get under way, was pencilled in for shortly after the politicians finally gave the go-ahead.

Securing this took almost 18 months. In France the process was straightforward: the Council of Ministers approved the choice on 14th January, 1987, twin Bills were introduced ratifying the Treaty of Canterbury and granting the concession, the Chamber of Deputies gave its unanimous blessing on 22nd April and on 3rd June the Senate concurred. At Westminster, however, the tunnel legislation came under the complex Hybrid Bill procedure, requiring the hearing of objections by Select Committees of both Houses and line by line scrutiny by Standing Committees; the one advantage was that such Bills did not automatically lapse if an election were called.

The 118-page Channel Tunnel Bill hit trouble the moment it was published in April 1986. Flexilink and a number of Labour MPs campaigning for all major infrastructure schemes to go through public inquiries branded the procedure a 'carve-up', and the Commons only voted against stalling consideration for a year - and jeopardising the proposed opening date of May 1993 - after its Standing Orders Committee had deadlocked on the issue. The Bill received its Second Reading on 5th June by 309 votes to 44, then went before a nine-member Select Committee, which aroused protests by declaring that its remit was to hear objections to specifics of the Bill and neither to the principle of the tunnel as such nor complaints about rabies, terrorism, drug smuggling or the transport of nuclear waste. The committee was swamped with 4,852 petitions of varying degrees of relevance from local councils, ferry operators, environmental groups and residents in Dover, Folkestone and beyond, many rounded up by Sealink. There were also protests from community groups around Waterloo station, which BR had designated as the tunnel's London passenger terminal after studying 12 alternatives, despite there having been a station there since 1848.

Sitting at Westminster and at Hythe near Folkestone - where it dealt with 155 objectors in four stormy days - the panel heard 220 hours of evidence covering 1,900 pages in 36 days of sittings. The Select Committee eventually recommended some 70 minor changes to the project, notably revised road access to the Cheriton terminal - the Bill also provided for a number of road improvements - and a less environmentally damaging line for the railway into the tunnel across the Holywell Coombe beauty spot.

A Commons Standing Committee next considered the Bill line by line, with safety emerging as the principal concern. Maritime unions and fire chiefs voiced concern that passengers carried through the tunnel in their cars would be incinerated if a fire broke out; a move to make Eurotunnel segregate passengers from cars was narrowly defeated, in the face of evidence that Swiss railways had carried cars with their passengers through Alpine tunnels for 34 years without a single casualty. The promoters of the tunnel detected the hand of the ferry companies, as segregation would have hit hard the economics of shuttle train operation, increased transit times and reduced service frequency. After ritual sound and fury on the floor of the House, the Bill cleared the Commons on 4th February, 1987. The most notable change had been the insertion of clauses forbidding the Government from subsidising construction or operation of the tunnel (as opposed to the rail and road links to it), and requiring BR to plan through tunnel services to the regions; this latter would return to haunt the operators of Eurostar when the economic case first for night services and then regional day services began looking bleak.

Proceedings in Parliament were now eclipsed by a tragic event outside. The sinking of the P&O ferry *Herald of Free Enterprise* off Zeebrugge with the loss of 180 lives on 6th March, 1987 exposed lamentable negligence by the vessel's operators - its bow doors had been left open - and torpedoed Flexilink's continuing attempts to prove that sea was safer. Eurotunnel management ordered staff not to gloat, but from this moment the argument over safety subsided.

By now, though, Flexilink had switched to the financial arena with deadly effect and its querying of Eurotunnel's forecasts undermined the company's efforts to raise capital. A bout of inertia had set in at Eurotunnel just when it should have been getting up to speed; boardroom strains culminated in the resignations of Sir Nigel Broackes, who had joined from EuroRoute in the hope of securing work for Trafalgar House but found Eurotunnel shambolic, and Michael Julien, a high-powered money man from the Midland Bank. Under heavy fire in the City, Lord Pennock stood down and on 20th February, 1987, at the instance of the Bank of England, Alastair Morton, an abrasive South African who came highly commended as chief executive of the Guinness Peat group and previously of the British National Oil Corporation, took over. He began by deferring Equity 3 till that autumn to lessen the chance of the project being stillborn through lack of capital.

Consideration of the Bill in the Lords started with an unopposed Second Reading, but controversy revived when a Government mix-up led to many objectors missing the 18th February deadline. Of 1,459 petitions lodged, many were challenged by the Government on legal grounds, but the Lords Select Committee showed its independence and gave objectors more latitude. Taking evidence for 30 days, it recommended 109 further minor amendments, then adjourned pending the General Election.

Standing Committee (which in the Lords means the whole House) began on 2nd July with opponents of the tunnel trying to refer the Bill back to the Select Committee. But the battle in practical terms was over; the Bill emerged on 6th July with only Government drafting amendments, hurried through its Report Stage and on 16th July was given an unopposed Third Reading. MPs accepted the Lords' amendments without debate, and on 23rd July, 1987 the Channel Tunnel Act received the Royal Assent.

Before work could formally commence, Eurotunnel still had to raise the bulk of the finance. On 12th May, 1987 the European Investment Bank had agreed to lend Eurotunnel £1 billion, and on 29th July a Rail Usage Agreement between Eurotunnel, BR and SNCF underpinning the tunnel's income from through rail services was signed; crucially to the tunnel's revenues, this provided for the two railways to guarantee their use of half the tunnel's capacity by through passenger and freight traffic, a target which has yet to be reached.

Next, £770 million had to be raised through a public flotation on the London stock market and Paris Bourse (Equity 3). While optimism ran high in the buoyant markets of the day, financial commentators attacked the issue as a risky one; even Eurotunnel admitted no dividend would be paid for a decade. When markets across the world crashed on 'Black Monday', 19th October, 1987, it looked briefly as if the issue would flop, but in the event enough shares were purchased at £3.50 apiece to rescue it - many by the buccaneering Robert Maxwell who on this occasion did not raid his employees' pension fund. The flotation, achieved partly through the offer of shuttle travel privileges once the tunnel was open, would not be the final call on the stock markets; soaring costs would require a rights issue during construction despite which less than 20 per cent of the final cost of the project would have been subscribed by private shareholders. Yet the success of the float was critical to concluding the final and most weighty piece of financing: a £5 billion loan and letter of credit facility negotiated with a worldwide syndicate of 198 banks. With Equity 3 accomplished, this agreement was concluded on 4th November, 1987, and on 16th November it was signed at a glittering ceremony at the City of London Guildhall where Alastair Morton promised banks and stockholders alike that the tunnel would 'amply repay' their confidence.

At last, work could begin.

Chapter Two

Construction and Commissioning

Eurotunnel now faced one of the greatest challenges in the history of transport engineering: to bore and waterproof a tunnel 51 km in length, 38 km of it beneath the seabed, equip it for the safe operation of a high-speed railway, construct terminals at each end to handle shuttle car, lorry and coach traffic and commission trains to transport them, and get the project completed and cleared for operation in 5½ years and within a budget of £6 billion. The Channel Tunnel would not be the longest in the world - Japan's 54 km Seikan tunnel, completed just before it, covers a fractionally greater distance - but with 149 km of bored tunnel, complex underground workings and extensive terminals it was a much more substantial project.

Completing it would prove a hard struggle. The greatest bugbear was the escalating cost of boring and equipping the tunnel which guaranteed an increasingly fraught relationship between Eurotunnel, its financial backers and its contractors, the consortium that became known as Trans-Manche Link (TML), as deadlines were discarded and the financial outlook deteriorated. The tunnel eventually took 13,700 workers 170,000,000 man hours to complete, with the total cost including Eurotunnel's shuttle trains reaching £10 billion. Boring the tunnel alone cost £2.7 billion, and when the work was at its height TML was spending £4 million a day.

More than once there was a real danger that the project might have to be abandoned, and it took an increasingly ruthless approach by Alastair Morton and his French counterpart André Benard toward TML, repeated intercessions by them to keep nervous Japanese banks from pulling out, pressure on all parties from the Bank of England, frequent threats of legal action in all directions and the negotiation of a hidden UK Government subsidy to the tunnel through BR's underwriting of a generous number of train paths, to get it ill-temperedly through to completion. Yet regardless of the rows and dramas, the work of boring and completing the tunnel was a triumph in itself.

The project in its entirety was both challenging and complex, requiring careful planning and a vast array of skills. The most obvious task was the boring of the running and service tunnels by Tunnel Boring Machines (TBMs) in four sections starting from the two construction sites at Shakespeare Cliff and Sangatte: 8.4 km landward from Shakespeare Cliff, seaward from Shakespeare Cliff and seaward from Sangatte (a combined length of 38 km) and 3.3 km between Sangatte and the French tunnel portal. The tunnel would run on average 45 m below the seabed, with a maximum clearance of 75 m, with the running bores generally 30 m apart. The initial landward kilometre from the Cheriton portal to Holywell Coombe was excavated not by TBM but by the New Austrian Tunnelling Method (NATM), larger-diameter caverns being hewn out and then shotcreted; the route across the Coombe, only just below ground level but in tunnel for environmental reasons, was constructed by cut-and-cover.

The two 7.6 m-diameter running tunnels would generate most spoil, but the smaller pilot or service tunnel was excavated first. It was used during construction to ferry supplies, workers and spoil, and on completion for ventilation and maintenance, to carry a fireman and for evacuating passengers and staff in an emergency. The running tunnels were bored on either side of the service tunnel, with the latter ducking under one of the running tunnels at each end to break surface to one side of the rail tracks. Altogether, just under 150 km of tunnel would be bored by TBM in 12 'drives'.

Two vast undersea chambers were needed to accommodate diamond crossovers between the two running tunnels, permitting single-line working through a portion of the tunnel should one part of the line be put out of action. There were further crossovers at each end of the tunnel, the French one in the open but that at the Kent end sited, for space reasons, partially in the section beneath Holywell Coombe. Of the undersea crossovers one was 17 km into the tunnel from Cheriton, the other 15.2 km from the French portal, leaving a central operating section of some 17.7 km. While under construction these imposing caverns had the feel of medieval cathedrals, the UK chamber being 163 m long, 21 m wide and 15 m high; remarkably this vast space was excavated by the NATM from the service tunnel which, as at the portals, had been slewed to one side of the running tunnels. All the spoil from the UK chamber had to be removed through the service tunnel, the running tunnel TBMs only reaching the site later. The French crossover cavern was created by building a huge concrete arch after the TBMs had passed through, with a 'roadheader' machine gouging out rock beneath it. Once the crossovers were completed, airtight sliding doors were fitted over the crossover tracks so that when trains were on their normal routeing these sections appeared like normal lengths of tunnel.

Every 250 m there were to be 'piston relief ducts' between the two running tunnels, preventing air pressure building in advance of high-speed trains. Every 375 m a further cross-passage would provide a connection between all three tunnels for use by maintenance staff and in an emergency. All these subsidiary tunnels, as well as three undersea pumping stations and numerous underground technical rooms, had to be dug out by hand.

The tunnels were bored almost entirely through a stratum of chalk marl, regarded as the 'ideal tunnelling medium'. It was the need to bring the tunnel to the surface without leaving this stratum that required the Kent terminal to be at Cheriton, rather than nearer Dover, and this added to the length of the tunnel. Boreholes had revealed, however, that there were some awkward sectors to be traversed, and with most of these off the French coast it was estimated that the TBMs boring out from Shakespeare Cliff would make faster progress. When work began, however, these machines soon hit a patch of extreme moisture which slowed them considerably.

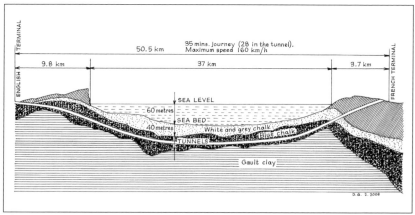

The geological profile of the Channel Tunnel as constructed. Its alignment to stay within the stratum of blue chalk can clearly be seen. *Eurotunnel*

Eurotunnel also had to prepare its twin shuttle terminals at Cheriton and Fréthun. The UK terminal, 8 km along the coast from Shakespeare Cliff, had to be squeezed into a 2.5 km by 900 m site between the M20 and the escarpment of the Downs; across the Channel there were no such space constraints and the French terminal, just south of Calais and barely 3 km from landfall at Sangatte, could be four times larger. Work on the UK terminal was further handicapped by the contractors being denied access to the site until early 1988, and the need to work round historic buildings and woods which Parliament decreed should be untouched by the scheme.

To construct the tunnel TML was formed, comprising Balfour Beatty Construction, Bouygues, Costain Civil Engineering, Lyonnaise des Eaux-Dumez, Société Auxiliaire des Entreprises, Société Générale d'Entreprises Sainrapt et Brice, Spie Batignolles, Tarmac Construction, Taylor Woodrow Construction Holdings and Wimpey Major Projects; the British and French contractors would operate as two separate teams (Translink Joint Venture and Transmanche Construction GIE), but their separate products clearly had to be compatible to provide a seamless transit.

The contract between Eurotunnel and TML was signed as early as August 1986 (very much on the contractors' terms, as it turned out), for there was much preparatory work to be done before serious tunnelling could begin.

Construction would be carried out from the time-honoured Sangatte site on the cliffs south-west of Calais, and from two sites at Shakespeare Cliff: a construction platform beside the Folkestone-Dover railway at the foot of the cliff, and a 'base camp' on the cliff top from which lifts would take workers directly to the tunnels without delaying the flow of materials below the cliff.

The new generation of tunnellers inherited the remains of the project abandoned in 1975, but these were not always of use. Most valuable were the results of the geological surveys conducted in 1974-75; these were now refined with the benefit of satellite readings and a further 180 seabed borings conducted during 1986-87. Also essential to the project were the construction platform beneath Shakespeare Cliff and the tunnelled road leading down to it from the cliff top. From the platform, a 5 m-diameter adit bored down to the level of the main running tunnels also lay ready for use. At the French end, the Sangatte site as ever was ready, but the workings begun in 1974 had been abandoned and the site cleared; this time access to the workings would be by a vertical shaft, not the diagonal adit used previously. Of even less use was the cutting head of the Priestley TBM which had excavated 300 m out to sea from beneath Shakespeare Cliff prior to the cancellation of the 1974 project and was entombed in concrete when the machine itself was removed. This proved extremely difficult to dislodge. A heap of concrete tunnel segments had been left stacked at Shakespeare Cliff when work was halted, but these turned out to be the wrong diameter for the new project and were tipped unceremoniously into the sea.

Site work began first at Sangatte in 1986; between that March and July a giant shaft 55 m across and 65 m deep, large enough for the Arc de Triomphe to fit into, was excavated, from which tunnelling could begin below sea level close to the water's edge. Next a dam was constructed on hills behind the shaft, creating a 'pond' of 1.4 million cubic metres capacity into which spoil from the tunnel mixed with water could be pumped. At the English end, by contrast, a coffer dam was built in the sea beside the construction platform and 3 million cubic metres of rail-borne spoil tipped straight into the space created, thus extending the site. When the project was complete, the spoil had added a 40-hectare extension to the United Kingdom; after being used to store tunnel segments to prevent the TBMs running out, it was christened Samphire Hoe and largely devoted to a nature reserve; by 2003 it was home to 118 species of plants, 79 species of birds and more than 200 invertebrates.

Work at Shakespeare Cliff began in earnest within days of the Channel Tunnel Act gaining its Royal Assent and the tunnel promoters formally acquiring (at the start of August 1987) the site and existing workings from the British Government. The concrete plug from the 1974-75 bore had already been removed, and an erection chamber was now constructed at the end of the tunnel, to which the service tunnel boring machine was brought in pieces down the adit for assembly. The TBM began its drive on 1st December - the official date for the start of construction - and advanced a somewhat disappointing 3.5 km in the first year; the seaward French service tunnel TBM *Brigitte* began its drive on 28th February, 1988, advancing just 200 m in the first six months because of technical problems and appalling drilling conditions in almost liquid ground. During that year further erection chambers for the two undersea running tunnels were excavated so that the TBMs for each could also be put together; a second adit from Lower Shakespeare Cliff was dug out at the start of 1988 to improve access to them. Before work could begin at full throttle, undersea marshalling areas for construction railways had also to be prepared at both Shakespeare Cliff and Sangatte.

The TBMs were remarkable machines, amounting to trains of up to 250 m in length. At the front came the rotary cutting head, feeding through an Archimedean screw as it revolved and progressed into a spoil conveyer system that ran the length of the TBM and emptied into railway trucks on construction tracks that were laid beneath the machine as it advanced. The heads on the British machines were armed with small picks to eat into the chalk marl, but the machines at the French end, where conditions were wetter, used revolving discs. Behind the head was a 'build area' where concrete segments, brought in by another conveyer from supply trains, were secured to form the tunnel lining, different machinery and processes installing upper and lower segments and, above the latter, concrete slabs to create a floor with a drain beneath. Next came the operator's cabin, from which both the speed of advance and direction of boring were controlled; laser guidance ensured that the cutting head never veered more than a few centimetres from true. To the rear lay the mechanism powering the shaft that drove the cutters, and behind the TBM the spoil wagons which at one point were taking out 2,000 tonnes of chalk marl every hour.

Altogether 11 TBMs were needed to bore the various stretches of running and service tunnel: six at the British end manufactured by James Howden and Robbins-Markham, and five at the French (one was turned round after finishing a first landward running tunnel to excavate a second) by Robbins, Kawasaki and Marubeni-Mitsubishi. The French TBMs were built like submarines to cope with the high moisture at that end of the workings; the British machines were more open and could thus proceed faster ... though water ingress did halt them for a short time in 1988. The French TBMs, observing a tunnelling tradition that would spread to the Jubilee Line Extension and in due course the tunnels on the CTRL, were given girls' names such as *Catherine*, *Europa*, *Pasqualine* and *Virginie*. The first of the four undersea running tunnel TBMs started work from Sangatte on 1st December, 1988, and the last from Shakespeare Cliff on 12th June, 1989; the final drive of all, on the southern landward running tunnel at the British end, began on 27th November that year.

The TBMs' progress, though not always rapid, caught the public imagination and a special Eurotunnel telephone line stating how far each had advanced in the previous week received many calls. TBM crews were pitted against each other, with lavish bonuses promised to those progressing fastest. In this atmosphere the share price also soared; having been floated at £3.50 in the autumn of 1987 the stock reached a heady £11.50 two years later before doubts over the project being completed on time, to budget or even at all injected a dose of reality; the slide continued after the tunnel was open and by late 1998 the share price was below 50p.

The first tunnelling breakthrough was achieved on 27th April, 1989, when the French landward service tunnel was completed after its TBM advanced 886 m (then a world record) in a month. After that one milestone after another was reached: 10 km of the English undersea service tunnel that 1st August, completion of the first section of running tunnel (from the French portal to Sangatte) on 18th December, 75 km of tunnel completed (21st April, 1990) and the passing of the undersea frontier by the English service tunnel TBM (20th June). With the French service tunnel now advancing more than 1,200 m a month as further records fell, the historic breakthrough beneath the Channel was now in sight. By late 1990 all the landward running and service tunnels at each end had been completed.

The tunnels themselves were lined with pre-cast concrete segments, the dimensions and means of assembly on the British and French projects differing somewhat. The British TBMs required eight segments plus a smaller 'key' segment at the top to line the running tunnels and six plus a 'key' for the service tunnel; those starting from France installed five segments plus a 'key' in all three tunnels. The French segments, which had special watertight joints because of the more porous strata being bored through, each covered more of the tunnel diameter, but each 'ring' advanced the process less: 1.4 m against 1.5 m for those fitted by the British-based machines. Finally while the French segments were manufactured on site at Sangatte - where all 340,000 concrete sleeper blocks for the running lines would also be produced - their British counterparts were cast at a special factory on the Isle of Grain, which between December 1987 and the spring of 1991 turned out 252,700 segments. The granite aggregate needed to cast the segments came to Grain by sea from the Glensanda superquarry near Fort William; most of the materials for the segments cast at Sangatte were quarried near Boulogne. In all, lining the tunnels used up 1.5 million tonnes of concrete.

On the TBMs and during fitting-out of the tunnels behind them, concern for safety had to be paramount given the obvious risks faced by the 13,700 workers. Sadly there were nine fatalities - eight of them British and four in an eight-month period from October 1989 which prompted a drive by TML to convince workers there could be no 'acceptable level' of accidents. In most cases falls by heavy equipment or components or crushing between them or construction trains were to blame. Though these deaths were tragic for the victims, their families and their colleagues and in most cases could have been avoided, the toll was less grim for a project of this magnitude and risk than most experts would have predicted; even the far less hazardous first phase of the CTRL produced two fatalities.

The immediate safety concerns beyond the operation and handling of equipment were the risks of the tunnel collapsing (unlikely once the segments were in place), inundation of an unlined working face from an unforeseen pocket of water (these were encountered but never on a serious scale, though powerful emergency pumps stood in readiness) and fire. The risk of fire was twofold: from the overheating or malfunction of equipment, and from a discarded cigarette. The two national consortia of contractors had different policies on smoking which reflected their approaches to the entire project: the British contractors treated the site like a coal-mine, issuing every man with a token to be surrendered on his return and confiscating all matches and cigarettes at the 'pithead' with smoking below ground a sacking offence. The French, by contrast, operated their site like a Gallic nuclear power station, with cleanliness and technology coexisting with a relaxed policy on smoking. This seemed also to apply to drink, as when the author made a transit by manrider in 1991, the best indication that the undersea border had been passed was a cairn of empty champagne bottles. British VIPs were allowed to imbibe when subsea ceremonies were held to mark some milestone on the project, though on one occasion their manrider arrived so late that they arrived to find their French counterparts had consumed all the champagne provided.

French workmen added a further touch near their undersea crossover: a shrine to St Barbara, the patron saint of miners, where many paused to pray. (Austrian tunnellers would erect a similar shrine on one of the underground sections of the CTRL.)

As far as working conditions were concerned, the three great challenges were dust, stale or poisoned air and noise. Given that the tunnelling operation involved mining large tonnages of chalk and other strata which were often dry despite their submarine location and installing and grouting half a million concrete segments, dust was inevitable and many workers were issued with protective masks. To maintain the supply of oxygen, powerful ventilation systems pumped fresh air into the workings from both Shakespeare Cliff - one of the adits continuing to be used for this purpose when the tunnel was complete - and Sangatte. They had their work cut out at the time when the service tunnel constituted a 20 km dead end with the TBM at its extremity; as soon as breakthrough was achieved, a crude and limited form of air circulation existed. To guard against anyone being trapped far under the sea in thin or noxious air, everyone venturing underground was issued with a self-rescuer, and behind each TBM a special closed manrider with stocks of oxygen was stationed to evacuate workers in an emergency. The ventilation system proved its worth in an incident in 1992, safely dispelling carbon monoxide pumped out *en route* by a defective diesel generator and encouraging the belief that in the event of fire it would remove smoke without assisting the blaze. As for noise - a problem acute in the TBMs and considerable with other processes - rigorous maximum levels were enforced, but some workers nevertheless needed earplugs or muffs.

Many of the 8,000 people employed on the British end of the tunnel (mainly by TML) were recruited locally, a considerable number from the dying Kent coalfield, but the largest construction project in Europe at the time had to draw labour from further afield. To house 1,100 workers from Scotland, Ireland and the rest of England, a temporary settlement known as Farthingloe Village was constructed atop Shakespeare Cliff. Opened in January 1989, its facilities included a shop, sports hall and other leisure facilities; it had, nevertheless, something of the air of a prospecting camp in the Klondyke, and occasional stories of heavy drinking and fisticuffs reached the tabloids. One story that, fortunately for TML, never did so concerned two male construction workers who became the first members of an informal 'Mile Deep Club'.

Above ground, work was advancing on the tunnel terminals after a major site preparation task at each of them. To create a suitable base at Cheriton, sand was dredged from the Goodwin Sands and offloaded at Sandgate from where it was pumped with seawater through a pipeline before being dried and used as fill. Among many earthworks needed at Cheriton was a tunnel to conceal the loop carrying turning shuttle trains from the adjoining hamlets of Newington and Peene.

At Coquelles a flatter but marshier site was made firm with a combination of chalk excavated from the Beussingue Trench, the cutting where the railway emerged from the tunnel portals, and sand; a volume of water seven times greater than the mass of the great pyramid of Cheops had to be pumped out before construction could begin. On these bases grids of trackbed, shuttle platforms and overbridges for shuttle traffic began to take shape plus new sections of motorway including, on the French side, the dramatic Fort Nieulay interchange positioned over a circular lake. By the end of 1990 tracklaying had begun on the main line at Cheriton linking BR's existing Folkestone-Ashford route with the tunnel portal.

Despite these signs of advance, strains over the financing of the project and TML's grip on it were growing. Opening in 1993 was starting to look a tall order, and any delay would land Eurotunnel with heavy interest charges without any revenue to meet them. The cost of construction was moving steadily ahead of projections as recriminations broke out between Eurotunnel and TML: Eurotunnel claimed that delays by TML would cost it £2 million a day if the opening date slipped, while TML blamed repeated changes in specifications. On the boring of the tunnel TML was allowed a 16.5 per cent markup on the contract price, and had to shoulder 30 per cent of extra costs. Terminals and fixed equipment were installed for a fixed price, obliging TML to absorb any extra expense. And for the rest of the fitting-out, 10 per cent of the works in all, TML negotiated a price for each contract, plus 11.5 per cent commission. The friction alarmed Eurotunnel's bankers who feared their money was at risk, with some (notably in Japan) seeking to bale out. Matters came to a head on 19th February, 1990, when TML refused to sign an agreement which it had negotiated with Eurotunnel the previous month that the contractors would pay 30 per cent of all tunnelling costs above revised target levels. With the liquidation of Eurotunnel on the agenda for a company board meeting two days later, bankers headed by NatWest demanded a showdown; at a tense meeting at which Robin Leigh-Pemberton, Governor of the Bank of England, lost his temper, Alastair Morton realised something must be done to break the deadlock; he left the room to make a telephone call and returned with the news that John Neerhout, previously a vice-president of the American construction giant Bechtel, would join Eurotunnel the following week to take charge of relations with TML. Neerhout's new Project Implementation Division, shadowing the contractors, would in time bring fresh frictions with TML, but critically there was now a buffer between them and Morton; TML signed up, and the banks released urgently-needed funds. Financial pressures were eased for a time by a further loan of £300 million from the European Investment Bank in May 1990, an extra £1.5 billion in credits from the banks that October and the following month £570 million more from the shareholders; a loan of £200 million from the European Coal and Steel Community followed in November 1991.

The stage was now set for the historic undersea breakthrough that would end Britain's status as an island after 10,000 years of isolation. The gap between the TBMs boring the service tunnels from Shakespeare Cliff and Sangatte narrowed rapidly, and on 30th October, 1990 the advancing French TBM met a probe pushed out from the British machine which had stopped five days earlier. The laser guidance system had worked with astonishing accuracy; the centrelines of the two bores differed by just 358 mm horizontally and 58 mm vertically. Breakthrough achieved, the British machine was slewed sideways and entombed in concrete, finding further use as an earthing point for the tunnel's electrical system; of all the TBMs used on the project, only one, from one of the English landward running tunnels, emerged intact for preservation, being put on display initially at Eurotunnel's visitor centre close to the Cheriton terminal, before raising £39,999 for charity when auctioned on eBay in April 2004. The French machine involved in the breakthrough, like all others not abandoned beneath the sea, was dismantled and the pieces removed by rail; it could not be taken out intact as its cutter head was larger than the lined tunnel. Miners then gouged out the brief linking section of tunnel to connect the two countries by land for the first time since the Ice Age and on 1st December, 1990, pictures of the breakthrough ceremony, with tunnellers (and the British and French transport ministers Malcolm Rifkind and Michel Delebarre) meeting beneath the Channel, were beamed around the world.

Breakthrough was achieved 4 km on the French side of the internationally-recognised undersea frontier. Initially it made sense for the point where the two TBMs had met to be the *de facto* border; there was a gap between the two construction railways and, for a time, an iron gate marked the dividing line. But once tunnelling had finished and fitting-out was in full swing, the frontier was demarcated on 30th November, 1992 with a ceremony unveiling markers on the wall of a running tunnel at the legally correct point.

The opening of, technically, a thoroughfare between two countries created a need for passport control for the trickle of people who started to transit on business, starting with the VIPs who transited to Shakespeare Cliff after the breakthrough ceremony and including in March 1991 the first press party whose passage by manriders took over five hours. Initially customs and immigration officials from the ports of Calais and Folkestone attended arrivals through the service tunnel, but on 25th November, 1991 a frontier control protocol was concluded between the British and French Governments under which, unprecedentedly, each country would have officers from the relevant services in position at the other's terminal.

The breakthrough also aroused public concern over the perceived threat to Britain from rabid animals - though intriguingly not healthy humans - who might sneak through from the Continent, publicity over which incensed Alastair Morton. A detailed set of defences including moats, electrified fences, baited traps and thick metal mesh sunk into the ground to deter burrowing creatures had been prepared; its purpose was to ensure, as one Eurotunnel executive put it, that any animal heading into the tunnel in search of food or a mate would find itself thwarted. It would be ironic that as the tunnel was completed, the incidence of rabies in northern France and in Belgium would plummet; the only successful intruder detected in the first five years of operation would be a Russian merchant seaman who jumped ship in Scotland and almost made it to France.

Now the service tunnel had been bored, the task of excavating and equipping the running tunnels and various other undersea works became simpler as men and materials could be moved more easily, and in fresher air. A considerable amount of tidying-up still had to be done in the service tunnel, but it now became a thoroughfare rather than an elongated construction site. The pace of tunnelling quickened; in the final week of March 1991 one of the English undersea running tunnel TBMs posted an all-time record advance of 428 m a week, and on 22nd May that year breakthrough was achieved in the northern undersea running tunnel. The final undersea breakthrough took place soon after, on 28th June, 1991, with completion of the southern running tunnel. But in that brief period an intruder who had set out to 'walk to France' from Cheriton earned Eurotunnel's unofficial 'loser of the week' prize by trying to make the transit through the only uncompleted tunnel out of the three available.

With both running tunnels and the service tunnel bored through, the nature of the project changed. While some connecting passages and other underground spaces not bored by TBM still had to be mined, the tunnelling equipment and (eventually) construction railways could be removed and the running tunnels fitted out. This was not simply a question of installing track, overhead electric wiring and signalling; lighting, power supplies to pumping stations and other undersea machinery, pipework for drainage, firefighting and cooling systems, ventilation and fire doors, data transmission and radio systems all had to be installed. No less than 1,300 km of electric cabling had to be installed, and in all more than 300,000 items of fixed equipment were involved, over and above the track and overhead wiring. This was the point at which the project began slipping seriously behind the targets set for it, because contractors moving in to fit out the tunnel found that equipment they were ready to install had not arrived or, in some cases, not even been ordered.

Tracklaying began on the terminal sites in November 1990 and in the first English running tunnel on 15th July, 1991. The task was a massive one and a special consortium, Channel Tunnel Trackwork Group, was formed to undertake it. In all 200 km of track had to be laid, half of it in tunnel, with 176 sets of points including two diamond crossings; Continental-type steel rail weighing 60 kg to the metre was used in preference to the lighter-weight rail traditionally used in Britain. Track in the terminals was ballasted, and that in the undersea running tunnels laid on a concrete bed. Once the tunnel had been cleaned, concrete was poured in to form a floor with inbuilt drainage. Track was laid in 180 m 'strings', welded together from shorter lengths at British Steel's Workington mill and the SNCF workshops at Moulin Neuf-Chambly north-west of Paris. The track, with small concrete blocks rather than full sleepers to hold it in place, was carried into the tunnel by standard gauge diesel-hauled trains which bore the tracklaying gantries as well as carrying four 'strings' each. At the end of the track already laid was a further, temporary, track panel mounted on wheels, onto which the train moved before backing away so that the gantries could carry out a fresh tracklaying cycle. Before this could begin, the temporary track was disconnected and wheeled further into the tunnel. As soon as each pair of 'strings' was in place, steel crossties were bolted on to make sure they were precisely in gauge. The only interruption to this pattern occurred in the undersea crossover chambers, where wooden sleepers were used for the purpose-made trackwork. Tracklaying was completed in the first English running tunnel on the last day of July 1992, and by the following April all the undersea track was complete. Above ground, track in the French terminal was connected to the SNCF's new TGV Nord route on 26th November, 1992.

Once the track was in place, electrification trains moved in to install 950 km of catenary, kept in place by 15,000 supports which made it zig-zag to lessen pantograph wear. When the service tunnel was no longer needed by contractors' trains, the rails were lifted and a concrete roadway for service and emergency vehicles laid; one of the last tasks for construction trains in the service tunnel was to install a high-pressure firemain running its entire length. The shuttle of rubber-tyred vehicles for maintenance workers through the service tunnel could not cope with demand during the final stages of fitting-out, and as productivity suffered in the autumn of 1993 TML bought 200 mountain bikes to get workers into position on time.

The shift from construction project to operating transport system was now well under way. Spoil disposal ended in mid-1991, and with an end of boring the proportion of workers employed by TML fell steadily, though the overall workforce remained at 13,700 for some time. During 1992 Eurotunnel began the recruitment of terminal and operating staff, some of them former TML construction workers. The tunnel, three-quarters of whose power would be used for traction, was connected to the British and French national grids in August and November 1991 respectively and catenary in the Cheriton terminal was energised on 25th April, 1992 . . . but the catenary in the running tunnels did not go live until the third quarter of 1993, months after the date originally set for the tunnel to open. However, almost as importantly, the two massive ventilation plants at Shakespeare Cliff and Sangatte - where the colossal construction shaft was now being roofed over - and the accompanying cooling plants which between them kept the air right through the tunnels bearably fresh and cool, were switched on to schedule.

For Eurotunnel, the project had by mid-1992 entered its most frustrating stage. The romantic stage of boring the tunnel was over, but every individual item in dozens of safety-critical systems had to be tested before the company could accept the completed tunnel from TML and even more testing to satisfy the Inter-Governmental Safety Commission (IGC) set up under the Channel Tunnel Treaty was needed before revenue-earning trains could run. The IGC's stipulations had already increased the cost of the project, and probably delayed the start of services, when in the spring of 1991 it ordered the redesign of the doors on the car shuttle wagons to increase their fire resistance; the doors of wagons that eventually entered service were guaranteed to withstand a spreading fire for 30 minutes.

Tunnelling had been completed more or less to the schedule set in 1985, but the fitting-out programme fell severely behind amid recriminations between Eurotunnel and TML; in January 1992 the Appeal Court in London effectively told TML it was free to halt work if Eurotunnel did not pay outstanding bills for £1.1 billion. Work did not stop, but several international panels of experts were called in to mediate, their work continuing well after the tunnel was opened. Each week's delay in opening increased the massive burden of interest charges that was now causing fresh concern over the viability of the project, and some tasks had slipped so badly that construction, testing and commissioning took place simultaneously. Eurotunnel announced in February 1992 that its target opening date had been put back from 15th June, 1993 to late that summer. By the start of 1993, relations between Eurotunnel and TML over who should bear responsibility for the soaring cost of the project had reached their frostiest.

On site, however, milestones continued to be passed. Eurotunnel's operational headquarters at Calais opened on 11th January, 1993. Eighteen days later the new British Ambassador in Paris, Sir Christopher Mallaby, travelled through the tunnel to take up his appointment. He did not, however, travel by Eurostar - the dedicated fleet of international trains was still being delivered and the catenary was not yet live - but through the service tunnel in a luxurious manrider nicknamed the Maggiemobile, after the former Prime Minister for whom it had been adapted (though not used - *see page 53*); his journey took 3 hrs 40 mins. The first passenger train, carrying a party of guests from the European Investment Bank, passed through the tunnel under diesel haulage on 12th March, and on 20th June the first Eurostar was towed through to England, again by a diesel locomotive. High-speed train tests, with diesels running at up to 160 kph, began in February 1993, and that September after the 25 kv AC overhead wiring had finally been energised, Eurotunnel's shuttle locos were put through their paces, reaching 140 kph on a test freight shuttle and 175 kph on a passenger car train.

Eurotunnel and TML announced on 27th July, 1993 that the operating company would take full control of the tunnel that December, with phased opening now to follow during 1994: through international freight trains in January, HGV shuttles in March, passenger shuttles commencing once the Queen and President Mitterrand had formally opened the tunnel on 6th May, Eurostar trains from July and coach shuttles that autumn. Though upbeat, this statement implied a further financially-damaging delay in opening (forecast revenues for 1994 were cut from £504 million to £260 million), and with the total cost of the project now nearing £10 billion Eurotunnel was locked in litigation over cost overruns. The company was disputing a bill of £1.4 billion from TML for additional work, arguing that the true debt was nearer £600 million, and was also aggrieved at a 66 per cent cost overrun to £388 million on the shuttle rolling stock being manufactured by Bombardier, which claimed changes in specifications meant it was losing money on the contract. The latter dispute was more serious as, while TML had almost completed its work, Bombardier had halted work on the vehicles at its Belgian plant for three months and the shuttle services could not begin without them.

Despite a fire caused by an electrical fault in mid-November 1993 which severely damaged 750 metres of one running tunnel, TML handed over the system in full operating order on time on 10th December. The same day Eurotunnel whisked a trainload of 242 journalists, railway officials, contractors and others through the tunnel from Cheriton, having to use a unit of dual-voltage Thameslink stock – No. 319 009 - because Eurostar trains had yet to receive their safety clearance; Chris Green, then Managing Director of Network South-East, could not help observing: 'The first passenger trip to France since the Ice Age, and it's on a train provided by us'.

Even after that euphoric glimpse of the future the delays and the frustrations continued; the extension of Eurotunnel's concession by 10 years to 2052 at the close of 1993 offered long-term rather than immediate relief to the company's finances. The main problem now was that the IGC felt evacuation procedures in case of fire were not effective, and a series of exercises were ordered, culminating in the detraining in mid-tunnel of a packed Eurostar train, before consent was finally given by the Commission for the tunnel to open. Other difficulties were experienced after Eurotunnel took charge of the system: emergency alarms triggered every 24 seconds; inadequate flow of air from the ventilator pumps and leakages through holes in the tunnel wall which had to be plugged by hand; differing computer software between shuttle locomotives and inexperienced train crews who struggled to master the 'over-sophisticated' shuttle technology.

With the opening date set, festivities marking the completion of the tunnel got under way. On 26th February, 1994, eight hundred dignitaries sat down to a commemorative lunch in the British crossover chamber, 17 km into the tunnel from Cheriton, as guests of the now Sir Alastair Morton and his co-chairman André Benard. The highlight was the cutting by Lady Thatcher of a ceremonial cake wheeled in to the triumphal march from *Aida*. M. Bénard told her: 'Without you, this dream would not have been realised'.

The undersea banquet should have been rendered impracticable by the regular passage of international freight trains, but their start had again been delayed as commissioning and safety tests continued. The opening of 'Le Shuttle' - as it was originally branded - for heavy goods vehicles in March 1994 also failed to materialise, and the following month Eurotunnel admitted that it could not launch 'Le Shuttle' for passengers in time for the peak holiday season, offering refunds to car drivers who had already booked passages from 5th June.

The opening ceremony on 6th May, 1994 took place not only without the tunnel already being in regular public use but with the starting dates for the various services still a matter for conjecture and the strain on Eurotunnel's finances growing daily. Organising a joint opening by two of the world's most prestigious and protocol-encrusted heads of state was not an easy matter, and touchy courtiers in Buckingham Palace and the Elysée were quick to detect slights in the planning. But in the event the opening went ahead almost without a hitch.

At 9.30 that morning the Queen cut her first ribbon of the day to open the Eurostar terminal at Waterloo International before boarding her Eurostar for Coquelles. At around the same time President Mitterrand opened the less grandiose departure facility at the Gare du Nord in Paris before boarding a TGV to Lille-Europe, where he opened the TGV and Eurostar station and was met by the European Commission president Jacques Delors and the Belgian Prime Minister Jean-Luc Dehaene who then joined his train for the French tunnel terminal. The trains were due to arrive simultaneously at Calais, pulling up nose-to-nose, but while the Presidential TGV had an untroubled 300 kph cruise across northern France, the Royal Eurostar, having crossed Kent at less than half that speed, entered the tunnel seven minutes late and smart running was needed to recover the time. BR blamed 'congestion in the south-east', not an unusual phenomenon, but part of the delay was caused by a last-minute scare when the Kent Constabulary observed an abandoned paint can by the lineside near Dollands Moor shortly before the Queen's train was due to pass; fearing a bomb, they tried to abort the journey but were overruled by the British Transport Police, who said the suspect object was 'theirs'. The Queen passed safely through the tunnel with her trainload of VIPs and the two trains duly pulled up together on the French side at 11.28 am. At Coquelles the two heads of state cut another ribbon to mark the opening of the tunnel and unveiled a commemorative plaque. After the inevitable speeches and a banquet of terrine of sole, fillet of duck and ice cream soufflé, the Queen invited the President to board her Rolls-Royce Phantom VI which was then driven onto a shuttle wagon for the transit to Cheriton. This terminal, too, was declared well and truly open and the happy crowds dispersed.

Three days after the formal opening but with no revenue-earning services yet able to operate, European Passenger Services (EPS), the company that would operate Eurostar as far as the UK was concerned, was hived-off from BR into a separate Government-owned company, with a view to eventual privatisation. A week later, on 16th May, 1994, with Eurotunnel warning its shareholders that they could not expect a dividend before 2003 because the cost of the project had reached £10.5 billion, the IGC finally gave its certificate for a limited HGV shuttle service to commence. The long, frustrating wait was almost over.

Chapter Three

Construction Railways

The excavation and completion of the Channel Tunnel was a logistical triumph, and it depended, crucially, on an efficient and reliable internal railway system within the tunnel workings at all stages of the project. It also placed considerable demands on the conventional railway systems on both sides of the Channel.

Narrow Gauge Systems

For over five years during construction of the tunnel, from 1987 to 1993, two extensive narrow-gauge rail networks reached out from Shakespeare Cliff and Sangatte, playing a vital role in the project before retreating to make way for permanent standard-gauge tracks. At its busiest, the English narrow-gauge construction system, with nearly 500 drivers operating 144 locomotives around the clock over 180 km of track, was the third largest railway in the United Kingdom after British Rail and the London Underground. Between April 1988 and March 1993 it brought out 17 million tonnes of spoil and delivered 7 million tonnes of building materials and equipment. Around 11 million single passenger journeys were made - 4,000 a day - and in the busiest month 154,000 train kilometres were operated to serve eight different tunnelling groups. The more sophisticated, though slightly shorter, French system was just as busy and almost as complex.

Both systems were constructed to 900 mm gauge. This was chosen primarily because it would enable two running lines, one in each direction, to be squeezed into the service tunnel which served as the main artery during construction for workers, spoil and materials. But it also had the advantage that as a widely-used gauge for industrial and mining railways, there was a large amount of second-hand motive power and rolling stock available, saving the construction consortium the need to commission a new and costly range of vehicles for a very limited period.

Despite their apparent similarity, there were three important differences between the two systems radiating from each end of the tunnel. The most fundamental was that while the French system was on a single level, stretching out both to seaward and to landward from the foot of the Sangatte construction shaft, a short but extremely busy section of the English system operated on the rack-and-pinion principle to connect the Lower Shakespeare Cliff construction site, where materials were delivered, with the tunnel workings below. There was even a fragmentary third level of operation, higher up the cliff. A second difference between the systems was that while the track on the English system stood on shingle ballast, the French permanent way was supported by steel girders. And the final contrast concerned signalling and train operation. The English system was operated like a colliery railway from a control point close to the marshalling area beneath Shakespeare Cliff, with basic mechanical (though colour-light) signalling and point control; in the tunnels where it was felt visual signalling systems would break down in the harsh environment, train movements were governed by radio communication between drivers and central controllers, with designated employees on the spot marshalling trains close to the workface. By comparison, the French narrow-gauge lines were controlled electronically from a gleaming console at Sangatte.

The English system began operations in the late summer of 1987, and expanded rapidly. It started above ground at Lower Shakespeare Cliff (the Upper Shakespeare Cliff construction site was not connected to the national rail network) on the construction platform inherited from the 1974 project. Standard-gauge exchange sidings beside the main Folkestone-Dover line enabled tunnel segments and other materials to be transhipped directly onto narrow-gauge trains for onward transport into the tunnel. Altogether there were eight narrow-gauge sidings in two sets of four, with stacks of segments in between; from the more northerly (landward) set of sidings a double-track neck served cement silos and a stockpile of aggregates. Immediately to the south of these sidings stood a four-road workshop where all the locomotives and rolling stock of the English narrow-gauge system were maintained.

Toward the eastern end of the site the sidings converged to form four running lines for construction and spoil trains. Initially these lines led to a point beside the portal of BR's tunnel leading toward Dover, from where the original adit from the 1974 project headed down to the tunnel workings. As soon as a second and more convenient adit was completed between a less easterly point on the construction platform and the marshalling area beneath, joining the tunnel workings further to seaward, this took over as the route for construction trains. The original adit was adapted to take the main conveyor for spoil to the surface (the spoil trains being unloaded below ground), but one track did remain in it alongside the conveyor. In December 1987, during the brief period when the 1974 adit formed the sole rail access to the tunnel (and before the conveyor had been set up), four 8 ton spoil wagons broke away in it from a train being hauled up by a Hunslet battery-electric locomotive when a coupling broke, careering down the adit for 300 metres before derailing at the cost of several minor injuries.

Trains on the five tracks in the adit itself, on a 15 degree (1 in 7) gradient, were hauled by electric rack-and-pinion locomotives. Battery-electric locomotives were tried at first both on the surface, in the adits and in the tunnel workings themselves, the idea being that they could work trains into areas underground where it would not have been safe or practical to instal overhead catenary, notably sections of tunnel that had only recently been excavated and lined. Before long, however, the construction consortium concluded that the battery locomotives could not haul heavy loads reliably over the long distances involved; first more high-powered battery-electric locomotives were ordered, and then the battery fleet was first supplemented and eventually replaced by diesels.

On the rack system - at first through the original adit - TML used locomotives drawing power from overhead wires which began, like the rack rails, only a couple of metres before the tracks started their sharp descent. Shortly before the foot of the adit, the rack tracks diverged to form a bewildering grid: one pair veered sharply left to take construction traffic to and from the three landward tunnels, another pair split into three peeling right as each of the seaward tunnels were reached, each single line at the height of the system's activity immediately doubling to permit two-way working; the single line between the two pairs continued straight ahead into the hoist from which personnel, and occasionally supplies and materials, were lowered from Upper Shakespeare Cliff. The trackwork at surface level connected to this hoist was, however, modest, comprising a small fan of sidings and the odd shed; motive power was provided by a pocket-size diesel shunter.

Rack locomotives handed over almost at once to battery-electrics, and later diesels, on direct trains between the adit and the landward routes, which eventually extended over 8 km to reach the Cheriton terminal site despite the fact that the final

The English tunnel portal, as envisaged in a full-scale model of a Cheriton terminal, built by the British Transport Commission's publicity department in 1962. Note the conventional rolling stock, including BR guard's van. *British Transport Commission*

Vehicles entering a mock-up of a Channel Tunnel vehicle-carrying shuttle at the Road Research Laboratory, Crowthorne, in May 1971. *W.H.R. Godwin*

The route proposed by British Railways in 1973 for a high-speed link between London and the Channel Tunnel. Controversy over the environmental impact and cost of this route was a key factor in the British Government's halting of work on the tunnel early in 1975.

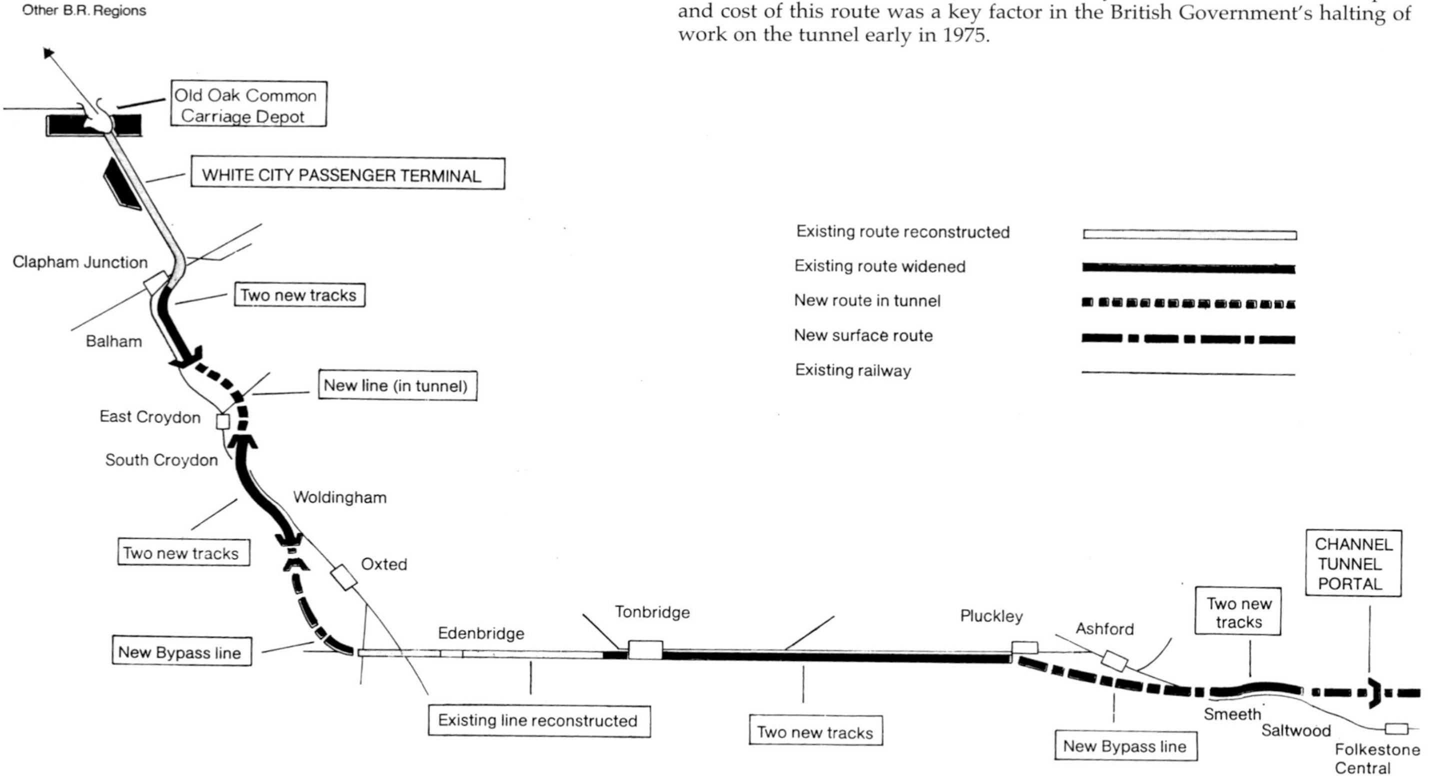

Existing route reconstructed

Existing route widened

New route in tunnel

New surface route

Existing railway

Other B.R. Regions

Old Oak Common Carriage Depot

WHITE CITY PASSENGER TERMINAL

Clapham Junction

Two new tracks

Balham

New line (in tunnel)

East Croydon

South Croydon

Woldingham

Two new tracks

Oxted

New Bypass line

Edenbridge

Existing line reconstructed

Tonbridge

Two new tracks

Pluckley

Ashford

New Bypass line

Two new tracks

Smeeth

Saltwood

Folkestone Central

CHANNEL TUNNEL PORTAL

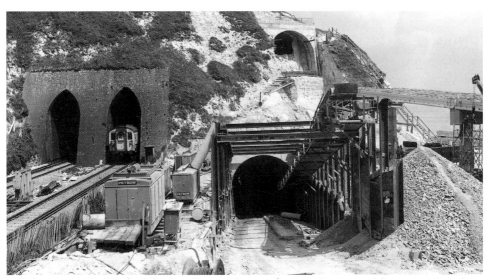

The entrances beside the Folkestone-Dover railway to the two adits prepared for construction of the 1970s tunnel. This photograph was taken on the day in 1973 when breakthrough was achieved on the adit above and to the right, to take road traffic from Upper Shakespeare Cliff to the construction site behind the camera.   *British Channel Tunnel Co. Ltd*

Workmen poised for action in 1973 at the end of the 480 metre tunnel bored into Shakespeare Cliff to the point where the drive to Sangatte subsequently began, only to be abandoned.
British Channel Tunnel Co. Ltd

Sir Alastair Morton, in his initial capacity as deputy chairman and chief executive of Eurotunnel. Against formidable odds, and taking few prisoners, he would see the Channel Tunnel through to completion. *Eurotunnel*

André Bernard, co-chairman of Eurotunnel as the link became reality and Europe's largest construction project turned into a vital transport link. *Eurotunnel*

One of the many protests against the building of a Channel Tunnel - some more spontaneous than others - that erupted across Kent *circa* 1983. *Eurotunnel*

The go-ahead: Margaret Thatcher and François Mitterand endorse the Treaty of Canterbury, signed by Sir Geoffrey Howe and Roland Dumas on 12th February, 1986. *Eurotunnel*

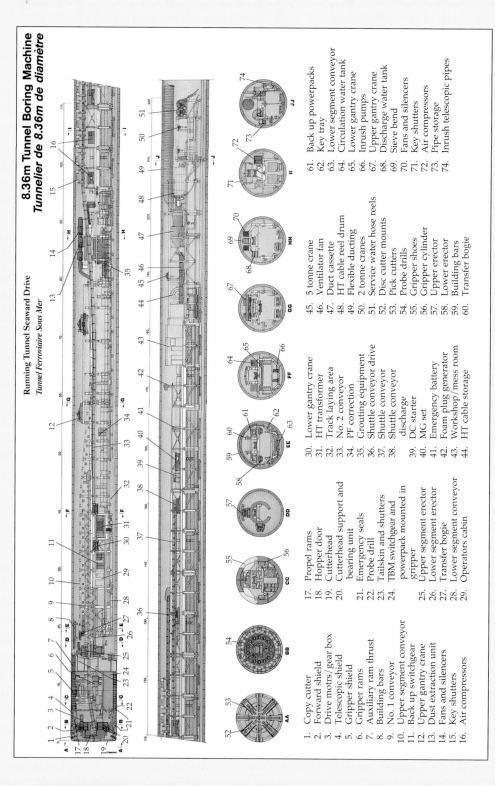

8.36m Tunnel Boring Machine
Tunnelier de 8.36m de diamètre

Running Tunnel Seaward Drive
Tunnel Ferroviaire Sous Mer

1. Copy cutter
2. Forward shield
3. Drive motrs / gear box
4. Telescopic shield
5. Gripper shield
6. Gripper rams
7. Auxiliary ram thrust
8. Building bars
9. No. 1 conveyor
10. Upper segment conveyor
11. Back up switchgear
12. Upper gantry crane
13. Dust extraction unit
14. Fans and silencers
15. Key shutters
16. Air compressors
17. Propel rams
18. Hopper door
19. Cutterhead
20. Cutterhead support and bearing unit
21. Emergency seals
22. Probe drill
23. Tailskin and shutters
24. TBM switchgear and powerpack mounted in gripper
25. Upper segment erector
26. Lower segment erector
27. Transfer bogie
28. Lower segment conveyor
29. Operators cabin
30. Lower gantry crane
31. HT transformer
32. Track laying area
33. No. 2 conveyor
34. PF correction
35. Grouting equipment
36. Shuttle conveyor drive
37. Shuttle conveyor
38. Shuttle conveyor discharge
39. DC starter
40. MG set
41. Emergency battery
42. Foam plug generator
43. Workshop / mess room
44. HT cable storage
45. 5 tonne crane
46. Ventilator fan
47. Duct cassette
48. HT cable reel drum
49. Flexible ducting
50. 2 tonne cranes
51. Service water hose reels
52. Disc cutter mounts
53. Pick cutters
54. Probe drills
55. Gripper shoes
56. Gripper cylinder
57. Upper erector
58. Lower erector
59. Building bars
60. Transfer bogie
61. Back up powerpacks
62. Key tray
63. Lower segment conveyor
64. Circulation water tank
65. Lower gantry crane
66. Inrush pumps
67. Upper gantry crane
68. Discharge water tank
69. Sieve bend
70. Fans and silencers
71. Key shutters
72. Air compressors
73. Pipe storage
74. Inrush telescopic pipes

Above: Cross-section of the British seaward running tunnel TBM, from the cutter and shield (*top left*) and motors through the gripper mechanisms to the conveyors, silencer and ventilation system.

Eurotunnel

Left: Aerial view of the Lower Shakespeare Cliff construction site. Work is well under way but tunnelling still has a long way to go to fill the lagoon in the foreground which is now the Samphire Hoe nature reserve. The 1973 roadway down from the cliff top can be seen at the rear to the right.

Eurotunnel

Breakthrough! French and British workers remove the final sliver of rock separating the two halves of the service tunnel, 1st December, 1990, connecting the countries for the first time since the Ice Age. *Eurotunnel*

A new *entente cordiale*: a historic handshake follows breakthrough on 1st December, 1990. *Bob Sweet*

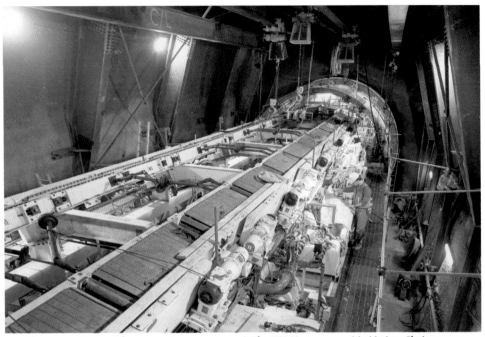

The support train of the seaward running tunnel. The TBM being assembled below Shakespeare Cliff, early in 1989. *Eurotunnel*

The service tunnel in one of its quieter moments, late in the construction process with much traffic now able to use the running tunnels. *Eurotunnel*

The Coquelles terminal at an early stage of construction, facing north. The first bridge to the vehicle loading platforms can be seen top centre, the curve towards the tunnel bottom left, the SNCF Boulogne-Calais line on the right.

The grille which marked the end of the French section of the service tunnel, March 1991. The narrow gauge track ran on only a short distance - it was a further year before the two systems were briefly connected. *Author*

Activity in the British crossover chamber, March 1991. Note the giant ventilation tubes. *Author*

The Cheriton terminal site with construction under way. The M20 motorway is to the right, the railway trackbed to the tunnel portal (*top*) bisects the picture and the loop for shuttle trains is taking shape in the foreground, with the hamlet of Newington only a stone's throw away.

Tracklaying on the Cheriton terminal site at an advanced stage: the main line to the tunnel runs left to right to enter the English portal (*top right*); behind it are the vehicle loading platforms.

Eurotunnel

TML Channel Tunnel handover to Eurotunnel at the tunnel portal on the UK side on 10th December, 1993, with Bo-Bo-Bo shuttle locomotive No. 9016 in the background. The line-up is (*left to right*) Peter Costain (Costain), Tony Palmer (Taylor Woodrow), Neville Simms (Tarmac), Sir Alastair Morton (Eurotunnel), Joe Dwyer (Wimpey) and Sir Robert Davidson (Balfour Beatty). *Brian Morrison*

The Queen and President Mitterand declare the tunnel well and truly open, even if full services are months away, Coquelles, 6th May, 1994. *Eurotunnel*

Cheriton on 6th May, 1994 as Bo-Bo-Bo No. 9017 arrives with the Queen and President Mitterand having brought them back from the Channel Tunnel inauguration ceremonies on the French side. *Brian Morrison*

As part of the opening celebrations a steam shuttle, 'The Harbour Master', was operated from Folkestone Harbour station on 7th May, 1994. Motive power came in the form of BR Standard 2-6-4T No. 80079. *David Winter*

A rare shot of the minimal construction railway at Upper Shakespeare Cliff, March 1991.
Author

Schoma 185 hp narrow gauge diesel No. RS009 prepares to head down the service tunnel from the marshalling area below Shakespeare Cliff.   *Eurotunnel*

kilometre to the portal was excavated by roadheaders under the New Austrian Tunnelling Method and not by rail-served TBMs. However, despite the existence of a direct connection, many trains for the landward section went first from the new adit to the marshalling area for the change of traction to be made. Once out in the open at Cheriton, the narrow-gauge tracks played a modest role in shifting materials for construction of the terminal.

To seaward, rack traction continued for over 200 metres to the marshalling area, the 'pit bottom' which was the operational heart of the English narrow-gauge construction railway. It was here that trains carrying workers, equipment, materials, supplies and empty spoil wagons for sites far along the tunnel were formed, and dispatched in the correct order behind powerful pocket-sized locomotives. In the marshalling area the flow of wagons and loaded trains brought down the newer of the two adits by rack locomotives was joined by manriders whose occupants had come down the hoist from Upper Shakespeare Cliff, and by trains of empty spoil wagons bound for the workface and other excavation sites which had discharged their previous loads into the bunker feeding the conveyor that ran up the original adit to Lower Shakespeare Cliff. It was also in the marshalling area that battery-electric locomotives lined up to recharge until their use was discontinued.

From the marshalling area, in the three parallel erection chambers where the seaward TBMs had been put together, double-track routes ran into each of the tunnels (though for the first few months' operation of the running tunnel TBMs a single track was managed with, the spoil and segment trains being shunted into position by a locomotive at the rear which later hauled them out), and continued right up to the workface.

The service tunnel was the main artery throughout the excavation process despite its tighter diameter and headroom, the latter reflected in the very limited loading gauge and clearances of wagons and manriders alike. By the time breakthrough was achieved, it stretched over 30 km from the marshalling area to the rear of the TBM, and through it absolutely everything had to be transported - including spoil from the vast undersea English crossover chamber which was partially excavated before the TBMs reached it. The service tunnel in the region of a crossover was during construction as noisy, as dimly-lit (though not totally dark) and as claustrophobic as at any other point along its route; it slewed to one side so that the running tunnels could open into the chamber. Visitors to the crossover disembarked from their manrider on a section of plain track once other movements on the section had been halted, before stumbling to their objective through a narrow tunnel floored with powdery (and usually dryish) chalk.

The ride through the service tunnel was always slow and jolting. Although there was officially a general speed limit of 30 kph it was seldom reached because of the weight of trains and the volume of traffic, and many local speed restrictions were always in force, mostly around working sites *en route*. The need for these was underlined by the fact that three of the fatalities in the tunnel occurred when workers were struck by moving trains. After the first, on 23rd January, 1989, all workers underground were ordered to wear high-visibility clothing, pedestrian refuges were sunk into the tunnel walls and flagmen were stationed at all working sites along the system's running track. Space in the service tunnel was tight, and as the number of crossovers along it was limited any sort of work inside it required single-line working for several hundred metres, inevitably causing disruption to the heavy construction traffic, or total closure.

The gradients within the service tunnel as it dipped from either end also presented a hazard; in June 1992 two runaway concrete mixer wagons in the English landward service tunnel achieved a speed of 50 kph, but fortunately no other traffic was in the way. With the exception of a section 2.5 km long where the tunnel dipped as it approached the French coast, the gradient profile of the workings formed a perfect 'U', with the lowest point 35.2 km from Cheriton and 24.8 km from Coquelles. While the tunnel was engineered to avoid unnecessarily steep gradients, around a third of it, mostly at the English end, was bored to a ruling gradient of 1 in 91 or 1 in 92. This would not be much of a challenge for electric-hauled shuttle and international trains operating at high speeds, but heavy construction traffic hauled by diminutive battery locomotives or diesels it was quite enough.

The narrow-gauge lines in the running tunnels never carried the same volume of traffic as those in the service tunnel, except during the months after the service tunnel breakthrough when spoil from the running tunnel TBMs continued to be hauled out through these bores until they, too, broke through and were halted. By this stage the service tunnel had become the formal channel of communication between Shakespeare Cliff and Sangatte, though the two national systems continued to be run separately. The 'English' and 'French' tracks were separated by an opening steel grille with perhaps 200 m of rail-less concrete trackbed on either side. The systems were only joined briefly in April 1992, allowing the Duke of Edinburgh to make a unique through journey by manrider from Shakespeare Cliff to Sangatte and TML to transfer a batch of Schoma shunters from one system to the other.

Once past the breakthrough point, the process was reversed, traffic building up steadily as the French section of the service tunnel headed toward Sangatte. The average spoil train on the French narrow gauge system comprised seven or eight wagons, with a locomotive at each end.

More brightly lit than their English counterpart, the French workings had a clinical appearance despite having largely been dug through very difficult and moist strata. Once again, construction trains initially were electrically-hauled, the landward section from Sangatte boasting overhead catenary and trains operating under battery power nearer the work sites. As on the English system, electric traction gradually gave way to diesels during construction, the French catenary being removed in February 1992.

As the service tunnel approached the bottom of the 'well' at Sangatte the double tracks in the service and running tunnels opened out into a parallel series of marshalling areas which were interlinked to allow a degree of operating flexibility. Close to the foot of the shaft, spoil trains discharged their load six wagons at a time into 'tipplers'; the chalky spoil was then mixed with water to form a substance resembling yoghurt and pumped up the shaft to the settling ponds above. Because the high water content of the spoil at the French end even before that mixing process made it seem more like mud, the empty trucks were then hosed down to prevent a slimy and dangerous build-up forming on the tracks before being sent back into the tunnels for a further rendezvous with a TBM. Other traffics, notably tunnel segments, were winched up and down the Sangatte shaft, with wagons being loaded and unloaded at surface level. Most maintenance of the French construction locomotives and rolling stock was carried out below ground; eight ton battery packs from the battery-electric construction locomotives had to be hauled halfway up the shaft every so often to be recharged in a special facility.

To landward of the Sangatte shaft, the construction tracks continued in the running and service tunnels until they broke surface in the Beussingue Trench 2.8

km away. The lines ran on in daylight to a yard and depot at Coquelles and a waste disposal area, later being cut back to form 'necks' within the trench, allowing trains emerging from one tunnel to return to Sangatte through another.

Initially workers on both systems were transported to and from their sites in loco-hauled manriding wagons, but as the workforce grew manriding trains were introduced, comprising rakes of 'passenger' cars with a cab at each end. Workers in the English manriders sat in twos, the openings through which they boarded the train protected at first purely by a guardrail but later, after a number of minor accidents, by thick webbing; no such precautions were taken at the French end, where the casualty rate was nevertheless consistently lower.

As the tunnel lengthened, workers travelling to their sites (and especially those bound for one of the TBMs) faced an ever-longer journey; by the time breakthrough was achieved journey times of 90 minutes each way were not uncommon. When the first press party made its transit in March 1991, the journey by English and French manriders from Shakespeare Cliff to Sangatte took nearly six hours in all, including the obligatory section on foot between the two systems. At this stage all traffic not concerned with the running tunnel TBMs was having to use the service tunnel, which particularly near the under-shore construction bases was a noisy and congested artery.

The wide variety of materials carried required an equal range of specialised wagons: flat trucks for tunnel segments, bolster wagons for rails to extend the construction railway, higher-sided wagons for loads of grout and electric cabling. In addition fleets of special 'bullet' wagons were used to convey large tonnages of concrete and special types of mortar to points along the route. Most loaded trains coming away from the workface comprised tipper-wagons full of spoil, which were unloaded into hoppers in the two marshalling areas beneath Shakespeare Cliff and Sangatte.

Once the TBMs had finished their work, the narrow-gauge railways continued for a time to perform a vital role carrying personnel and materials; in the service tunnel fitting of water pipes and electrical equipment in the apex of the tunnel was carried out from platform trucks on the narrow-gauge lines until the roof was concreted.

The narrow-gauge operation, by now entirely diesel-operated away from the adit at Shakespeare Cliff, began to wind down in mid-1992 and that autumn a start began on removing the construction tracks in the service tunnel so that rubber-tyred vehicles could operate there. In the English tunnels the construction rail was removed by a moving crane that ran along a ledge moulded into each side of the tunnel. Most construction track was removed from the French tunnels during October 1992. A special train to mark the end of the construction railway made one last trip into the tunnel from Shakespeare Cliff on 22nd March, 1993, and the very last section of rail, from the single rack-and-pinion track left in Adit 1 at Shakespeare Cliff, was taken up that May.

Narrow Gauge Locomotives and Rolling Stock

The hardware operated on the English system alone was impressive: 144 locomotives, 16 powered manriders plus 900 segment-carrying flat cars, materials cars, muck wagons, manriding cars and a 'hygiene train' which serviced each TBM at every shift change. And even more impressive was the 94 per cent availability achieved round the clock, 365 days a year, by TML's maintenance team. On the

French side a total of 700 items of rolling stock - locomotives, manriders and wagons - were in use at the height of operations.

The rack sections through the original adit and later Adit 2 were operated by 18 Hunslet/GMT electric locomotives each weighing 20 tonnes. Rated at 350 hp, they were equipped with batteries for surface operation in the segment stacking area. The first batch of eight was numbered RR1 to RR8, the initial four being delivered on 15th July, 1987. A further 10 electric rack locomotives from Hunslet were numbered RR11 to RR20; RR17 has been preserved by Eurotunnel at Cheriton.

There were also two 150 hp diesel rescue locomotives, RR9 and RR10, delivered by Hunslet/GMT between the two electric batches; other narrow-gauge engines on the project were painted white, but the rescue locomotives were turned out in green. RR9 had two 'lives' with TML: withdrawn from duties in the adit and transported to the consortium's Sevington disposal centre by 16th August, 1991, it was brought back to Cheriton the following month and put to work in the service tunnel from the English portal, being finally signed off by July 1992. Originally earmarked for preservation, it was disposed of in 1997 and RR10, which had arrived at Sevington during 1992, was kept by Eurotunnel instead.

The heavy work of shifting materials in the tunnels was initially carried out entirely by battery-electric locomotives, drawing power from 550-volt overhead catenary set into overhead parallel bars and hauling the heaviest trains in pairs. Hunslet first supplied twenty 175 hp locomotives numbered RA1 to RA20, the first eight arriving on site in 1987. However these proved underpowered, and TML ordered from Hunslet a further 40 battery-electrics, this time rated at 200 hp, which were numbered RA21 to RA60; the first two were delivered at the end of 1988 but the bulk arrived in 1990. The original 20 were withdrawn by early 1992, ten (RA15, 16, 19, 20, 17, 18, 5, 6, 7 and 8) being converted by Hunslet to 200 hp diesel shunters with Deutz engines and returned to the tunnel numbered RS301 to 310 respectively. (They would later also be converted to standard gauge, details below.) The last six survivors of the first batch - RA1, 2, 4, 9, 10 and 13 - had to contend with a steady cutback in the overhead catenary on the construction system during 1991 and in their final months had to be matched with flat-wagons converted into makeshift battery carriers. The final survivor of RA1-20 in its original form was RA14, which was returned to Hunslet in June 1994, around which time the rest of the class were broken up.

The later batch of battery-electrics carried out the lion's share of work on construction and spoil trains until withdrawn in favour of diesels by the end of 1991. All 40 battery locomotives still in stock, and some other surplus motive power, were then conveyed in redundant segment-carrying wagons to TML's equipment disposal site at Sevington sidings, where a price tag of £50,000 each was put on them; most failed to attract bidders for further use and were broken up between 1994 and 1997, but RA55-59 were returned to Hunslet and rebuilt as four locomotives for use on constructing London Underground's Jubilee Line extension.

The landward tunnels were never electrified during the construction phase, having fewer problems with ventilation, and for them, initially, a fleet of 53 assorted diesels was acquired from Schoma. There were thirty-three 185 hp engines numbered RS001-027, RS032/33 and RS042-45 for use on spoil and other heavy trains; eighteen 150 hp locomotives for lighter equipment trains numbered RS034-41 and RS046-55; and two 200 hp tandem units for rescue duties, numbered RS028-31. All but RS001-6 were delivered new; this batch had been constructed in 1980-82 for Breschling, Austria, and were reconditioned by Schoma for work on the tunnel. The very first Schoma locomotive to be delivered was named *Tinkerbell* by its crew; almost all the others eventually gained more orthodox girls' names.

When a connection between the two narrow-gauge systems was briefly made in the spring of 1992, 10 Schoma diesels from the batches RS001-45, by then surplus to requirements at the English end, were cascaded through to assist with dismantling the French system. The first items of stock to be exchanged through the tunnel, they were Nos. RS007, 008, 009, 011, 013, 014, 019, 020, 021, 022 and 026. Many of those that stayed had little time more to work; by early June 1992 diesels from the tunnel workings were following the battery-electrics to Sevington for disposal, though the final narrow-gauge construction trains did not run until early the following year.

A separate fleet of diesels was acquired for shunting in the yard above ground at Shakespeare Cliff. Seven 150 hp shunters numbered RS101 to RS107 were bought from RFS, together with two Simplex 112 hp shunters which originated with the National Coal Board (RS201 and 202). The former were soon downrated to 100 hp because of wheel slip, and as battery-electric traction fell out of favour a number were sent down the adit to work in the tunnel itself.

For passenger haulage, TML bought from Schoma sixteen 80 hp type D60 diesel manriding units numbered RU001 to RU016; nine were three-car units and seven two-car.

The UK-based Schoma fleet, distinguishable from most other construction locomotives and rolling stock by its boxy, upright look, included two curiosities. The first was the Maggiemobile, the unpowered manrider from one of the three-car units (maker's number 5069) that had been fitted out with carpets and upholstered seats for the expected visit of the Prime Minister to mark the tunnel breakthrough. By then Mrs Thatcher was out of office, and the Maggiemobile missed its moment of fame; however it was used occasionally by VIPs, among them the Duke of Edinburgh. Used on the final narrow-gauge run in March 1993, the Maggiemobile was normally sandwiched between two spruced-up power car manriders nicknamed the 'Disneys'.

The other unusual vehicles were 'winch wagons' numbered RZ100 to RZ108: former flat wagons that were converted to propel themselves along the tunnel during fitting-out without the need to tie up a locomotive. As they could be required to stop at one metre intervals, propulsion by means of a winch was quite adequate.

Most of the locomotives and rolling stock from these two immense narrow-gauge systems passed on without ceremony for scrap - especially the battery-electrics whose use elsewhere was limited - or to work on other construction projects. A handful, including a Hunslet battery locomotive and a Schoma railcar, remained on site until 2000 before being cut up. Most of the 55 Schomas did find a further use, on schemes ranging from the Jubilee Line extension to the Stor Belt in Denmark, the Valencia, Taipei, Josephburg (Germany) and Lisbon Metros, the Lesotho Highlands water project and the Heathrow Express tunnels. In addition, three of the second batch of more powerful Hunslet battery-electrics survive in preservation, RA38 at the Eurotunnel exhibition centre at Cheriton and RA36 at the National Railway Museum, York; a third has been acquired by Dover Transport Museum.

Of the diesels used, the Schoma 3-car manrider RU013 was preserved by Eurotunnel at Cheriton; other manriding vehicles were resold by the makers as far away as Australia. One trailer car from a manriding unit has been preserved at Dover Transport Museum, as has a Hunslet diesel locomotive. Both the 1979 Simplex ex-NCB diesel shunters used at Shakespeare Cliff were also bought for preservation: RS201, rebuilt to 2 ft gauge, by a supporter of the Midland Railway Centre's Golden Valley narrow-gauge line where it eventually entered service in May 1999, and RS202 by the

Leighton Buzzard Narrow Gauge Railway Society; also regauged to 2 ft, it arrived at the Bedfordshire line the following month.

The French narrow gauge construction fleet is less well documented, partly because of tight security at Coquelles and also because fewer French enthusiasts take an interest in industrial locomotives. Motive power was at first supplied by 69 battery-electric locomotives, from SIG of Neuhausen in Switzerland, with motors from GEC-Alsthom, and 50 four-wheel diesel-hauled manrider vehicles from Senafer. Later at least 31 diesel industrial locomotives operated on the French site. Apart from the Schoma diesels later acquired from TML, all locomotives on the French narrow-gauge system had twin cabs.

The SIG battery-electrics (with UK-manufactured batteries) were in two classes. There were 24 20-tonners, numbered TU20 58001-24, and 45 more powerful 38-tonners, numbered TU 59001-45. The Senafer manriders comprised 22 power cars numbered TU51001-22 (though 51010 was a red-painted fire and rescue vehicle) and 28 trailers. Each of the power units could work as a single-unit railcar or hauling one, two or even occasionally three trailers. These latter were numbered TU20 51101-6, 51201-12 and 51051-60.

Some workings at the French end were diesel-hauled from the start, but the proportion steadily increased from 1990 and a wide miscellany of motive power was used. First came a handful of small 0-4-0 shunters in the TU20 50xxx series, one being no more than a permanent way trolley. There were at least five more four-wheelers numbered TU20 55003-7, and one tiny 0-4-0 numbered TU20 55668. Class 'EM20' 56001-7 (and maybe more) were standard type D25 French small industrial diesels. The Schoma four-wheelers transferred from the English end were renumbered TU20 56601-10. At least two Belgian-made 0-4-0s were taken on and numbered TU20 56402 and 56404, and a larger French 0-4-0 operated as TU20 56503.

Standard Gauge Construction Trains

Once the boring of the running tunnels was completed, the way was open for the laying of permanent way for the international and shuttle trains that would ultimately use them and for the installation of the panoply of equipment required for safe and rapid railway operation. And as soon as standard-gauge trackwork was laid into the tunnel portals in July 1991, a new generation of construction trains moved to supplant the narrow-gauge workhorses which, by the autumn of the following year, had almost vanished after barely five years of operation. For a brief period the two systems coexisted, and at the foot of Adit 2 beneath Shakespeare Cliff a crude temporary 'swing bridge' had to be constructed to enable narrow-gauge traffic using the service tunnel to pass over the standard-gauge track which had already been already laid in a running tunnel and was in use by construction trains.

While the narrow-gauge construction networks revolved around the marshalling areas beneath Shakespeare Cliff and Sangatte with a minimal presence above ground, the standard-gauge traffic involved in fitting out the tunnel operated from the open-air terminal sites at Cheriton and Coquelles, in whose preparation such trains were also involved. Operationally the construction railway was now less flexible, as each running tunnel contained a single track only and the two-track versatility of the narrow gauge line through the service tunnel was lost with its removal late in 1992. Only in the crossover chambers could construction trains on the running tracks switch tunnels.

The first task of the standard-gauge construction fleet, brought together like its diminutive predecessor from sites and railways all over Europe, was tracklaying, initially in the terminal areas and before long in the tunnel itself. Though delivering the 'strings' of track was a major job in itself, the construction fleet would be involved before the tunnel was handed over to Eurotunnel in December 1993 in several other kinds of work. Most demanding was the haulage of giant 580 m concrete-making trains which could reach 2,000 tonnes in weight; the exhaust fumes from the high-powered locomotives needed to shift these trains alarmed the health and safety authorities, who required all diesel locomotives working in the tunnel to run with separately-towed 'scrubber' units to filter out the most harmful gases. Other construction trains installed the overhead catenary, took in pipes for the tunnel's cooling system and laid electric cables, while in the run-up to the handover of the tunnel special loading gauge test trains were run.

Mr John Davy
6 Riverway
Wednesbury
WS10 0DN

Standard Gauge Construction Locomotives and Stock

The first standard-gauge locomotives used on heavy construction and tracklaying trains in the tunnel were eight former Deutsche Bundesbahn (DB) class '211' B-B 1,100 hp centre-cab diesel hydraulics, still in their DB black livery. Built by Deutz, Henschel and Krupp and put into service on branch lines from 1978 to replace steam traction, they were withdrawn from DB's Wurzburg depot in 1986-87 and arrived at the Cheriton base of the Channel Tunnel Tracklaying Group (CTTG) in the spring of 1991. They were numbered 21 (ex-DB211.118.3), 22 (211.134.2), 23 (211.267.0), 24 (211.118.5), 25 (211.160.7), 26 (211.189.6), 27 (211.162.3) and 28 (211.249.8). Initially they operated right through the tunnel, but by the end of the year they were relegated to work on the English terminal site after making themselves unpopular on works trains in the tunnel because of the amount of smoke they generated. None of the '211s' was retained by Eurotunnel after being transferred to the French end at the start of 1993, though a couple saw further use in Switzerland.

Despite the '211s' propensity for making smoke, TML brought in a steam locomotive to test the tunnel's smoke detection system. The locomotive which steamed into the tunnel through the Beussingue portal on 11th June, 1993 was former SNCF 4-6-0 No. 230.G.353, the sole survivor of a class of 170 built at the turn of the century.

From December 1991 until the following June most standard gauge construction trains were hauled by former BR class '20' single-ended 1,000 hp Bo-Bo diesels built by English Electric in 1957; some of the class are still in service today with Direct Rail Services, and were until recently on provincial lines in France. In all 30 class '20s' were used on the project: a trial batch of four, a main order of 21 and five for spares. They were hired from RFS Engineering, Doncaster, which had refurbished them after acquisition from BR and even loaned them from the odd preservation society. They operated from both Cheriton and Coquelles, where they played an important role too in the construction of the French terminal site, between November 1991 and June 1992, numbers on the French side being augmented at the end of that period and some staying in use well into the following year. There were never more than a dozen on the project at any one time, and the swift comings and goings were reflected in the fact that there were briefly two class '20s' on site each bearing the CTTG numbers 31 and 32. The full roster of class '20s' was as follows:

BR No.		RFS No.	CTTG No.	Arrived	Left		Based
20001	(a, m)	2011	11	2.3.92	by 5.93		Coquelles
20040						(f)	
20047	(k)	2004	4	19.12.91	by 8.93		Coquelles
20048	(b, m)	2014	33	18.3.92	25.5.93	(l)	Cheriton
20051				23.1.92		(g)	
20056	(c)	2012	12	5.3.92	by 5.93		Coquelles
20066			31	6.1.92	1.3.92		
				Returned 26.6.92		(j)	Cheriton
20084	(k)	2002	32	23.12.91	by 17.9.93	(l)	Cheriton
20085				10.2.92	-.8.93	(h)	
20087			29	5.11.91	-.6.93	(l, j)	Cheriton
20088	(o)	2017	37	10.2.92	-.8.93	(l)	Cheriton
20095	(k)	2020	39	29.5.92	19.8.93	(l)	Cheriton
20102	(k)	2008	8	24.1.92	by 8.93		Coquelles
20105	(o)	2016	36	10.2.92	18.8.93	(l)	Cheriton
20107	(d)	2013	34	18.3.92	-.4.93	(l)	Cheriton
20108	(n)	2001	1	23.12.91	by 9.93		Coquelles
20113	(k)	2003	31	23.12.91	.9.93	(l)	Cheriton
20119	(i)		32	6.1.92	1.3.92	(k)	Cheriton
20120	(k)	2009	9	25.1.92	by 8.93		Coquelles
20127	(k)	2018	38	5.5.92	23.8.93	(l)	Cheriton
20132	(o)			-.9.92	-.6.93	(k)	
20133	(k)	2005	5	19.12.91	by 9.93		Coquelles
20138	(o)		30	5.11.91	19.8.93	(l)	Cheriton
20145	(n)	2019	29	31.5.92	23.8.93	(l)	Cheriton
20159	(k)	2010	10	25.1.92	-.6.93		Coquelles
20166	(e)	2015	35	21.3.92	by 27.6.93	(l)	Cheriton
20173						(f)	
20175	(k)	2007	7	31.1.92	by 8.93		Coquelles
20194	(k)	2006	6	19.12.91	by 9.93		Coquelles
20208				2.1.92		(g)	

(a) Owned by Class 20 Locomotive Society.
(b) Owned by Midland Class 20 Association, returned to the Midland Railway Centre.
(c) Owned by Caledonian Railway.
(d) Owned by East Lancs RPS, returned to Flixborough Wharf, Humberside.
(e) Owned by Bodmin & Wenford Railway.
(f) Scrapped at MC Metals, Glasgow.
(g) Scrapped at RFS Kilnhurst.
(h) Scrapped at RFS Doncaster.
(i) Stored at Toton 1995-2003, bought for preservation and transferred to Barrow Hill for restoration.
(j) To BR Derby and Toton.
(k) Subsequently owned by Direct Rail Services, 20113/175 scrapped at Carlisle 12/03.
(l) After use/storage at Coquelles.
(m) Also used later on construction of the CTRL.
(n) At MoD Smalmstown until broken up by Harry Needle Railroad Co., 2005.
(o) By 2005 stored at MoD Smalmstown.

BR's ubiquitous class '08' 0-6-0 diesel shunters were also heavily represented, at least 21 being hired in by contractors. At various times Nos. 08331, 08407, 08417, 08472, 08498, 08517, 08542, 08562, 08603, 08700, 08705, 08713, 08764, 08785, 08802,

08823, 08828, 08834, 08866, 08874 and others all operated on site, many of them returning direct to BR. For electrification work from Cheriton, Balfour Beatty hired No. 08596 from RFS; renumbered 19, it bore the distinctive RFS livery of grey with a blue and yellow tick on each side. (All the '08s' on site hired from RFS bore names ending in -ence, for instance No. 08764 *Florence*.)

Numerous other diesel locomotives were hired by TML, CTTG and individual contractors like Balfour Beatty for work on the closing stages of the project. The first to be delivered for TML, in November 1991, were five 427 hp diesel-electrics (Brush Nos. 801-805) which had been used by the Tyne and Wear Metro to haul works trains and carry out rescue duties until displaced by three new Hunslets. Brought to Cheriton and repainted at Dollands Moor from their old yellow Metro livery, the Brush diesels were renumbered 60 to 64. Redundant from mid-1994, they later saw service at Normanby Park steelworks, Scunthorpe.

TML's next locomotives were already old Tunnel hands: eight of the 10 Hunslet former narrow-gauge electric and later diesel locomotives from the RS301-310 batch. Converted to standard gauge, renumbered 65 to 72 and painted yellow, they were delivered from the end of November 1991. After two to three years' service on site, they returned to Schoma for yet another rebuild and new life.

TML also hired three diesel shunters from Yorkshire Engine Company, Rotherham, between May and September 1992, numbering them 56-58. The first was Yorkshire No. 2807, the second Thomas Hill No. 173V, and the third F. Hibbert No. 3958.

CTTG, meanwhile, reinforced its fleet in the spring of 1992 with four Ruston & Hornsby MoD-type shunters hired from Yorkshire Engine Co. Three, whose Army numbers had been 426, 428 and 421, were renumbered 91-93; one of these later returned to MoD service at Bicester along with the fourth shunter, whose Army number is unknown. A further Ruston & Hornsby shunter, works No. 417889, was briefly hired to work at Cheriton from Trackwork Associates of Doncaster.

Balfour Beatty also put into service Hunslet No. 7106 (Yorkshire Engine Co. No. L101), which it renumbered 20. In addition the contractor took on a pair of ex-DB Gmeinder diesel shunters built in 1955/56 and withdrawn from Göttingen depot in 1990; renumbered 50 (ex-DB 323.674) and 51 (DB 323.539), these tiny twins (weighing just 17 tonnes each) went on to Hong Kong to work on the Lantau Airport project and after spells in store at Derby and Ashford were put on sale by Balfour Beatty in April 2003. Contractors on the project also operated a number of smaller shunters, as well as Unimog road-railers.

A highly mixed brigade of standard-gauge construction locomotives was also hired by contractors for work at Coquelles, using from May 1993 the old narrow-gauge traction maintenance depot which had been re-gauged. This also housed passenger stock used by the contractors. At least one of the ex-DB class '211s' banished from the tunnel showed up there, and the ragtag fleet also boasted TT9, a Bo-Bo diesel-electric built by General Electric in the United States and shipped over to France after D-Day, TT10, a 1946 Baldwin-built A1A-A1A diesel-electric which the SNCF had numbered 62073 and was now owned by the heritage group Trains à Vapeur du Touraine, and two ex-SNCF Co-Co diesel-electrics, formerly numbered 65004 and 65012; these too came from Trains à Vapeur du Touraine. When the first Eurostar set was hauled through the tunnel to Britain, the locomotive taking the strain was another SNCF A1A-A1A, No. 68041. There was also a Bo-Bo diesel-electric built by Brissonneau and Lotz in 1962, a 4-wheel diesel-hydraulic shunter built by Renault in the same year, a Spie et Batignolles diesel-mechanical four-wheeler similar to the SNCF type 3M and a Moyse diesel-electric 0-4-0.

For the closing stages of work at the French end, CTTG acquired three 34-ton Sentinel locomotives (works Nos. 10037, 10070 and 10164) in March 1992 from RFS, Kilnhurst. One with a Rolls-Royce engine, works No. 10280, went to Coquelles as well.

With the tunnel open, the locomotives used in construction became redundant and were returned to their hirers as a new maintenance fleet was acquired. Most of the construction rolling stock similarly became redundant, as purpose-built stock was sought for ongoing maintenance.

*   *   *   *   *

Once permanent track was in place in the tunnel and on the lines leading to it, an exotic variety of diesel units and railcars was used to ferry workers into and through the bores. Because a speed limit of 30 kph was enforced until signalling was installed, the gearboxes of the power units were modified to prevent this being exceeded. As with the freight locomotives, their exhausts were also adapted.

From the British end, the need was met by three 3-car diesel-mechanical 'heritage' slam-door units dating from 1959 which had been ousted from Birmingham suburban lines by more modern stock; they ran in their BR blue and grey livery. Stock numbers were 51076, 51099 and 51149 (a class '119' Gloucester-built cross-country unit), 51372, 51414 and 53897 (a class '117' Pressed Steel suburban unit), and 59753, 59754 and 59490 (a Derby-built class '117' with a Pressed Steel trailer). The introduction of the diesel multiple units in place of the narrow-gauge manriders transformed the task of getting tunnel workers to their tasks, even with stops and the strict speed limit. With each unit carrying up to 370 people, a rigid timetable was operated at the start of every shift. One train ran 'fast' from Shakespeare Cliff to the middle crossover, then stopped to drop off workers until it reached the notional junction with the French tunnels, where it waited until the end of the shift; a second stopped at the crossover, then ran non-stop to the point where the first train was waiting. Up to 30 works trains a shift then moved in behind them. Passengers entered and left the dmu trains via the guard's door.

From the French end, workers were conveyed by the most bizarre vehicles to have transited the tunnel to date: five single railcars formerly of the SNCF's series X3800, better known as 'Picassos'. These extraordinary vehicles, built in the early 1950s, were instantly recognisable by the 'bubble' to one side of the roof in mid-carriage from which the driver operated the train, usually as a double unit; the overall effect was that of an open gull-wing door on a de Lorean car, or a South Eastern & Chatham Railway (SE&CR) 'Birdcage' brake turned on its side. The 'Picassos' were acquired from various private railways to which the SNCF had sold them, and were refurbished and given a standard white livery by the Société Auxiliaire de Diesels (SAD) at Florange, near Thionville, before arriving at Coquelles.

These railcars were supplemented by former Belgian Railways No. 4001, a single three-car unit in distinctive red and yellow livery hired by TML from the Chemin de Fer des Trois Vallées.

These vehicles handled staff traffic both before and after the catenary was switched on in September 1993 and the commissioning of shuttle trains, Eurostars and class '92' freight locomotives began. The first standard gauge 'passenger' working for the European Investment Bank on 12th March, 1993, comprised a rake of 'Corail' carriages hauled by SNCF diesel No. 66411. And when the completed project was handed over to Eurotunnel on 10th December, 1993, the dignitaries who travelled through the tunnel from Cheriton were conveyed in a four-car Thameslink dual-voltage unit – No. 319009 - borrowed for the day from Network South-East and named *Coquelles* to commemorate the occasion. Class '319s' were used again in the hours after the Royal opening of the tunnel to allow the public a little way in.

When the overhead catenary in the English terminal was energised on 25th April, 1992, a BR electric locomotive - class '87' No. 87205 *County of Cheshire* - was brought in to test it.

After the catenary in the running tunnels was energised that September and more so after the tunnel was handed over to Eurotunnel in December 1993, trial trains on the terminal layouts and in the tunnel itself were increasingly worked by electric haulage.

Construction Services Above Ground

Construction of the Channel Tunnel generated many extra freight workings on the national railways of Britain and France as aggregates and other materials were brought to the working sites. The impact on BR was considerably greater for three reasons: tunnel segments were not cast on site as they were at Sangatte, and had to be brought by special trains from the fabrication plant on the Isle of Grain, the Sangatte site was not rail-connected, and more of the tunnel was in any event bored and fitted-out from the English end.

Pride of place must go to the segment trains from Grain to Shakespeare Cliff. The segment works at Grain was on the site now taken up by Thamesport, close to the eastern tip of the island and near the end of the freight-only branch from Hoo Junction yard, east of Gravesend; the plant received its supplies of aggregate by sea through its own dedicated wharf on the Medway. It lay close to the long-abandoned passenger ferry terminal of Port Victoria (a steam passenger service from Gravesend that forked north to Allhallows-on-Sea from Stoke Junction Halt, a mile or so west of the plant, had lingered on to the end of 1961).

Production of segments began in October 1987, and the first trainload of TML bogie boxwagons left Grain on 27th November. The traffic had been earmarked for haulage by new class '60s', but there were not enough in service until 1990 so almost invariably the segment trains were hauled by pairs of 'Crompton' class '33' diesels; to mark the thousandth shipment on 8th November, 1990 No. 33021 was named *Isle of Grain* and No. 33051 *Shakespeare Cliff*. But for the formal opening of the plant by the Transport Minister David Mitchell on 23rd March, 1988 the preserved Bulleid 'West Country' Pacific No. 34016 *Bodmin* was brought in to do the honours, though only for the initial portion of the journey.

Between November 1987 and the end of May 1991, 1,250 segment trains made the run; during peak production, three trains of 24 wagons made the journey each day. Positioned for loading at Grain by Rolls-Royce diesel shunters hired from BP, the segment trains were too heavy to use the steeply-graded direct route to Dover via Faversham and the North Kent line. Instead they made a 100-mile loop to Shakespeare Cliff by way of Dartford, the Lee curve, Sevenoaks, Tonbridge and Ashford, nudging 60 mph south of Orpington. After 12 hours unloading at Shakespeare Cliff, the now far lighter trains returned to Grain by the direct route, reversing at Hoo Junction.

Shakespeare Cliff enjoyed from the outset the bonus of direct rail access (to the Folkestone-Dover route); when tunnelling was at its height, 7,500 tonnes of materials were being delivered there every day.

The segment trains were the best-publicised traffic, but amounted to barely one-fifth of the total supplying the tunnel. For a start, separate trains of ballast, sand and cement for Shakespeare Cliff also originated from the Grain branch, class '37' and class '56' diesels providing motive power. In addition there were heavy deliveries of stone and aggregates from other locations for the tunnel and associated works, notably the wall constructed to create the lagoons at Shakespeare Cliff which spoil from the tunnel turned into Samphire Hoe. Foster Yeoman had brought one million tons of stone to Lower Shakespeare Cliff by the time its last train ran on 12th May, 1992. Other loads included steel piles for the sea wall, cast iron, bison slabs and running blocks for use in the tunnels. Further heavy freight flows, in the later stages of the project as other construction traffic wound down, were of overhead line equipment, sleepers, and 'strings' of rail from British Steel's Workington plant; these were delivered direct to the Cheriton terminal site, where the tracklaying operation was concentrated, via a siding laid at Dollands Moor.

Much of the incoming materials traffic was handled not at Lower Shakespeare Cliff but at a spacious railhead created at Sevington, just east of Ashford on the south side of the main line to the tunnel. The fan of four sidings at Sevington acted as a sorting centre for many items delivered by rail (and also by road, though strict limits had been imposed by Parliament on road-borne construction traffic). A shuttle service of trains transported materials for the tunnel itself as required from Sevington to the exchange sidings with the narrow-gauge construction system at Lower Shakespeare Cliff; haulage was usually by class '37' or class '33' diesels. Some other materials, such as minestone for the Cheriton terminal which formed the final traffic from Snowdown Colliery, were rail-delivered to Sevington, then brought to the site by road. The Sevington site also became TML's disposal centre for surplus equipment, and as such housed its narrow gauge construction railway stock pending resale; after several years of disuse it was reactivated late in 1999 to handle aggregates for the Channel Tunnel Rail Link, and it was later considered by Eurotunnel as a potential intermodal terminal for through freight trains from the Continent, with swap-bodies transhipped to road vehicles. The TML box wagons were transferred to other traffics; astonishingly one rake, still in TML livery, turned up in a Yeoman stone train at Woking yard in the summer of 2004.

The disposal of spoil from the tunnel on the spot at Lower Shakespeare Cliff and Sangatte ruled out the need for even-heavier traffic flows to landfill sites elsewhere in Britain and France. Eurotunnel estimated that removing the spoil from the English tunnel workings alone would have required a train every 30 minutes round the clock for three years, or a lorry every 30 seconds over the same period.

There was less scope for rail-borne construction traffic at the French end, not least because the concrete tunnel segments and sleeper blocks for those contracts were manufactured on-site at Sangatte. Nor was such traffic as conspicuous, as heavy freight shipments are more commonplace on the SNCF network than they had become on the Southern Region by the late 1980s. No special sidings were constructed to handle tunnel construction traffic as there were already ample facilities for unloading bulk freight trains in the Calais area, handy at least for the Coquelles terminal site. In the later stages of the project, materials were delivered direct to Coquelles on a spur from SNCF metals at Fréthun, one such traffic being rail from Moulin Neuf-Chambly. As for the Sangatte construction site, its location high up and close to the cliffs made installing a rail connection impracticable, and materials were delivered by road.

Chapter Four

Through the Tunnel

Anyone using the Channel Tunnel for the first time, even now it has been operating for some years, looks ahead to the journey with a mixture of anticipation and apprehension. Anticipation because of the excitement of being able to travel seamlessly between two land masses hitherto divided by a formidable piece of sea; apprehension because a journey beneath the seabed of 38 km defies the laws of nature. The author's then five-year-old son prefaced his own first shuttle trip through the tunnel by donning his frogman's mask and snorkel, and many adults approach the transit with equal foreboding despite the assurance of a calm crossing even on a day when the Channel is choppy.

Yet the tunnel's engineering achievement in linking England to France is equalled by the ability of either form of transport through it - the international high-speed trains or Eurotunnel's own vehicle shuttles - to make the trip, once begun, seem positively ordinary. The feeling of wonderment only surfaces, if at all, at the moment the train bursts out of the tunnel portal into daylight at the conclusion of the passage, and regular travellers become decidedly *blasé*.

To the disappointment and embarrassment of railway planners, the vast majority of traffic through the tunnel arrives and departs by road. At the French end of the tunnel, where we shall start a journey which by rail will end when Phase Two of the CTRL reaches St Pancras, motorists and HGV drivers reach Coquelles on the A16 coastal autoroute which links Calais, just to the north of the terminal, with Boulogne and Abbeville. Most traffic from Paris and points south travels up on the A1 to Lille and then the A26, joining the A16 from the Belgian border at a cloverleaf junction 6 km (and three exits) east of the terminal.

Coquelles

The Coquelles terminal (*see plan on page 206*) is an international transport interchange on a grand scale, in fact the largest in Europe. At 450 hectares - much the same size as Charles de Gaulle Airport - its area is over three times as large as its English counterpart, not so much because of the Gallic preference for *grands projets* but because it is set in flat, open country free from the severe constraints imposed on the English site by the steep hillside behind Cheriton. Indeed there is space on the Coquelles site to double the existing passenger and rail infrastructure should that prove necessary.

Lying just to the south-east of Calais, the sausage-shaped terminal site (a configuration determined by its railway layout) lies on a south-west to north-east axis. To seaward it is bounded by the A16, constructed at the same time as the terminal, and to landward by the Calais-Boulogne route of the SNCF, which was both realigned and electrified (for a handful of trains a day) in concert with the tunnel scheme. The main railway line into the tunnel from the TGV-Nord skirts the terminal site to the south.

Despite its proximity both to the sea and the tunnel portal, neither can actually be seen from the terminal. The site is only a few metres above sea level; moreover, trains have to make a 90-degree turn to join the high-speed line to and from it. Cars, coaches and lorries enter the terminal from the A16 via the Fort Nieulay interchange, an elegant Y-shaped viaduct constructed above a circular man-made lake 400 m in diameter. Entry by this route is so simple that one can easily find oneself within the terminal complex having missed the chance to call at the famed 100-hectare Cité Europe and its 120 shops, 11 outlet stores, hypermarket, 20 restaurants and 12-screen cinema, which is a destination in its own right for many trippers from the UK because of the bargains available; 15 million shoppers pass through it each year, 35 per cent of them from Britain. Cité Europe, incidentally, is just the largest and highest-profile part of a considerably larger commercial zone developed by Eurotunnel at the request of the French Government to boost local employment; at one stroke, in November 2002, three hotels were opened there. Plans for a wind farm beside the terminal are also now being worked up; an agreement with Boralex SA that, subject to planning permission, could lead to five turbines of two-megawatt capacity being put into operation was signed in the spring of 2003.

You can also park within the Coquelles terminal and shop at Eurotunnel's own stores, which offer a fair range of what until 1999 were duty-free goods; the loss of duty-free hit Eurotunnel considerably, though not as hard as the competing ferries. However, most tunnel travellers are keen to be on their way (though there are Freight and Club Class lounges at both terminals for those with time on their hands) and the terminal's shops are not a money spinner. In 2000 the airport operator BAA, which originally managed them, sued Eurotunnel over the low level of business, especially since the ending of duty-free, and in an out-of-court settlement its contract was terminated in March 2001; management of the shopping at Coquelles was taken over by Hachette. There are also four fast-food outlets in the terminal building, including a McDonald's.

The terminal complex also houses Eurotunnel's hangar-like principal maintenance centre for shuttle locomotives and trains, which operates round the clock. It lies just inside the terminal loop of track on the landward side of the terminal; outside and to the south of the loop at that point lie first the realigned Calais-Boulogne line, and then the SNCF's Fréthun international freight terminal, besieged by asylum-seekers during 2001-2, where class '92' haulage through the tunnel starts and finishes and where tunnel sleeper trains would have switched to and from Continental traction, and the SNCF's control centre for domestic services in the area.

The principal maintenance shed has four rail tracks, all wired overhead, and a floor area of 20,000 sq metres; three of the tracks can be slewed to allow outsize loads into and out of the building. Originally it was half the size, but in June 1998 an extension was opened which doubled its length to 828 metres, making it the longest in the world and allowing an entire shuttle train, rather than one of its two rakes, to pass through at a time, thus reducing turn-round time. Each shuttle train, with its locomotives, makes a weekly call for maintenance, being moved through the depot under remote radio control; only when major work is necessary is a wagon taken out of a shuttle train for individual attention. There is another workshop for heavy repairs; it again has four tracks, but no electric catenary. Between them Coquelles' two servicing facilities employ 145 of Eurotunnel's 160 train maintenance staff. Coquelles also hosts Eurotunnel's corporate operating headquarters, a duplicate control centre in case that at Cheriton is put out of action, and the company's French exhibition centre, formerly at Sangatte.

Four lanes of car traffic approach the French tollbooths, with their futuristic suspended pagoda-style roofs; motorists who have already reserved are asked to hang a lettered ticket from their car mirror to show which scheduled shuttle they are booked to travel on. Once your ticket has been passed through an electronic scanner, you can park in the terminal, whose buildings were designed by Paul Andreu, director of architecture for the Paris airports authority, and relax in the restaurants and shops until it is time to head for the shuttle. For motorists arriving in France, an Elf filling station is almost the first thing you see after leaving the train.

Driving from the terminal to the train, you pass first through French and then British passport control, usually without being stopped. (On the outward journey from Cheriton - and most tunnel passenger round-trips originate in the UK - motorists correspondingly go through French as well as UK border controls.) The route also takes you through a series of gaugers designed to weed out any vehicles which are too high or wide for the double-deck car shuttles, such as 4x4 vehicles more than 1.85 m in height; these are directed toward special wagons in the passenger shuttles which also carry coaches (including dedicated coaches for cyclists which operate between the French and English terminals), campers and caravans. Almost before you know it, you are in the queue for the shuttle train itself which builds up on the concrete bridges over the platform area. Truck drivers follow a similar procedure, but use a separate route through the terminal to prevent HGVs being held up by peak-season tourist traffic. To cope with the pressure of illegal migrants trying to board HGVs at Coquelles, 37 km of wire fencing has been erected around the terminal, and some 200 CCTV cameras have been installed as well as passive detection systems; security precautions at the SNCF's nearby Fréthun sidings have also belatedly been tightened, though the site is not yet policed round the clock, preventing a full service of tunnel freight trains from operating. The entire process of loading and unloading shuttle trains at Coquelles, of checking for unwanted guests and of keeping traffic flowing smoothly through the terminal, is monitored from a control room on-site; all other operations are controlled from Cheriton.

There are 10 railway tracks at Coquelles for the boarding and unloading of passenger and freight shuttles (originally eight were provided but two extra platform lines were opened on 21st October, 2002 to cope with the planned increase in HGV shuttles to a maximum seven a hour); in each case a single platform, with an entry ramp at one end and an exit ramp at the other, accommodates both functions. These terminal platforms are on a 1.7 km unidirectional loop of track, mainly of three running lines but narrowing to two as the platforms are neared. Shuttle trains are limited to 80 and 90 kph respectively on the two lines into the terminal, 70 kph as they navigate the loop, 60 kph over the points in the arrival fan and – academically - 70 kph in the platforms. (In terminal sidings all trains are restricted to 30 kph.)

By the time shuttle trains from Cheriton pull up at the platforms to unload, they have travelled most of the way round the loop, having passed *en route* Eurotunnel's maintenance depot and shuttle sidings, all of whose complex trackwork lies inside the loop. Before this complex is reached an emergency siding peels off, outside the loop, some distance from the others and shielded from the running lines by high banks of earth; this stands ready to take a train that has caught fire in the tunnel and has to be isolated while the blaze is tackled. A rudimentary platform is provided to disembark passengers, should the need arise, and concrete bunkers for the firefighters. On the one occasion so far that the facility could have proved useful, however, the train burned so fiercely inside the tunnel that it could not be towed out until the flames had been extinguished.

The entire Eurotunnel rail system consists of an elongated figure of eight, with trains operating clockwise around the Cheriton loop and anti-clockwise around its

French counterpart in order to equalise wear on their wheels. The effect of this is that trains leaving Coquelles to enter the tunnel have to burrow under the lines emerging from it (and also under the high-speed tracks carrying Eurostar and through freight traffic) so as to reach the portal on the left-hand track.

Just to the south of the terminal site is the double-track triangular junction through which passes all international passenger and freight traffic other than the shuttles, plus the infrequent TGVs between Paris and Calais-Ville, the more intensive Calais-Boulogne local service and some domestic freight. The westerly pair of tracks carries Eurostars between the tunnel and Paris, a few of which halt almost immediately south of the junction at Calais-Fréthun, 3.4 km from the tunnel portal; there is also a further track which links the local platforms at Calais-Fréthun station with the lines heading for the tunnel. The northerly pair takes all the tunnel's through freight traffic (trains heading for the tunnel, like the shuttles just to the north, pass under both of the high-speed Paris lines before joining the route for England). After halting at the Fréthun sidings beside the Coquelles complex for a locomotive change, most freight trains that have left the tunnel pass the SNCF's local freight yard to reach a further triangular junction at Les Fontinettes; here trains for Calais peel off to the left, and those for Dunkerque, Hazebrouck and Lille to the right. The south-easterly side of the Fréthun triangular junction carries Calais-Boulogne traffic (serving the low-level platforms at Calais-Fréthun) and the occasional TGV.

No sooner have tunnel-bound trains cleared the triangular junction and the four tracks merged into two than Eurotunnel's own tracks bear in from the right, looking toward the portal. First the two lines carrying shuttle trains that have just begun their journey pass under the main route, very soon the shuttle lines running into the terminal merge into the main line emerging from the tunnel, and finally the tunnel-bound tracks combine; two separate tracks for shuttle trains continue some way into the cutting christened the Beussingue Trench during construction, to provide line capacity when trains of various types 'back up' inside the tunnel. However Eurotunnel's policy of starting trains at each terminal from the closest point to the tunnel portal enables delays caused by other traffic to be kept to a minimum; indeed there is more of a problem for Eurostars arriving at high speed and having to brake because a shuttle or freight train is 'in section' just ahead.

The number of tracks in the Trench decreases from five to four to three, and close to the portal a bi-directional crossover enables trains from any route to transit the tunnel in either direction should part of the system be switched out; this replicates the crossover at the English portal which, because of lack of space between there and the Cheriton terminal, is largely set back into the tunnel itself. Just beyond the crossover, two single running lines each disappear into their round tunnels (they are in fact oval, the shape of an egg balanced on its point, but the bottom part has been filled in to provide the trackbed).

Above these twin portals and to the left, atop the cutting, stands Eurotunnel's French electricity substation providing power for the terminal complex and one half of the tunnel. To the right, above track level but well within the cutting, a well-metalled road enters the genuinely round pilot tunnel giving Eurotunnel vehicles access for maintenance and, if necessary, rescue. This starts to one side of the running tunnels, but very soon moves to a central position in order to provide convenient access to both.

An Undersea Adventure

When the time comes for cars to board what was originally branded 'Le Shuttle', Eurotunnel marshals direct them along one of two overbridges and down to the platform where the train awaits after discharging its incoming traffic, onto the train and its upper (by ramp) or lower deck until the car in front comes to a halt. Each train fills from the front, but will leave when scheduled even if there are spaces unfilled. Eurotunnel staff check with drivers that every car's handbrake is on, and once every vehicle is in place the public address system broadcasts announcements in French and English about the journey ahead and highlights essential safety precautions; for a start, smoking is strictly prohibited. Lorries join the freight shuttles in the same way as cars, moving forward through the train after boarding until instructed to stop. As each lorry halts, its front wheels are clamped to keep them securely in place during the transit. The drivers are then transferred, with any passengers in their cab, by courtesy bus to the club car behind the train's leading locomotive.

While the lorry crews relax together with free refreshments, motorists and their passengers stay put in their vehicles; they only need to leave them to use the toilets which are provided in every third carriage. Motorcyclists who prefer not to stay with their machines have the choice of a special compartment; pedal cyclists can make the journey by shuttle in dedicated motor coaches. Passengers in their cars can while away the journey by listening to Eurotunnel's own FM radio station, whose programmes of music and information are transmitted into the shuttle trains. Instructions to passengers are also flashed regularly onto dot matrix information screens in each air-conditioned shuttle wagon.

When departure time for the shuttle train arrives, metal-shuttered fire doors seal off each carriage. The 'right away' is given, and the shuttle pulls smoothly away from the terminal platform for a scheduled 35-minute transit (40 minutes for a freight shuttle, though times as low as 34 minutes have been recorded by the newer and more powerful class '97xx' shuttle locomotives), to the accompaniment of appropriate announcements on the public address system. Passage of the initial short distance onto the tunnel main line by shuttle may be hesitant if there is a through passenger or freight train to clear; freight trains are more of a problem for other traffic as they run at a maximum 100 kph in the tunnel against 120 kph for a freight shuttle (reduced from 140 kph after the fire of November 1996), 140 kph for a passenger shuttle and 160 kph for a Eurostar. But by the time the shuttle approaches the tunnel portal, having cleared the terminal complex at a maximum 80 kph, it should be accelerating well toward its maximum running speed. Shuttle trains emerging from the tunnel at Coquelles slow to negotiate the lengthy loop, but still maintain a healthy speed until they near the terminal platform.

Freight trains starting from the Fréthun sidings after a change of locomotive to a class '92', and Eurostars that have stopped at Calais-Fréthun, are picking up speed as they negotiate the triangular junction and head down the Beussingue Trench to the tunnel portal. But the through Eurostars from Paris, the Alps, Avignon, Disney and Brussels start coasting from their maximum speed some distance away, and actively brake as they pass through Calais-Fréthun and the portal becomes visible to the driver.

The approach to the tunnel is not entirely risk-free even for Eurostars travelling at speed. Although the sea is not visible, salt spray from it can at times of very high winds stick to the overhead wiring and disrupt the power supply; after gales in late October 2002, Eurostar services had to be suspended for two days.

In the reverse direction, passengers experience a sharp acceleration as the Eurostar passes the terminal, away to its north, clears the junctions and Calais-Fréthun station and heads for Lille. Before very long the train captain will announce that the train has reached its maximum speed of 300 kph or 186 mph - whether it has or not.

As Eurostars near the French tunnel portal there is a comparable announcement that the train is about to enter the Channel Tunnel, the transit time being given as 20 minutes. Unless they have stopped at Calais-Fréthun or there is a hold-up in front, most such trains will approach the tunnel close to Eurotunnel speed limit of 160 kph. Until 1998 all trains approaching the portal from Coquelles had to check to 90 kph at the point where the Eurotunnel and SNCF signalling systems meet; removal of this requirement has benefited Eurostars in particular.

One moment the passenger sees chalk cutting sides, converging tracks and electric catenary from the carriage windows, the next only grey concrete tunnel walls. And after a very short opening section which is well lit, the view from the windows turns to near-darkness; there is the bare minimum of background lighting although 20,000 light fittings are provided in the tunnel for maintenance and emergency use.

The running tunnels, though an upright egg-shape in construction, have as been mentioned been boxed into a less exotic outline by the need to fill in the trackbed and to make way for a multitude of services. Signalling cables run below the walkway for emergency and maintenance use. Cooling water pipes in each direction run along one side, and a firemain and catenary tension weights along the other. Above the trains are tensioning weight pulleys keeping the catenary steady and a bundle of lighting and other lower-voltage electric cables, including two earthing cables connected at intervals to the track. Each tunnel lining also contains a 25kv feeder cable to boost the traction power supply *en route*.

Generally when a train enters a tunnel at speed, there is a 'whoomph' as it impacts on the static air within the tunnel, and passengers along its entire length experience a sudden change in air pressure. In the Channel Tunnel, however, the system of regular piston ducts linking the running tunnels (and arching over the service tunnel) acts to limit the build-up of pressure and there is no such sensation. Quite a few passengers, though not nearly as many as in the far shorter North Downs tunnel on the CTRL, do feel their ears 'pop' during the journey: Eurostars are fitted with inflatable door seals to protect passengers against sudden pressure surges, but the shuttles, despite being air-conditioned, are less comprehensively insulated.

Trains enter the French portal on a north-westerly alignment, and this is broadly maintained until the English shore is approached, save for one northward kink in mid-Channel to keep within the stratum. The transit begins on a 1 in 91 downward grade that applies for the first 2.7 km of the journey, almost to the foot of the Sangatte shaft, just before which it eases infinitesimally to 1 in 92. This steady slope - by a fraction the steepest gradient in the tunnel - both enables shuttle trains setting out from Coquelles to build up enough speed to avoid delaying Eurostars, and assists those braking as they near the end of their transit from Cheriton. Though it was challenging for heavy but relatively low-powered construction trains, this gradient is not so steep as to cause any difficulties for class '92s' hauling international freight trains out of the tunnel, and Eurostars take it in their stride.

The former Sangatte worksite is reached 3.2 km into the tunnel, or less than two minutes for most passengers. All traces at running tunnel level of the complex works tunnels and trackwork that marked its role as nerve-centre of the French construction effort have disappeared, though passengers may catch a change in the noise the train makes as it passes the site. Above ground at Sangatte, the maze of activities around the shaft has been replaced by emergency facilities and an air-conditioning and cooling plant whose futuristic vents snake down into the shaft itself. This shaft is now sealed off for all other purposes, to quell air pressure surges from passing trains. It has also been ballasted with 130,000 tonnes of concrete to prevent it 'floating' upwards as the historic groundwater table returns following the draining of the strata during construction. Yet Sangatte retains a crucial function in ventilating the tunnel and cooling it to between 25 and 35 degrees Celsius (the target level is 31°), by remote control from Coquelles. It also possesses a powerful emergency generator which could provide enough power and light to keep essential systems going in the event of a total failure of the French public supply - though not enough to keep the trains running. Above ground Sangatte also became at the turn of century the site of a Red Cross hostel for asylum seekers; the impact on tunnel services of attempts to reach Britain by occupants of this centre and other would-be migrants is outlined in Chapter Nine.

Beyond Sangatte the running lines continue to burrow downwards at a gradient of 1 in 92, save for one short section at 1 in 500, for a further 3 km. The most important landmark on this stretch is entirely invisible: the point some 400 m beyond the Sangatte shaft where the tunnel passes under the French coastline and continues beneath the waters of the Channel. Equally invisible is the water ingress which is a greater problem over the first few kilometres out from the French coast than anywhere else on the tunnel; even on this stretch, though, it is much less than had been feared, and save for some early disruption of track circuits which upset the signalling and train control system it has not yet caused any operating difficulties.

From this point onward the gradient profile in the tunnel, and in consequence the tractive effort needed by the locomotive units, is governed by the need of the tunnellers to keep within their chosen chalk marl stratum. Though this generally forms a U-shape in line with the seabed above, there are variations en route, changes in level and sudden narrowings of the stratum which produce in turn after Sangatte short stretches at 1 in 500, 1 in 92, 1 in 143, 1 in 172 and 1 in 500 to a point some 13 km from the French portal where the tracks are 100 m below sea level.

From here the running tracks actually rise again for 2.5 km at 1 in 400 - not enough to affect the progress of trains in either direction. At the 'dip' before this brief upgrade lies the first of three sophisticated undersea pumping stations, from which water that accumulates in the bores is pumped up a main above the service tunnel to the surface. The downgrade then resumes on a gradient of 1 in 500 to the French crossover chamber, 15.22 km into the tunnel (or 44.78 km from the English portal) and thus almost 30 per cent of the way through it, and 46 m below the seabed.

The French crossover is the first of three in the tunnel (plus the one just outside the French portal), and one of two beneath the sea. The chamber was constructed after the TBMs had already bored out the running tunnels; 11 small overlapping tunnels were bored around where the chamber was to be, and lined with concrete to form a continuous arch 170 m long, 19 m wide and 12 m high before the cavern itself was excavated from within. Only then were the original tunnel lining segments removed to enable the crossover to be installed.

The location of each crossover chamber was partly dictated by operational requirements: to divide the tunnel into three 18 km sections where single-track operation could be imposed if necessary - allowing engineering possessions 18 km or, if unavoidable, 36 km long - and to do so where the running lines were nearly on the level, so that trains slowing down to change tunnels did not have to accelerate up a difficult gradient. But their siting also stemmed from the geological need to gouge out these large cavities at a point where this could be done entirely within the stratum.

Travellers normally pass the crossover chambers completely unawares; there is a slight change in the lining of the tunnel where the heavy 'bomb-proof' steel sliding doors that roll back for the crossover to be used replace the concrete wall segments, and there are the inevitable clicks from the rail joints over the points at either end of the diamond crossover. Even these sounds are muted, as the tracks and pointwork in the chamber are surrounded by rubber seals to reduce the risk of derailments and make the sliding doors more airtight.

When, for maintenance or other reasons, trains are switched into the 'wrong' tunnel at a crossover, passengers get just a glimpse of the majestic sub-sea hollow through which their train is passing. They are alerted to the existence of the crossover by the sharp though steady reduction in speed to 60 kph required of trains changing tracks, and in the subdued light which has replaced the glare of the arc lights used during construction, they are left only vaguely aware of passing through a man-made cavity of remarkable size.

For this crossover as for the others, the service tunnel was slewed to one side to enable the running tunnels to connect. Passengers, except in the thankfully rare event of an emergency disembarkation, never see this tunnel which, in its routine communications and maintenance role, is a busy thoroughfare in its own right. Rubber-tyred maintenance (and rescue) vehicles use it to ferry crews and materials between working sites at a maximum speed of 50 kph, driving - it should be noted - on the left-hand side of the road. But the service tunnel performs several other essential functions, carrying the tunnel's firefighting main (with every hydrant armed with English- and French-style nozzles for whichever brigade arrives first), control and communications cables and, in the crown of the tunnel, a main carrying water pumped from the tunnel's lowest points for dispersal at Sangatte or Shakespeare Cliff.

During each shuttle train's journey the train captain keeps an eye on each carriage in turn by closed-circuit television, which can zoom in on any potential problem. Should there be a mid-tunnel emergency requiring evacuation of the train, emergency doors in each wagon will unlock so that passengers can detrain and make for the service tunnel and safety. Each shuttle train is equipped with automatic fire alarms and others that can be operated by passengers; to guard against false alarms, two must be activated for the alert to be registered. Air-conditioning systems (on a passenger shuttle) will then be shut down as the train crew go to investigate. Portable extinguishers are provided to deal with a minor fire; with anything more serious all passengers will be evacuated from the affected wagon to other parts of the train, and if smoke density continues to increase, Halon, highly effective but a notorious greenhouse gas, will be released to put the fire out. (What actually happened when a fire did break out on a freight shuttle just north of the French crossover, seriously damaging 600 metres of the southern running tunnel, is outlined in Chapter Eight.)

With a locomotive at each end, shuttle trains in an emergency can be driven out of either end of the tunnel, one locomotive and, if necessary, the disabled portion of the train having been detached. If the entire train is immobilised, one of Eurotunnel's diesel-electric rescue locomotives would tow it out. Eurostars, too, can be divided in an emergency. The power units at either end of the train can be uncoupled, or the train's two rakes separated in the middle. By virtue both of their higher speed and the fact that they not carrying dozens of tanks of highly combustible petrol and diesel, Eurostars are considered less prone to fire *en route*, but have an equal capacity to disembark passengers in an emergency should one occur. In such an eventuality, each carriage's retractable footboards would open out onto the walkway at the side of the tunnel. Before the Inter-Governmental Safety Commission allowed Eurostar services to start, several full-scale evacuation drills were staged in the tunnel to make sure a train could be emptied with sufficient speed; a power supply failure during one such exercise contributed to delays in commencing the service.

Beyond the French crossover the running tunnels continue their descent, first at 1 in 500 - transiting northbound the section of tunnel damaged by the fire which required heavy restoration - and then for shorter stretches at 1 in 125 and 1 in 238, and during this descent the official sub-Channel boundary between the United Kingdom and France is reached. The border line is nearer to the French portal - and indeed to the French coastline - than to the English, a consequence of the tunnelling work having proceeded faster from Shakespeare Cliff than from Sangatte and of there being a longer stretch of tunnel beneath land on the English side than the French. It is passed at slightly different points in each tunnel: in the northern (France-bound) running tunnel at 22.082 km from the French portal and 27.918 from the English, in the service tunnel at 22.098 km from the French portal and 27.902 from the English, and finally in the southern (England-bound) running tunnel at 22.119 km from the French portal and 27.881 from the English. The border was officially demarcated on 30th November, 1992, by a plaque in one of the running tunnels, but this was subsequently removed by souvenir-hunters and repeated efforts to replace it have met with a similar fate.

Now running beneath officially British seabed, the tunnels dip for a further 2.7 km to the low point of the crossing, almost 150 m below the surface of the Channel, which is reached 24.8 km from the French portal. This is the location of the largest of the three sub-sea pumping stations, with a pair of tunnels between the running tunnels accommodating an electrical sub-station and pumps capable of operating even when totally submerged, and a 172 m-long sump running at right angles to the tracks. This last includes a 'dangerous goods sump' where noxious or inflammable liquid released into the tunnel by a spillage can be isolated and stored for safe removal.

The tunnel's low point is less than halfway from Coquelles to Cheriton, 35.2 km away, and just beyond it is the neutral section of catenary separating the French and UK electric power systems. This break is essential to the safe operation of the tunnel, as the two national systems for technical rather than political reasons must never be directly connected. Like the less heavily-trafficked current breaks on the scissors crossings in the crossover chambers, and neutral sections near each portal to separate running tunnel and terminal current supplies, the mid-tunnel neutral section comprises a short earthed section of contact wire, separated at either end from the live catenary by an insulated glass-fibre rod. A pantograph traversing the neutral section will barely be stirred; most passengers are unaware that they have passed from one nation's power system to another, but occasionally the carriage lights will dim slightly.

From the neutral section, the tunnel begins a steady climb which continues right up to the British portal. Overall the ascent is steeper as the Cheriton terminal is considerably higher above sea level than Coquelles. The upward gradient is 1 in 357 to start with, then as the stratum rises more sharply there is nearly 4 km at the more demanding 1 in 91, before a short stretch at 1 in 333 amid which the UK undersea crossover chamber is sited.

This second crossover completes a section of running track 17.69 km from its French counterpart, which is some 20 m lower; it is situated almost 33 km from the

French tunnel portal and just over 27 km from that at Cheriton. Superficially it resembles the French crossover and operationally it is identical, but it was constructed by different means. Whereas the French TBMs passed through the area first and the chamber was then hollowed out, the English undersea crossover was excavated prior to the arrival of the TBMs, all the spoil being shipped out via the service tunnel. In its raw state the cavern was 163.8 m long, 21.2 m wide and 15.4 m high, but a strong inner concrete lining installed after the TBMs had passed through reduced its dimensions to 156 m by 18.1 m by 9.5 m. As with the French undersea crossover, only the clicking of wheels over rare rail joints and a slight change in the configuration of the tunnel wall where it gives way to the sliding doors - each 6.6 m high, 32 m long and weighing 92 tonnes - gives any indication that the chamber is being transited, unless the train is slowed to cross to the opposite running tunnel.

By now the route of the tunnel is bearing more west than north as the English coast draws nearer. After a short stretch at 1 in 500 where the last of the three undersea pumping stations is sited, the tunnel climbs at 1 in 250 before the gradient stiffens to 1 in 91 for the final 3 km to the shoreline. On this section, by contrast with the upward approach to the French portal, all trains initially used the gradient to slacken speed, as the line speed for Eurostars on joining the BR network shortly after exiting the tunnel was lower than the 160 kph maximum within it until completion of the first stage of the Channel Tunnel Rail Link.

By the time the tunnel passes under the English shore after a 38 km sub-Channel transit it is heading almost due west, with 9 km still to go before daylight is reached. At this point, as a brief stretch at the less taxing gradient of 1 in 149 gives way to 1 in 92, the former worksite below Shakespeare Cliff is reached.

As with Sangatte, there is no discernible evidence to the passing train traveller that this was one of the two hubs of Europe's largest construction project of its day. Yet behind the scenes the labyrinth of tunnels that operated during the construction process or were left from earlier projects is still there. And, like Sangatte, the site still retains an important role in the operation of the tunnel. Above ground on the site of the former exchange sidings and pile of tunnel segments, next to the spoil-created Samphire Hoe and beside the Folkestone-Dover railway, stands an impressive ventilation and chilling plant which controls air freshness and temperature in the British half of the tunnel. One of the four gigantic chillers cools the landward section of tunnel from Shakespeare Cliff, the other three the stretches to seaward.

From the ground-level installations at Lower Shakespeare Cliff, ventilation, cooling, drainage and firefighting pipes run down to the service and running tunnels 40 m below through Adit 2, the main artery for construction trains for all except the very early stages of the project. Supplies can also be ferried down the adit to the service tunnel, but maintenance vehicles must continue to the English portal. Adit 1, dating from 1974, also survives but is put to fewer uses. At tunnel level below Shakespeare Cliff is located the tunnel's second emergency generator to sustain vital services, though not to power the trains - in the event of a total current failure, Eurotunnel's fleet of diesel rescue locomotives would have to work overtime.

From Shakespeare Cliff the tunnel, now running on an east-west axis, passes inland of Folkestone as the climb to the surface continues at 1 in 92 for almost 7 km to the point, beneath Sugar Loaf Hill, where the English TBMs originally began their journey. Before the tunnel was excavated, there was a hollow here named Holywell Coombe, but partly to preserve the view and partly to improve security the tunnel was continued across this dip in a concrete box instead of opening out into a cutting, and then landscaped over.

The section of tunnel thus created above the original ground level now houses a third crossover, not the scissors crossover of the two subsea chambers but (for trains approaching the English portal) a trailing followed by a facing crossover, 49 km from the French portal and 16 km from the English undersea chamber. The staggered nature of the crossings actually results in the final few yards of the landward crossover protruding from the tunnel entrance. The service tunnel, meanwhile, slews from its established position between the running tunnels to the seaward side of both as the portal looms.

For the final few hundred metres under Castle Hill, the tunnels were constructed by the New Austrian Tunnelling Method, hacked out and shotcreted rather than bored by the TBM-and-segment method used for the rest of the system (with the exception of the crossover chambers). For this distance, trains run through a flat concrete box at a gradient slightly eased to 1 in 97. The lighting improves and the noise level for passengers rises as their train emerges from the tunnel.

Viewed from the terminal, the tunnel portal is a far more brutalist construction than its French counterpart. Beneath a flat concrete raft can be seen three rectangular openings of unequal width, separated by thick concrete uprights: from left to right the northern running tunnel into which tracks are still converging, the southern running tunnel with a single track, and finally the service tunnel.

Cheriton

Britain's Channel Tunnel terminal is shoehorned into such a tight space that it is hard to conceive that it handles the same amount of traffic as its French counterpart - though, by definition, it must. There was just enough room between the built-up area stretching landward from Folkestone and the steep escarpment of the North Downs to squeeze in a terminal at Cheriton measuring at most 2.5 km by 900 m and covering 350 acres or 140 hectares, just over a quarter of the ample area provided at Coquelles. Even so, it was impossible to construct the terminal and squeeze into it the full range of facilities required without intruding severely on the ancient hamlets of Newington and Peene; some buildings in each had to be demolished, but the bulldozing of sizeable earth embankments to block out the sights and noises of the terminal enabled most residents to remain. One other piece of site-clearing had, sadly, already taken place three decades before work began on the terminal: the lifting of the former SE&CR Elham Valley branch linking Folkestone and Canterbury, whose trackbed ran north-west across the western end of the Cheriton site.

The Cheriton terminal lies on an east-west alignment immediately to the north (landward) of the M20 (which was extended to and beyond the terminal under the Channel Tunnel Act) and, some 200 m nearer the sea, the Ashford-Folkestone-Dover railway between Sandling and Folkestone West. By contrast with its French counterpart, the Channel can be glimpsed from parts of the terminal. Eurostar passengers will be lucky to catch it at all as the through tracks are fairly low down, and the seaward view is obscured by anti-noise shuttering (which doubles as a barrier to keep animals out) shielding residential areas close by; however they may just see it shimmering through the arches of the viaduct carrying the Ashford-Dover railway through the town.

Despite its tight location, Eurotunnel's English terminal crams in as wide a range of services as does its opposite number - and indeed has a considerably larger passenger terminal (2,500 sq. m against 1,500 sq. m) than at Coquelles. This was achieved in part by burying the terminal loop of shuttle railway track (1 km long as opposed to Coquelles' 1.7 km, but with a much tighter radius of curves) in a cut-and-cover tunnel at its north-western end. Double-track for most of the distance before fanning out to three tracks as the terminal platforms are approached, the Cheriton loop was laid with wooden sleepers, rather than the concrete blocks used everywhere else except on the crossovers in the tunnel. On the ground freed up above the loop are the inspection facilities for HGV traffic using the freight shuttles.

Shuttle trains within the English terminal generally operate to lower maximum speeds than at Coquelles, save for the 30 kph maximum in the sidings. Braking sharply from a maximum of 100 kph on the arrival lines (slightly faster than entering the French terminal), they must slow to 60 kph in the first part of the terminal loop and then to 50 kph in the loop tunnel; the 60 kph limit in the arrival fan is, however, less restrictive that at Coquelles, as the immediate approach at Cheriton is straighter.

Once out of the tunnel, Eurostars and international freight trains slice through the seaward side of the terminal area (*see plan on page 209*). Two tracks head westward from the junctions with the terminal loop to join with the branch from Dover and Folkestone as it comes in from the southern side of the terminal site to a junction parallel with Dollands Moor; from this link the CTRL diverges to either side, the up line level with the eastern end of the terminal's loading platforms and the down line at their western end. The two tracks connecting to Network Rail pass over the M20 to reach Dollands Moor to landward of the running lines, where freight trains halt for clearance, and crew or driver changes. Eurostars formerly had to slow to little over 100 kph coming out of the tunnel for a brief further distance over Eurotunnel metals to Continental Junction, where the route from Dover joined from the left and the third-rail pick-up of current began.

During construction of the CTRL Continental Junction was eliminated, two new junctions replacing it: one – Cheriton Junction - not far from the tunnel entrance at which the CTRL merges with a residual double-track connection from the domestic line from Ashford to the tunnel, and the other the divergence of that line from the Folkestone route at the west end of Dollands Moor. This connection between Network Rail and the tunnel, with overhead catenary, was the sole access for Eurostars in the closing stages of work on the CTRL but now sees little traffic except when the CTRL is closed for engineering work, as international freight continues, as before, to pass through Dollands Moor. The CTRL begins its life on two separate alignments, the southbound track running just north of the Dollands Moor sidings and the northbound immediately south of the Network Rail running lines, crossing the route from Dover and Folkestone on a rising alignment.

Incoming shuttle trains diverge almost at once from the through lines to the left (seaward), beginning their long journey round the terminal loop but, as at Coquelles, with their speed limited to 60 kph. Very soon an emergency siding diverges, comparable to that at Coquelles; its principal use has been for quarantining EWS freight trains on which illegal migrants are found to have travelled through the tunnel until police and immigration staff can arrive.

On a shuttle's arrival at the Cheriton terminal platforms (*see plan on page 206*), having traversed almost all of the loop (much of it in tunnel to save space and for environmental reasons), the loading process is reversed. The bridging plates from the club cars and the loading wagons are lowered to cover the gap to the platforms, HGV drivers are ferried back by bus from their club car to their vehicles, instructions for driving out are given over the public address system and the dot matrix indicators in each shuttle wagon, and at a signal from Eurotunnel staff the vehicles drive out, some 40 minutes (45 for freight) after being driven on board.

Cars and HGVs leaving the shuttle trains at Cheriton leave the platform by turning sharp right onto one of two terminal bridges, then right again onto a slip road that takes them straight out of the terminal, joining the M20 at Junction 11A by a direct connection 3 km due west of the point where they left the train; as at Coquelles there is an Elf station on the way out. As all passport and customs checks - if any - will have been carried out at Coquelles before the vehicles join their trains, motor cars leaving the Cheriton terminal have no further controls to pass through. In theory the same absence of checks on leaving the shuttles applies to HGV traffic, but since the upsurge of illegal immigration through the Channel ports and the tunnel, lorries leaving shuttle trains in the English terminal are susceptible to spot checks by UK police and immigration officers. Provided there are no stowaways on board, the HGV driver's journey through the Channel Tunnel is safely at an end, and he too can continue on his way.

Shuttle trains loaded at the Cheriton terminal platforms have a very short distance to get up to speed before they enter the tunnel, and indeed are limited to 80 kph until they reach the portal. This is less of an operational disadvantage than it would be at Coquelles - or at least it was until Eurostars began arriving at speed on the CTRL from London - yet it is still a constraint on the tunnel's capacity. As Cheriton approaches, the Eurostar train captain announces that the tunnel will soon be entered. The approach to the former Continental Junction was, until completion of the first phase of the CTRL, where Eurostar passengers bound for the Continent experienced their first 'buzz' of speed, from the surge of power as their train left the third rail and accelerated over the couple of kilometres of Eurotunnel metals before storming into the tunnel portal, still gaining speed. Yet that acceleration, though rapid, paled beside the greater surge when the train bursts out into the Beussingue Trench and accelerates to maximum TGV velocity beyond Calais-Fréthun.

Almost all of the terminal lies to the north of the through railway tracks that slice through it. The small southern portion of the site houses a number of sidings for spare shuttle wagons and a maintenance building where simple repairs can be carried out and checks done. Within the single-track through shed and a two-road facility with rail access at one end only, Eurotunnel's diesel-electric and Unimog maintenance are also carried out. Spot repairs to shuttle trains in service can be dealt with by teams of troubleshooters on each terminal's platforms; anything major is handled by the main servicing facility at Coquelles, and just 15 of Eurotunnel's 160 train maintenance staff are based at Cheriton. At the terminal's extreme south-western corner is the Longport access point from the A20, downgraded since the completion of the M20 but still well used by local traffic which uses the road to reach the terminal either direct from Folkestone or by leaving the M20 at Junction 12, beside the terminal site's southern boundary. It is at Longport that Eurotunnel drivers sign on; next to the slip road from the A20 stands the terminal's police station, and across the M20 outside the perimeter of the terminal lies Eurotunnel's exhibition and media centre.

The north of the terminal, from west to east, reflects the steady progression of vehicles through it as they approach or depart from the shuttle platforms. Motorway traffic enters and leaves the terminal just to the north of the international railway tracks, incoming vehicles passing through an impressive toll plaza with seven two-sided booths under a humped canopy reminiscent of a row of hang-gliders. Beyond the tollbooths, the route forks; motorists in a hurry can head straight for their shuttle trains, while HGV traffic turns hard left to the freight inspection facility in the north-western corner of the site, on a concrete raft over the shuttle loop tracks beneath, and car and coach traffic with time to spare bears half-left to the sizeable car park of the passenger terminal.

In this tent-shaped building with its striking fabric roof through an aperture in which light beams into the night sky, travellers by road can while away the time in three fast food outlets - and since 2000 a 350-seat food court - and 11 shops, or be tempted by a larger area selling what used to be called duty-frees. For regular travellers there are - as at Coquelles - Freight and Club Class lounges with their own small gift counters. The complex, like that at Coquelles, was managed by BAA until the settlement of its legal dispute with Eurotunnel over poor revenues; remodelled in the spring of 2001, most retail outlets at Cheriton are now managed by Alpha Retail.

HGVs bound for the shuttle head due east from the inspection facility along the northern perimeter of the terminal, in the shade of the Downs, to join the two bridges that approach and span the platforms for departure: one at the rear of each train, the other halfway along. Just to the south of the lorries' route stands the tunnel's control centre, whose functions are described in the next chapter; from the distinctive control tower which resembles the bridge of a ship complete with mast, there is a panoramic view of almost the entire terminal site, but the controllers actually operate at or below ground level and monitor shuttle loading and unloading operations within the terminal by closed-circuit television - essential when a Channel fog sets in.

By contrast, cars from the passenger terminal bound for the shuttles take a circuitous route: back to the roundabout at which they entered the terminal's car park, then south-east briefly to join non-stop incoming traffic for a series of width, height and security checks. Heading north-east past the rear of the terminal building, they go first through a laser check, then past two series of futuristic booths at which first UK and then French immigration officials may ask to check passports - though in practice they seldom do. Having gone through this process, motorists become fully aware of the constraints of the site as they turn a sharp right and then zig-zag back into holding queues for boarding their trains. A further 180-degree bend just to the east of the control centre brings them finally onto the approach roads for the platform bridges, and from there it is only seconds onto the train.

The 10 departure/arrival platforms (increased from eight, as at Coquelles, from October 2002 to cope with the imminent increase in the HGV shuttle to a maximum seven trains an hour) run due west-east along the eastern half of the terminal site. The through international train tracks lie just to their south, while to the north, beyond the two added platforms, stands the building where train crew sign on and take their breaks. Despite the cramped dimensions of the site, space was allowed for even more shuttle platforms, and some of this is now designated for sidings and transhipment aprons so that Eurotunnel-operated intermodal freight trains can operate through the tunnel to and from Cheriton and the M20; work was due to start in January 2004 but was put on hold when Eurotunnel's banks refused to finance it in revenge for comments about them by the company's new Board. At the extreme east of the site, to landward of the shuttle tracks as they converge to enter the tunnel, stands the tunnel's English electricity supply sub-station.

Chapter Five

Operation and Signalling

The Channel Tunnel has not just proved a stupendous feat of engineering: its core is an intensively operated railway network whose safe operation depends on sophisticated and interlinked systems of train control and signalling. Theoretically the tunnel can handle 20 trains per hour each way, but with the differential speeds of the trains using it - Eurostars at a maximum 160 kph, car and HGV shuttles at 140 and 120 kph respectively and international freight trains at 100 kph - the practical limit is 16 trains per hour, though Eurotunnel's operating licence sets a maximum of 12. This ceiling has applied since extra safety precautions were imposed after the fire of November 1996, with the maximum speed of HGV shuttles reduced from 140 to 120 kph, and a clear 4-minute interval required before and after each such train. To prevent capacity being wasted, it makes sense for trains of the same type and speed to run behind each other whenever possible rather than entering the tunnel in random order. Originally this was reflected in the Eurostar timetable which, despite lengthy gaps, provided for its trains at the busiest times to set off four minutes apart (the minimum time-interval between tunnel trains set for safety is three minutes); from the opening of the CTRL, this 'flighting' was largely abolished to ease passenger congestion at Waterloo, but it is likely to be reintroduced once St Pancras becomes London's Eurostar terminal. Flighting can still be practised for London-bound Eurostars, as trains arriving in England in rapid succession have started from a variety of terminals on the Continent and congestion at the Gare du Nord or Brussels Midi is thus not an issue. The principle of not letting trains of varying speeds through the tunnel at random has, however, been maintained as far as possible, for this could, without careful control, impose considerable delays. Moreover Eurotunnel has stipulated from the outset that any Eurostar which arrives on its system having missed its path for the tunnel through late running on the Network Rail or SNCF networks will have to take its place behind scheduled shuttle traffic.

Traffic growth since the tunnel hosted its first revenue-earning trains in 1994 is just starting to press against the envelope of capacity at its busiest times; at any one time there can be seven or eight trains in each tunnel. At peak periods the system is now fully used. When demand is at its highest, five passenger and five HGV shuttles in an hour will operate, and there is now capacity for up to seven HGV shuttles an hour. Up to 30 Eurostars between Waterloo and various Continental destinations now operate on the busiest days, the demand bunching so that three paths an hour through the tunnel are required at some times. And while growth in through international freight traffic has proved disappointing, up to 20 trains a day were running, primarily at night, before the disruption of 2001/02, and the service remains intense during the hours when a police presence at Fréthun permits trouble-free operation. Paths also have to be found for works train and light-engine workings. Yet there is usually still enough leeway to allow Eurotunnel's operating staff to alter schedules and add extra trains if traffic requires. The timetable expert Barry Doe has calculated that 315,000 paths a year through the tunnel are available for traffic, a further 35,000 being required for maintenance. Of those 315,000, 100,000 are used by Eurotunnel's shuttles and 50,000 by Eurostar and freight operators, leaving 165,000, or 52 per cent, as spare capacity.

Moreover in off-periods during the night the tunnel may still only be handling in an hour two passenger shuttles, one or two HGV shuttles, and maybe only one one freight train and no Eurostars at all.

A good indication of when the peaks and troughs in demand occur is given by a typical day's working timetable for a period when operation of international freight services was not hampered by less-than-24-hour security at SNCF's Fréthun yard. Friday 8th September, 2000 was a day on which tourist car traffic was still high after the summer holidays, HGV and rail freight traffic was getting back into its stride after the August break in France - and a French lorry drivers' protest which had blockaded the Coquelles terminal the week before - and Eurostar was experiencing its busiest day of the week. From midnight to midnight, the tunnel handled 211 trains: 97 freight shuttles, 59 passenger shuttles, 35 Eurostars, 18 international freight trains and two works trains. Two light engines also ran.

The busiest hour southbound was between 1100 and 1200 when 13 trains ran: five HGV shuttles left Cheriton, four passenger shuttles, three Eurostars and one freight train. Northbound, traffic was heaviest between 1400 and 1500, when 13 trains, again, left Coquelles: five HGV shuttles, five passenger shuttles and three Eurostars. By contrast the quietest periods were (southbound) between 0300 and 0400 when just two HGV shuttles and one passenger shuttle ran, and (northbound) between 0500 and 0600 and 0600 and 0700, during each hour of which two HGV shuttles and one for motorists operated. The longest gap between trains entering the tunnel was 0229 to 0315 southbound and 0339 to 0423, 0439 to 0523 and 0539 to 0623 northbound. One reason for this flighting was the presence of works trains in one section of running tunnel, which meant that single-line working was imposed in the small hours over an 18 km stretch.

Apart from illustrating clearly the predominance of HGV shuttle traffic and the disappointingly slow build-up of international freight, the day's working timetable also shows the very different types of demand at differing times of the day and night. Of the 18 southbound freight trains, 10 entered the Cheriton portal between 0004 and 0719. By contrast, no southbound Eurostar services approached the tunnel between 2203 and 0731. Consequently, the two sets of long-distance rail traffic, travelling at very different speeds, almost avoided each other. The southbound HGV shuttle service operated at full throttle with five departures an hour from 0909 to 0044, reduced to three trains in the hour from 0100, two during the small hours, three in the hour from 0700 and four from 0800. The passenger shuttles kept more social hours: two in the hour after midnight BST, hourly during the night, two in the hour from 0700, four from 0800, then varyingly two, three or four an hour until the late evening, with four trains in the hour from 2300. The pattern northbound was little different.

Shuttle provision is determined by the fact that most cars and coaches leave Cheriton in the morning for the Continent, while heavy lorries that have mainly come from the Midlands and North peak in the afternoon. From Cheriton, lorry traffic is heaviest in the morning and car and coach traffic greater in the evening as Brits return home. Lorry traffic, understandably, is heavier during the working week; car shuttles are busier at weekends. Nevertheless the precise pattern for such an individualistic industry is hard to predict, as Eurotunnel discovered late in 2004 when it tried to get hauliers to guarantee their use of the tunnel in advance.

Despite the headline transit time of 35 minutes, the timings for individual trains vary considerably, in part because transits during single-line working are slower through the requirement to decelerate to 60 kph over the crossovers. Eurostars are timed at from 21 to 26 minutes, the slower times probably connected with stops at Calais-Fréthun which require lower speeds at the French portal. Passenger and HGV shuttles alike are timed to take between 34 and 43 minutes, despite the former having a higher maximum permitted speed; the arrival of more powerful freight shuttle locomotives has reduced the differential to a minimum. International freight trains are allowed a maximum 43 minutes to make the transit and a minimum 27 minutes, which given the speed restrictions on such trains in the tunnel looks almost unattainable, even behind a class '92'.

Trains using Eurotunnel's rail network are each given a four-figure 'mission number' - Eurostar's being 9, which explains the numerals that appear above each train listed in the Eurostar timetable: 90xx for Paris, 91xx for Brussels, 92xx for other destinations. The other codes used are 4xxx for international freight trains, 6xxx for Eurotunnel passenger shuttles, 7xxx for HGV shuttles and 8xxx for Eurotunnel works trains. The 9xxx series also integrates Eurostar workings with the Thalys trains from Paris to Brussels and beyond, but there the interlocking with the SNCF train description system ends; the French national railway uses the 7xxx code for its domestic high-speed services on the LGV-Nord.

Although the tunnel provides a 24-hour service, routine maintenance has to be regularly undertaken and, to facilitate this, a single portion of one running tunnel is out of commission during three nights of any one week. The effect of this is that single-line operation comes into force over roughly one-third of the tunnel's length, trains that would normally use the affected section of tunnel being diverted to run 'wrong-line' at one crossover chamber and returning to their normal route at the next. Such running reduces the capacity of the tunnel in two ways: for a start, single-line operation over one-third of the route has an obvious impact on paths available in each direction, and secondly maximum speeds for shuttle and through trains over the entire network are reduced during maintenance periods to 100 kph for Eurostars (though few operate at such times), 80 kph for passenger shuttles and 60 kph for freight trains and HGV shuttles. Even at the busiest times of year, the tunnel is able to cope within these limitations. But on the rare occasions when maintenance also affects track in two sections or in one of the crossover chambers and single-line operation is needed over some 36 km of tunnel, delays to users are almost inevitable.

The four sections into which the tunnel is geographically divided by the crossovers have no block status where signalling of the route is concerned; they are far too long to accommodate just one train. How the tunnel is signalled will be gone into shortly; suffice it to say here that the system in use is based on 500-metre block sections in each running tunnel, for bi-directional use if necessary. However, the four sections between each crossover: in turn from the French to the English portal 15.22 km, 17.69 km, 16 km and 1 km respectively, have an obvious operational function as the units into which operation of the tunnel can be divided if the entire system is not available for use for any reason. The flexibility created by the existence of the crossovers proved itself in the aftermath of the fire of November 1996, when a revised timetable was quickly able to handle much of the tunnel's pre-existing traffic - though HGV shuttles were admittedly suspended for a time pending safety checks.

Even though Eurotunnel's car and HGV shuttles operate a 'turn up and go' service, each day's timetable is set in advance by the company's rail traffic planners. The paths allocated to each particular train are calculated to achieve maximum efficiency in power consumption for the speed profile of that particular service. The daily shuttle schedules take into account train and staff availability, tunnel capacity and any planned maintenance work, as well as the volume and timing of scheduled through passenger and freight trains. Those timings are fed into Eurotunnel's operating computer, and paths for each train are created automatically. Should a sudden surge in demand require the running of an extra shuttle train, the timetable will simply be amended and the computer will take into account the additional working and its effect on other train movements, adjusting them if necessary.

Eurotunnel's entire 'main line' is regulated from a high-tech operations room in the control tower at Cheriton, at the rear of this distinctive building, not on the 'bridge' but partially below ground. This Rail Control Centre, heart of the tunnel's operations, is dominated by the world's largest LED panel - 24 m long and 3 m high, involving 1.5 million diodes - on which the entire Eurotunnel rail network, down to every siding in each terminal, is depicted, Cheriton to the left, Coquelles to the right, together with the exact position of every train, reported in by monitoring track circuits. On this vast display, designed by the French firm Vecteur, the running lines on the tunnel system are marked out in green, with the position of each train shown in yellow. Eurotunnel's boundaries with Network Rail (just to the east of where they pass over the English tunnel's terminal loop) and the SNCF network (just south of the flying junction bringing shuttle traffic out of the French terminal) are also indicated, with the sections of track beyond again shown in green. Below this giant railway map, on the same panel, is illustrated in green the entire circuit of electric catenary, and above the map is a plan of the tunnel's ventilation and cooling systems. Behind the display is a complex but orderly mass of wiring, kept behind roller shutters at the rear which afford easy access for maintenance.

The controllers sit at three curved rows of desks facing the LED display. Should the control room system fail, running of the system would automatically be switched to a waiting duplicate control room at Coquelles, identical except that there is no comparable LED display there. In normal times, however, the Coquelles control room handles only in-terminal shunting activities away from the main running lines. Right at the front is a work station at which all fire alarms are monitored. Installed as a first line of response after the fire of 1996, the controller at this desk alerts the entire control centre the moment any alarm is triggered; all trains are immediately slowed to 100 kph so that all 24 piston relief ducts can be closed, together with the crossover doors if they are open. Once a month Eurotunnel's response to a fire alert is tested: an empty HGV shuttle train goes into the tunnel with orders to stop at a crossover and report that fire has broken out; when the control system is alerted, the full emergency system is put into operation with senior management in attendance. Behind the fire alarm controller sit three controllers dealing with, in turn, the Eurotunnel train crews, management of rail traffic, and the operation of equipment such as power supply, communications, ventilation, drainage and cooling.

Eurotunnel's railways are controlled by a fully computerised Rail Traffic Management system (RTM) computer; linked to the LED display. While regular train operation is entirely computerised, control room staff can monitor operations at all times, so that they can intervene as appropriate and if necessary take over full manual control. But they are only actually alerted if something happens that requires their intervention; even when a portion of one running tunnel is closed for maintenance, the single-line working in the other bore remains governed by the computer. Moreover the computer system is 'fail-safe', so that in the event of any equipment failure, safety precautions are automatically taken, up to and including the halting of all trains if signalling pulses through the rails were to stop. Computers also plot the progress of through international trains heading for either portal on the British and French domestic systems; those on time are cleared automatically onto Eurotunnel's metals and into the tunnnel. If they are running late and a shuttle train is already moving into the tunnel, the Eurostar or freight train may have to wait its turn.

The progress of train movements, and the availability of paths, is not the only information fed into the RTM computer. It also records the temperature at various points along the tunnel, the number of cars and HGVs arriving at each terminal to catch a shuttle and the strength of current in the catenary.

There are in fact two electronic control systems operated from the Cheriton centre. The Rail Traffic Management system controls train movements, while the Engineering Management System (EMS) handles the signalling and infrastructure; the two are manned by 30 bilingual staff.

Successful operation of the tunnel depends on trains entering, traversing and leaving it at very tight headways in busy times; under the Treaty of Canterbury, Eurotunnel was required to provide 20 train paths an hour, or one every three minutes, though, as has been explained, the practical maximum is 16 and the present legal maximum is 12. The computerised timetabling of shuttle trains and through international rail traffic takes the need for trains to run in close sequence into account, the operational system being based on the Swiss BLS route through the Lotschberg tunnel, which carries a similar mix of traffic.

Delivery of the tight headways required depends on a state-of-the-art system of signalling - yet there are no visible signals in the running tunnels. All that can be seen there are the yellow and blue 'flag' markers, also a familiar lineside sight in the terminals and on the LGV-Nord and the CTRL, that indicate the start of each 500-metre block section. Instead of operating colour-light signals (except in the terminals where single-aspect signals give a conventional 'right away'), trains in the tunnel are governed by cab signalling which is activated by information sent through track circuits to each train from Eurotunnel's computerised control system, just as those same circuits report on the movement of each train to the LED display. If a driver were to ignore a signal to reduce speed, or did not slow down sufficiently, an emergency braking system would automatically intervene.

Inherent in the tunnel's signalling and operational system, and indeed in its safety planning, is a system of Automatic Train Protection known as TVM430, an upgrade of the TVM300 system installed by SNCF on the Paris-Lyon and Atlantique TGV routes; this is fitted to all revenue-earning trains using Eurotunnel's metals: shuttles, Eurostars and through freight trains alike. All other motive power transiting the tunnel - such as new stock being delivered to UK train operating companies like South West Trains' massive 'Desiro' order from Siemens, trains being sent for overhaul, or special workings like the 1999 class '20'-hauled 'Train for Life' for Kosovo or the EWS class '37s' and '58s' sent to France and Spain for infrastructure work - must be hauled through it, dead, by locomotives that are so fitted, generally class '92s'.

At any one time, TVM430 (the initials stand for *Transmission Voie Machine*, track-to-train transmission) can feed the control system of a train within its ambit with a staggering 27,000,000 items of information. Using coded data fed through those track circuits to a specially equipped console in each train's cab, TVM430 - which also governs Eurostars on the LGV-Nord route from the French tunnel portal to Paris and now on the CTRL - allows its driver to know in real time the speed level needed to keep at the right interval from the train in front and the one following. The information is picked up from the rails by sensor coils in front of the train's leading bogie, and by other sensors on the leading power unit from loops of wire, or 'beacons', between the rails. Detectors mounted on the locomotive's axles also continually feed to the computer precise details of the train's current speed.

Despite the intensive timetable operated at peak times, TVM430 always gives a train driver in the tunnel nearly twice the distance he needs to stop, should some emergency befall the train in front. The system is posited on trains running three minutes apart at 300 kph - almost twice the maximum speed permitted in the tunnel for any train. Moreover, as with the ATP systems pioneered on parts of the BR system, if the driver ignores these warnings the train is automatically halted for him.

The purpose of ATP is not to bring a train to a jarring halt if another has stopped immediately ahead; it is to maintain smooth running of the scheduled service at optimum speed. The ATP control system will steadily slow any train as it approaches an obstruction, in the hope that it can pick up speed equally smoothly again as the other train moves off, but always with room to halt safely if necessary. Indeed if the system works there should never need to be an emergency stop; certainly there has never been one on the Marylebone-Aynho Junction section of Chiltern Railways where a German-designed version ATP has been successfully operating for some years. There were, however, problems in the tunnel's first months of operation with 'rogue trains' appearing on the LED as a result of highly conductive salt water in the tunnel affecting the track circuits. According to a shuttle train driver quoted in the *Sunday Times*, the problem at its worst led to five emergency stops a week by drivers who were suddenly notified that a 'train' was just ahead of them.

In the tunnels, TVM430 operates through a chain of track circuit blocks, the start of each being denoted by a 'flag' marker fixed to the tunnel wall. The purpose of the marker is to remind the driver that he is passing a point where the signal aspect in the cab may change, or where a speed reduction may be required. The critical information the driver needs at all times is the correct speed level at that point for his train as determined by the computer, and this is displayed on the console before him. The train's automatic controls allow a few kph in latitude, but if the set speed is exceeded significantly an automatic reduction is made; if a train ahead has come to a halt, gradual braking to a standstill is initiated. (A shuttle train travelling at 140 kph is reckoned to need three sections, or 1,500 m, to come to a non-emergency stop, though more is allowed.)

Normally the driver's console will show in green squares the maximum line speed for that type of train, for instance 160 kph for a Eurostar or 140 kph for a passenger shuttle. But if a slower speed is required because of a train ahead, the display will flash green during passage of a first section, then alter at the next marker to flashing black figures in white lozenges. The figures shown will represent the speed to be decelerated to by the end of the second section, 115 kph in the case of a passenger shuttle; if the driver does not reduce to that speed, the control system will do it for him. At the next section marker if the train ahead has not itself picked up speed, the flashing black-in-white-lozenge figure will go down from 115 to 80 kph, with the driver once again obliged to reduce to that speed by end of this third section. If the train ahead has still not cleared, at the next section marker '000' will show up in black on a red background, meaning that the driver must halt by the next section marker. In the interests of safety, this will not be the marker for the section occupied by the train ahead, but for an 'overlap section' kept clear of traffic before that train is reached. Were a train for any reason to run on into this 'overlap' section, three red squares would show on the console and the computer would trigger an emergency brake application.

The overall effect of the ATP warning and braking process is that the driver of a Eurostar or through freight train starts picking up warnings on his cab console 3 km before the start of a section in which a train is running or stationary; shuttle drivers get their warning 500 m later. The reason for this is that Eurostars require an extra

Hunslet battery-electric No. RA24 heads a works train in the service tunnel. *Eurotunnel*

Schoma diesel man-riding unit No. RU 005 pauses in one of the English seaward running tunnels during the construction stage. *Eurotunnel*

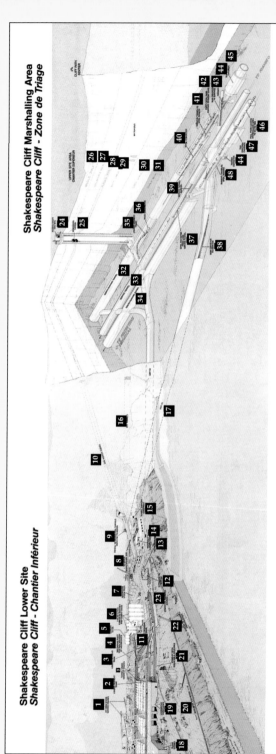

Shakespeare Cliff Lower Site
Shakespeare Cliff - Chantier Inférieur

Shakespeare Cliff Marshalling Area
Shakespeare Cliff - Zone de Triage

1. 20 t high speed gantry cutter
2. Loaded segment train
3. Tunnel lining segment stacks
4. Unloading point for rail delivery aggregates
5. Cement silos
6. 2x80 cu. m/hr concrete batches and cement silos
7. Aggregate stock piles
8. To Upper Shakespeare site
9. Portal to British Rail tunnels, main line to Dover
10. Site access
11. Empty segment train

12. Entrance to adit A2
13. Ventilation fans
14. Materials laboratory
15. Tunnel support equipment
16. BR tunnels
17. Adit A1
18. Plant stores
19. Locomotive workshops
20. Main spoil conveyor
21. Stand-by spoil conveyor and stockpile
22. Access to seawall construction
23. Conveyor transfer station
24. Access shaft (10 m dia.)

25. Personnel hoists
26. Middle chalk
27. Melbourne rock
28. Plenus marl
29. White chalk
30. Grey chalk
31. Chalk marl
32. Running tunnel north
33. Service tunnel
34. Running tunnel south
35. Loaded segment train
36. Rack and pinion locomotive
37. Spoil conveyor from land service tunnel

38. Main conveyor to surface
39. Service tunnel bunker
40. Spoil conveyor
41. Running tunnel north spoil bunker
42. Empty spoil cars
43. Main conveyor to surface
44. Feeder conveyor
45. TBM erection chamber
46. Full train leaving marshalling area to go to TBM
47. TBM erection chamber
48. Running tunnel south spoil bunker

Sectional drawings of the Lower Shakespeare Cliff working site and marshalling area beneath it, showing (above ground) the range of facilities needed to keep construction moving, and below the complex narrow gauge layout at the start of the tunnel workings. *Eurotunnel*

The French narrow gauge construction network breaks surface in the Beussingue Trench.

Eurotunnel

Passenger motive power on the French narrow gauge construction network: Senafer battery-electric power car No. TU 2051105, in the service tunnel, March 1991.   *Author*

Activity at the foot of the Sangatte shaft, 14th December, 1988. Note the unsecured track and the lifting gear.   *Eurotunnel*

The tunnel segment fabrication plant on the Isle of Grain on 8th November, 1990. A pair of class '33s' stand with a train. *Brian Morrison*

Not the usual class '33' but a '34' - Bulleid Pacific No. 34016 *Bodmin* hauls a train of tunnel segments away from the fabrication plant at Grain to mark its official opening on 23rd March, 1988.

RFS class '20' No. 2018 with the last long-welded rail train from Workington on 14th July, 1992.
Brian Morrison

Class 20' No. 20159 (RFS No. 2010) one of 10 based by CTTG at Coquelles, enters the Beussingue Trench with a fitting-out train, 12th July, 1993.   *Bob Sweet*

Mission accomplished. HGVs leaving their shuttle at Cheriton.   *Bob Sweet*

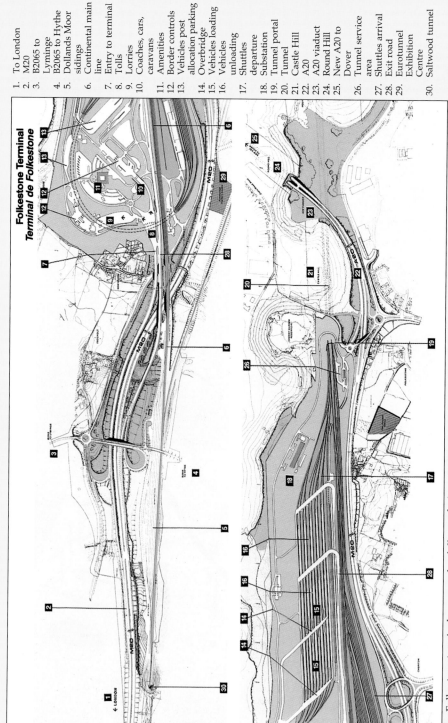

Folkestone Terminal
Terminal de Folkestone

1. To London
2. M20
3. B2065 to Lyminge
4. B2065 to Hythe
5. Dollands Moor sidings
6. Continental main line
7. Entry to terminal
8. Tolls
9. Lorries
10. Coaches, cars, caravans
11. Amenities
12. Border controls
13. Vehicles post allocation parking
14. Overbridge
15. Vehicles loading
16. Vehicles unloading
17. Shuttles departure
18. Substation
19. Tunnel portal
20. Tunnel
21. Castle Hill
22. A20
23. A20 viaduct
24. Round Hill
25. New A20 to Dover
26. Tunnel service area
27. Shuttles arrival
28. Exit road
29. Eurotunnel Exhibition Centre
30. Saltwood tunnel

The Folkestone terminal as opened at full stretch, from Dollands Moor (5, left) to the tunnel portal (19, right). The pre-CTRL connection to the BR system is shown (at 6). The terminal buildings lie just left of centre (11) and the vehicle unloading (16) and loading platforms (17) to the right.

Eurotunnel

A car shuttle train clears the terminal platforms at Cheriton and heads for the tunnel.
Bob Sweet

Cars begin to disembark from a lightly-loaded shuttle train at Cheriton. *Eurotunnel*

Two Eurotunnel staff cars pass in the service tunnel, demonstrating its width.   *Eurotunnel*

Engineers cycle to work in the service tunnel, September 1993.   *Eurotunnel*

Between trains in one of the running tunnels just short of the French portal, the light from which can be seen in the distance. *Eurotunnel*

The doors sealing off the crossover tracks in one of the undersea chambers. *Eurotunnel*

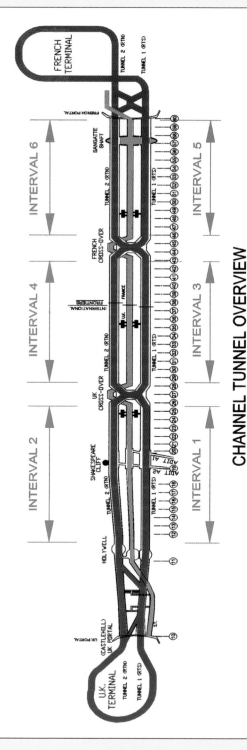

CHANNEL TUNNEL OVERVIEW

SIMPLIFIED VIEW FOR MEDIA PUBLICATION AS ISSUED BY THE PRESS OFFICE

Operational diagram of the Channel Tunnel showing the strategic positioning of the crossovers, the sections into which the route is divided and the way the service tunnel is sidelined to facilitate each crossover.

Eurotunnel

Three shuttle trains lined up ready to go at Coquelles, hauled by locomotives Nos. 9112, 9111 and 9007. *Eurotunnel*

Cars for a busy holiday shuttle being directed aboard at Coquelles. *Eurotunnel*

The first HGV shuttle club car about to be married to its train at Coquelles after delivery in October 1992. *Eurotunnel*

The first demonstration loading of an HGV shuttle at Cheriton in September 1992. Compare the 1971 mock-up exercise pictured on page 33. *Eurotunnel*

The 1510 to Fréthun stands at Dolland Moor on 13th October, 1995. It was the last working through the tunnel of an SNCF '22000' class. *Brian Morrison*

Nearing journey's end: EWS class '92' with a well-loaded automotive train heads away from the tunnel at Fréthun yard. *EWS*

Above: The nerve centre of the tunnel, the Rail Control Centre at Cheriton, dominated by the world's largest LED panel.
Eurotunnel

Left: Exterior of the Eurotunnel control centre at Cheriton.
Eurotunnel

500 m in which to pull up because of their speed, and that the braking systems on the class '92s' hauling freight trains are considered less effective, given their sometimes exceptionally heavy loads, than on the shuttle locomotives.

TVM430 also governs the speed of acceleration or deceleration by shuttle trains in Eurotunnel's terminals, and within the tunnel when one portion is out of action for planned maintenance. As a train nears a crossover where it will switch to the opposite running tunnel, a series of warning signals appears on the cab console advising of the deceleration necessary for safe negotiation of a crossover; the maximum speed over the junctions themselves for any train is 60 kph.

With any computerised control system, exceptions occasionally have to be made. For example, if a shuttle train breaks down in the tunnel, the train behind may be needed to push it out. In such a case, the Cheriton control centre would give the driver special permission to enter the 'overlap' section at low speed, with the emergency braking imperative overridden. Special provision is also needed for the operation of maintenance trains. While Eurotunnel's diesel-electric locomotives which haul such trains to their working sites are equipped with TVM430 cab signalling and can operate under it at 100 kph, the same does not apply to the 'sub-trains' into which maintenance trains are divided during possessions. These need and have the ability to move independently, and are permitted to operate at up to 30 kph under 'Move on Sight' rules. Once scheduled trains have been diverted from a portion of tunnel and the catenary de-energised, the control centre will hand over responsibility for safe movement to the person in charge of the maintenance train. At the end of the possession the train is re-formed and leaves the site, once again under diesel-electric haulage and TVM430. Habitually maintenance trains leave for a possession from one terminal, then continue through after it to the other; maintenance staff who complete their shift away from home are returned by shuttle.

As with any automated system, the risk of mishap is greater when some abnormal occurrence requires human intervention. One such occurred on 1st September, 2000 after an EWS freight train emerging from the tunnel at Cheriton with illegal immigrants clinging to it had been switched to the emergency siding. Once the train had been searched, the driver was ordered to reverse back onto the main line to continue his journey to Dollands Moor. However, the order to set back put the freight train directly in the path of a Waterloo-bound Eurostar; with the control computer raising the alert, both trains were halted and as an extra precaution the overhead power in the relevant section was turned off. The Eurostar was able to pull up short, but it was fortunate that no accident occurred as the trains came to rest barely 100 metres apart.

Ancillary services such as electric power, lighting, ventilation, drainage and the operation of the doors in the crossover chambers, are controlled by a separate Engineering Management System. This monitors the operation of all these mechanisms and makes changes when necessary, for example opening the crossover doors, isolating and earthing sections of catenary and closing piston relief ducts if a section of running tunnel is closed for maintenance. If more than one item of equipment being monitored requires attention, the computer will present the controllers on duty with an order of priorities for dealing with them.

To make sure that information and instructions from the control centre can reach all train, operating and engineering staff in the tunnel, no fewer than five separate voice communication systems are used. There is a radio link to the trackside and the trains, supplemented by Eurotunnel's radio system which other staff use throughout the tunnel complex and the terminals. There is a telephone system in the terminals and tunnels for routine communication, plus special emergency telephones along the running tunnels. In addition, the controllers can reach staff in the terminals, undersea cross-passages and the service tunnel by a standard public address system.

In addition to the Rail Control Centre at Cheriton, car and HGV traffic on the site is governed by a Terminal Traffic Management Control Centre (TTMCC) at the top of the control tower (Coquelles, sensibly, has its own). Staff monitoring each of Eurotunnel's control systems are permanently in touch with each other.

Furthermore a Major Incident Co-Ordination Centre (MICC), also in the tower, is available round the clock in case of an accident or other emergency. Here outside agencies, like the fire or paramedical services or the train operating companies, can pool their resources and information with Eurotunnel should some crisis require it. Facilities are kept ready to give an overview of the situation, with conference facilities and lines of communication both within the Eurotunnel complex and to wherever needs to be reached outside it. These were fully tested in simulation exercises before the tunnel was opened and, as we shall see, were put fully to the test when fire broke out in the tunnel on 18th November, 1996.

There is also - somewhere - according to *La Vie du Rail* a panic button for flooding the tunnel at one end or the other in case of war breaking out between Britain and France, or of either country being occupied by a foreign power. Its location, and how precisely it operates, is said to be a military secret.

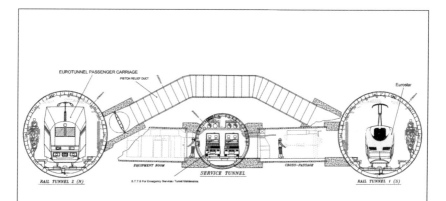

Sectional drawing of the Channel Tunnel showing the relationship between the two running tunnels and the service tunnel and one of the piston relief ducts connecting them.

Eurotunnel

Chapter Six

Motive Power and Rolling Stock

From the outset, it was clear that a pioneering high-speed undersea railway like that through the Channel Tunnel would require a completely new concept of train. Highly sophisticated locomotives and stock were commissioned to operate through it by Eurotunnel and national railways, and each variety - the Tri-Bo shuttle locomotives, the Eurostar international high-speed multiple units and the class '92' electric freight locomotives - has proved extremely successful in service. The same cannot, sadly, be said of the 'Nightstar' passenger stock designed for operation on international sleeper trains, as it never turned a wheel in revenue-earning service through the tunnel despite having cost UK, French, Dutch and German taxpayers some £130 million.

The locomotives and rolling stock that operate through the Channel Tunnel, either on shuttle or through international trains, have had to meet strict safety and technical standards as well as delivering exceptional performance. This is why most conventional stock has been banned from revenue-earning service through the Tunnel, and not just the 'heritage' rakes of the Venice-Simplon-Orient Express. Channel Tunnel trains must, naturally, be equipped for the tunnel's sophisticated system of Automatic Train Protection. They must be highly fire-resistant, and (except for international freight trains) be able to exit the tunnel under their own power even if the engine at one end is incapacitated. High standards of reliability are demanded, to keep the tunnel free of avoidable blockages. Tunnel trains must meet the aerodynamic challenge of transiting over 50 km of single-bore tunnel at 160 kph with a minimum of wind resistance, and be able to take gradients of up to 1 in 91 in their stride with a heavy load, even from a standing start. They must be able to cope with sharp changes in temperature and humidity as they enter and leave the tunnel. And all stock running onto the national systems of Britain, France and beyond also require power and internal systems compatible with each of these networks as well as those of the tunnel itself. Manufacturing such trains was quite a challenge, but it was met . . . successfully, if at a high cost.

Eurotunnel

The workhorses of the Channel Tunnel are the 58 Brush-built 136-tonne Tri-Bo electric locomotives which haul all the shuttle services - car, lorry and coach - operated by Eurotunnel between its terminals at Cheriton and Coquelles. Initially 38 were ordered in July 1989, four of them spares, at a budgeted cost of £2.1 million each (which was comfortably exceeded). As traffic has built up, 21 further Tri-Bos, the final seven of them being arguably the world's most powerful locomotives - have been delivered, one of these replacing fire-damaged No. 9030. The locomotives operate in pairs, one at each end of a train, sharing the tractive effort equally but controlled from the leading locomotive's cab.

Eurotunnel's shuttle locomotives are based on a batch of smaller but still impressively powerful Tri-Bos delivered by Brush to the 3 ft 6 in. gauge New Zealand Railways in the late 1980s. Given the shuttle locomotives' singular task - which includes being able to push the preceding shuttle out of the tunnel if it breaks down -

it is not surprising that they have some highly unusual features. For a start they are taller than most locomotives - 4.2 m from track to roof plus raised pantograph, against 22.008 m in length and 2.966 m in width. The Tunnel's generous loading gauge created the space for a really mighty engine, but the Tri-Bos' dimensions were limited just enough to permit them to travel over main lines on the Continent *en route* for a major overhaul; for attention at Brush they have to be conveyed by road because of the restrictive British loading gauge.

The Bo-Bo-Bo wheel arrangement - three bogies, each with two axles - is unusual for a locomotive (though not for a high-speed emu) but not unique. This arrangement not only enables the locomotives to take the tight curves at each terminal, especially Cheriton where the rail network was squeezed into a confined site, with less wear than a longer-wheelbase Co-Co would suffer; it also means that after one unit failure they can still operate on two-thirds power.

The third way in which these locomotives stand out is their pioneering use, for a 25kV overhead-powered locomotive, of the three-phase variable frequency drive. Power from the two pantographs (only one is normally used) is transformed down to a 1500V direct current and passed through solid-state inverters fitted with Gate Turn-Off semiconducting thyristors which convert it in turn into a three-phase alternating supply that can be used by traction motors that are relatively simple and easy to maintain. Each of the six motors, one per axle, is rated at 1,285 hp (total 7,710 hp). Microcomputers control the locomotives' power systems.

Each locomotive from the original batch has a main cab at its streamlined end and a smaller one, for shunting and light-engine running at up to 80 kph, at its rear, 'train', end; the train captain normally occupies the main cab of a shuttle's rear locomotive in readiness to drive the train out of the tunnel in an emergency. There is also scope to control the locomotive at speeds up to 33 kph from tiny cabs located in each rake of shuttle wagons; this facility is mainly used for manoeuvres on terminal sidings and in the Coquelles depot. In addition, low-speed movements by the shuttle locomotives can be carried out under radio control from the trackside. From the cabs a communication system enables the train captain to make announcements to shuttle passengers.

Each locomotive has a standard UIC screw coupling at the front so that it can assist another tunnel train; at its rear is a Scharfenberg coupling enabling it to couple and uncouple from a shuttle train automatically. All the information and control circuits, plus a 1500V power connection, pass through the couplings. There is also a fire alarm system linked to both ends of the train. Each shuttle locomotive is divided into four fire-detection zones where excessive heat will set off the cab alarm and trigger releases of halon gas to smother a blaze.

The shuttle locomotives' body shells were manufactured by Qualter Hall Engineering of Barnsley, and (after stress tests on one shell at BR's Derby technical centre) were fitted out at Brush's Loughborough plant, with propulsion equipment supplied by ABB's factories in Switzerland. The first completed locomotive was delivered to the running depot at Coquelles on 14th December, 1992 - by road and sea as even without its bogies it was too bulky for the BR loading gauge. The first few were delivered in works grey, but all were eventually painted in a standard 'Le Shuttle' livery; until the title was dropped and grey again became the dominant colour. Two of the early arrivals were sent to the Velim test track in the Czech Republic for a 50,000 km endurance test, which they passed with flying colours.

The first batch of shuttle locomotives were numbered 9001 to 9038, and between 1994 and 1997 were allocated names; almost all were named after opera singers, the first two being christened personally by Luciano Pavarotti and Dame Kiri Te Kanawa, but a handful were given the names of famous tunnels.

Eurotunnel's fleet of shuttle locomotives suffered its first depletion in the fire of 18th November, 1996, when No. 9030, which was on the point of being named *Montserrat Caballé*, was very seriously damaged and withdrawn; the name was bestowed instead on No. 9033. The scrapped locomotive's companion, No. 9006, was deemed repairable and eventually returned to service.

Soon after, Eurotunnel ordered five further Tri-Bos from Brush, four (9101-4) to cater for increasing traffic and one (numbered 9040 although there was no 9039) to replace the fire casualty; they were delivered in 1998. These locomotives are all distinguishable from the first in that they have no rear 'shunt cab' and thus cannot haul passenger shuttles. Between 1999 and late 2000 nine more similar locomotives were delivered, and numbered 9105-13.

Seven further Tri-Bos entered service between February 2002 and June 2003. Numbered in the 97xx series (not 92xx lest they be confused with the class '92' freight locomotives which operate through the tunnel), these have a continuous power rating of 7MW (developing 9,387 hp) compared with 5.6MW of the earlier batches, which were mighty enough. The 97xx series were introduced to handle longer and therefore heavier HGV shuttle trains, and these are being phased in as the number of more powerful locomotives increases. Paired together, they will be able to operate 3,000-tonne trains at up to 140 kph. Eurotunnel engineers reckon that only Swiss Railways' class 'Re 6/6' Tri-Bos, built from 1972, and conceivably the German class '103' Bo-Bo can pack a corresponding punch, but add that the Eurotunnel locomotives are capable of higher speeds and have lighter motors.

The 97xx also lack the second cab at the rear, but they differ from the four later 91xx locomotives by having an original grille on the non-driver's side, an improved air management system to prevent the tunnel heating up, and a more easily visible speed indicator on a video screen. Their extra strength - each 97xx is three times as powerful as a 'Deltic' - quickly demonstrated its worth in operation, not least in making up lost time, and in February 2003 a €150 million programme of uprating the 37 surviving original locos to 7MW as they each completed 10 years and 3 million kilometres in service was begun. The work being carried out at Brush's Loughborough plant, which includes a full internal overhaul with rewiring and replacement of traction motors and control equipment, is due to take until April 2009, after which a start is likely on overhauling (and uprating where appropriate) the later Tri-Bos. No. 9025 was the first locomotive to be upgraded, arriving at Loughborough in May 2003; it was delivered back to Cheriton in February 2004 as No. 9825; all uprated locomotives from the original batch will be renumbered in the 98xx series.

The second upgraded locomotive to emerge was No. 9821, and No. 9820 the third, re-entering service in August 2004 as the pace of conversion accelerated. Nos. 9804, 9814 and 9819 followed. The full consist of Tri-Bos to enter service to date is as follows:

9001	*Lesley Garrett*	9007	*Dame Joan Sutherland*
9002	*Stuart Burrows*	9008	*Elisabeth Soderstrøm*
9003	*Benjamin Luxon*	9009	*François Pollet*
9004	*Victoria de Los Angeles*	9010	*Jean-Philippe Cortis*
9005	*Jessye Norman*	9011	*José Van Dam*
9006*	*Régine Crespin*	9012	*Luciano Pavarotti*

*   Slightly damaged in fire of November 1996; returned to service.

9013	Maria Callas	9038	Hildegard Behrens
9014	Lucia Popp		
9015	Lötschberg 1913	9040	
9016	Willard White		
9017	José Carreras	9101	
9018	Wilhelmina Fernandez	9102	
9019	Maria Ewing	9103	
9020	Nicolai Ghiarov	9104	
9021	Teresa Berganza	9105	
9022	Dame Janet Baker	9106	
9023	Dame Elisabeth Legge-Schwarzkopf	9107	
9024	Gotthard 1882	9108	
9025	Jungfraujoch 1912	9109	
9026	Furka Tunnel 1982	9110	
9027	Barbara Hendricks	9111	
9028	Dame Kiri Te Kanawa	9112	
9029	Thomas Allen	9113	
9030*			
9031	Placido Domingo	9701	
9032	Renata Tebaldi	9702	
9033†	Montserrat Caballé	9703	
9034	Mirella Freni	9704	
9035	Nicolai Gedda	9705	
9036	Alain Fondary	9706	
9037	Gabriel Bauquier	9707	

*   Damaged beyond repair in the fire and scrapped.
†   Name originally allocated to the first No. 9030 but not carried.

Each pair of Tri-Bos tops and tails a rake of shuttle wagons of which Eurotunnel has over 900 in total. The 28-wagon passenger shuttle trains are 776 m long and the original 28-wagon freight shuttles 730 m; further freight shuttle trains delivered from 1998 have 32 wagons, hence the greater power of the 97xx series Tri-Bos ordered to haul them. Strictly confined to the Eurotunnel system, these wagons are the world's largest items of rolling stock, towering 5.6 metres above rail level and being 26.5 metres long; each weighs 63 to 65 tons (the double-deck car carriers are the heavier) and is designed to take a load of 24 tonnes. For the opening of the tunnel Eurotunnel ordered a total of 526 wagons, comprising nine passenger shuttle trains, eight freight shuttles and plenty of spares. 254 were enclosed wagons for tourist traffic from Bombardier (shells built in Canada and fitted out at Bruges) and 272 were HGV shuttle vehicles from BREDA-Fiat.

The passenger order comprised 108 single-deck wagons for coaches, high cars and vans, 108 double-deckers for cars and motorcycles, 18 single-deck loading wagons plus one spare and 18 double-deck loading wagons plus one spare. The loading wagons allow vehicles to enter from the platform beside the train before running forward to its place, or to gain the upper level in the double-deck cars, which to serve this purpose are the longest shuttle vehicles at 27.5 metres. The loading wagons also have a small cab at the end, for low-speed shunting in sidings and maintenance areas. Originally two such wagons were marshalled at the centre of each rake of vehicles, so that each nine-vehicle rake could be controlled from there when the train was split into two for servicing, but since a maintenance shed capable of handling an entire shuttle was opened at Coquelles the trains no longer have to be split and they have been replaced in the centre of the train by a single flat vehicle.

Likewise each passenger shuttle originally comprised two rakes of 12 wagons, each divided into four 'triplets', with a loading wagon at each end and two in the middle; again the need for wagons with cabs in mid-train has now evaporated, and a flat loading wagon has again been substituted.

The initial order for freight shuttle wagons comprised 35 loading and unloading wagons, one of them a spare, 228 honeycomb-sided carrier wagons including four spares, and nine club cars, one of them a spare. The loading and unloading wagons are open flats 25.1 metres in length designed for maximum manoeuvrability of a lorry and trailer, save for a marshalling cab at one end; when loading, hydraulic jacks beneath the wagons grip onto concrete walls below platform level to give added stability. Each of the original freight shuttles comprised 24 20-metre HGV wagons in two rakes, with four loading wagons and a club car. The original stock was supplemented late in 1996 by a further 16 freight shuttle wagons of identical design.

The 52-seat club cars for the HGV shuttles, with folding tables, non-alcoholic refreshments and toilets, are based on the first-class stock used on Italy's 'Direttissima'; being narrower than the shuttle wagons, they have retractable flaps for entrance and exit. One club car is marshalled in each shuttle train immediately behind the leading locomotive; when the train is ready to depart a bus takes drivers to the club car from the wagons where they have left their vehicles. Because HGV drivers do not stay with their vehicles, the freight shuttle wagons, save for the club cars, are not air-conditioned, whereas the passenger shuttles have full air-conditioning. Safety is the reason for segregating lorry drivers from their vehicles, and the precaution was borne out in the fire of 1996; another precaution against fire is that any oil leaking from the HGVs is channelled away for recycling.

During 2004 the consist of the HGV shuttles was changed as a fire suppresion vehicle - converted at Coquelles from a redundant BREDA vehicle loader - began to appear behind the club car in each train. These wagons, a consequence of the 1996 fire, enable sprinkler water to be pumped under pressure along the length of the train in the event of fire breaking out in one of the lorries.

The first tourist shuttle shells arrived at Zeebrugge from Canada in January 1991 and were taken to Bruges for fitting-out. In June 1993 the first completed wagons were delivered to Coquelles. The first shuttle wagon to arrive on site complete was an HGV loading wagon, delivered to Coquelles in April 1992. The first two HGV carrier wagons arrived at Folkestone by road that July, the month when Eurotunnel branded its Cheriton-Coquelles passenger and HGV services 'Le Shuttle', and the first club car was delivered from Italy that October. By the end of 1993 most of the original shuttle fleet was ready for operation.

As HGV traffic increased, more and longer shuttle trains became necessary and Eurotunnel turned to Arbel-Douai for a second generation of stock: wagons of a modified design to reduce and simplify maintenance, with much more open sides than the original fleet. The consist was also changed: from 24 covered wagons, four loading vehicles and a club car to 29 covered wagons, three loading vehicles (the two in the centre with cabs being replaced by a single ordinary flat wagon) and, once again, the club car. The first two 32-wagon shuttles from Arbel, plus three club cars built by the Italian manufacturer Costamansnaga, were delivered in 1999; there followed one further rake to replace wagons lost in the fire, two more in 2000 and four more by 2003, bringing the operational total to 16 sets (seven BREDA, nine Arbel). The acquisition of these vehicles brought the total of freight shuttle wagons to over 460, allowing for the losses sustained in the fire. Those that survived the fire have been split between other first-generation rakes to boost their capacity.

In March 2004, Eurotunnel's Europorte 2 subsidiary issued a letter of intent for the purchase of five Alstom Prima electric locomotives similar to SNCF's BB class '37000'. Able to operate on the German and Swiss 15kv AC voltage as well as France's 25kv AC and 1500v DC (south of Paris), they were an add-on to SNCF's order of 29 locomotives for delivery during 2004. These were not intended for operation through the tunnel, but to haul freight trains to it from Lille, Metz, Basel and Milan under the EU's 'open access' regime. Though French and UK Government approval for these services has been received, their operation - and indeed the procurement of the locomotives, two of which are options - has been put on hold as efforts are made to resolve Eurotunnel's latest financial crisis. Indeed it has been suggested that Britain's EWS may take over the option on the Primas to operate its own planned freight services in France. Eurotunnel had earlier considered operating these services with surplus class '92s'.

Apart from the Tri-Bos, Eurotunnel has a small stable of small but powerful diesel locomotives. Five 4w-4w MaK diesel-electric twin units, similar to a batch already in service in Holland with NS, were bought new from Krupp and numbered 0001 to 0005; the first arrived in December 1992. Based at Cheriton with a couple outstationed at Coquelles, they work into and through the tunnel as required, coupled to special exhaust scrubber units. Their main task is planned maintenance, but they are on 24-hour standby to pair up and rescue a shuttle or through international train from the tunnel should all its motive power fail, and on several occasions they have rescued a stranded Eurostar. They are capable, in tandem, of moving a 2,600 tonne shuttle train, with 'dead' electric locomotive, up a 1 in 90 gradient at 50 kph from a standing start.

Eurotunnel also has 12 four-wheel diesel hydraulics bought between 1993 and 1996 and each given girls' names, from 0031 *Frances* to 0042 *Nicole*. The first two were seen on BR's Old Dalby test track in January 1994, and others may also have worked there. Originally built by Hunslet to 900 mm gauge, they were rebuilt and regauged by Schoma before entering service with Eurotunnel. At first sight, bizarrely, they appear to be electric locomotives, but their cab-mounted pantographs are used purely to test and earth the overhead wires on the Eurotunnel network. The company also had two small diesels constructed by Schoma using the Deutz power units from a pair of TML narrow-gauge locomotives, but although these proved valuable in the tunnel's early days, little is known of their subsequent activity. In 1997 Eurotunnel found it necessary to bolster its maintenance fleet by hiring for six months the ex-BR class '03' 0-6-0 shunter D2199, the property of South Yorkshire Railway Preservation Society at Meadowhall. Eurotunnel's railed motive power roster also includes 'Unimog' road-railers for shunting stock and a railborne trackbed cleaning machine.

As rolling stock for maintenance, Eurotunnel has 32 'modules' ranging from gantries for catenary work to specialised cranes for pipework and cleaning-out tanks. Because not all are needed at any one time, just 15 flat wagons to carry them were obtained from the French company SOCOFER, supplementing three Bulgarian flat wagons acquired for the final stages of commissioning. The modules are normally hauled into the tunnel as a maintenance train by the Krupp diesels, but a 'sub-train' for a particular task may be left *en route* with a smaller diesel in charge.

Eurotunnel also operates some road vehicles inside the tunnel complex: LADOG lean-burn tip-up lorries for tunnel maintenance and deliveries, mainly in the service tunnel, and STTS long-wheelbase vehicles for firefighting and for delivering maintenance pods in the service tunnel.

Eurostar and National Railways

A very special train was needed for the flagship high-speed international passenger service planned for the Channel Tunnel, and in Eurostar we have it. The sleek white, dark blue and yellow 18-car units commissioned for 'Three Capitals' services from London to Brussels and Paris established the Eurostar brand from the moment they went into operation, and have proved as reliable as they are eye-catching. They are also extremely safe; when a Eurostar bound from Paris to London derailed at close to maximum speed on the TGV-Nord line near Arras in June 2000 after a piece of equipment became detached from a bogie, the train stayed on the alignment and of more than 500 passengers, not one was seriously injured, though the locomotive suffered structural damage. Perhaps the only criticism is that they are longer and more capacious than has proved necessary for the passenger numbers carried; 16 or even 14 carriages could have handled most of the traffic more economically, the need for shorter platforms reducing Eurostar's terminal costs and causing fewer operating headaches on conventional routes, especially in England.

With slightly smoother looks than their SNCF cousins, the Eurostars cram into a more restricted space not only the TGV's traction system but also the far more complex electronics needed to operate both in France and through the tunnel and under the vastly different current and signalling systems of Britain and Belgium.

Eurostar was the brainchild of a consortium set up in 1988 by BR, SNCF and the Belgian Railways (SNCB) to order 300 kph trains for services through the tunnel that would meet these requirements. External styling of the trains was by France's Roger Tallon, one of the architects of Corail stock and the TGV, with Britain's Roger Jones responsible for the power car's trademark round nose and the interiors of the cab and the catering vehicles. Jacques Tillman of Belgium designed the rest of the trains' interior. Although the British loading gauge required a narrowing of the TGV bodyshell from 2.9 m to 2.814 m, the trains were designed to the same standards of comfort as the pioneering French high-speed stock.

Thirty-one 18-car trains were ordered on 31st December, 1989, their ownership being divided 16:11:4 between SNCF, BR and SNCB (three of the SNCF units and one allocated to the SNCB were late additions because of more optimistic growth forecasts). Each train cost £23 million, making this initial investment worth a staggering £713 million. The contract to build them was won by an international consortium headed by GEC-Alsthom; other main contractors were Brush and British Rail Engineering, De Dietrich and ANF in France, and Belgium's BN and ACEC. Delivery of a successful train by a project management team working in three languages over half a dozen manufacturing sites was quite an achievement; the power cars were built at Belfort in France, then moved to Birmingham, where the carriages were constructed, to be 'mated' to the unit.

Each 'Three Capitals' Eurostar train comprises two identical but single-ended rakes of nine cars (one a buffet) and a power unit; the 20 vehicles have an overall length of 394 metres and weigh 752 tonnes (816 tonnes laden). The weight was kept down by making each passenger carriage (except for those at each end of a rake) share its bogies in the manner pioneered by Gresley's London & North Eastern Railway 'Quad' suburban stock. This arrangement required the coaches to be shorter than conventional long-distance stock so as to keep within loading-gauge on curves. Every full-length train has the capacity of two jumbo jets: seats for 210 first-class passengers and 584 second class, plus 52 folding seats in the vestibules. The sets operating the winter ski services run with a number of seats cordoned-off to accommodate extra luggage.

Each nine-car rake is numbered separately in the class '373' series; the power cars are numbered 3001-3022 (UK-owned units), 3101-3108 (SNCB) and 3201-3232 (SNCF). There is also a spare power car numbered 3999, originally kept at Le Landy and more recently at North Pole; it has occasionally been seen in use, notably early in 2001 after damage to No. 3007. In July 2005 it made a circuitous journey around west London to be turned, hauled by Eurostar locomotives Nos. 37603 and 73130. From April 2003, maintenance of the 26 half-sets still used by SNCF on 'Three Capitals' services (Nos. 3201-02, 3205-24 and 3229-32, was transferred from Le Landy to North Pole because of capacity problems at the Paris depot.

The first car of each rake has an eight-seat family area and 52 second-class seats, coaches two to five 60 second-class seats (coach five is for smokers). Coach six is a buffet bar with two catering stores, coach seven and eight are lounge cars with 39 first-class seats (one smoking, the other non-) and coach nine has 29 first-class seats, a disabled toilet, two customs compartments (little used in practice although at the design stage the UK customs and immigration services insisted that they needed one and a half coaches per train) and a baggage compartment. Under the Philippe Starck refurbishment which finally got under way in 2004, two seats in each carriage are being removed to create more space for luggage.

Eurostar's first-class seats are comfortably upholstered and passengers have folding tables; connections for laptop computers are now also being installed next to first-class seats. Seats in second class are mainly airline-style and steel-backed, an austere touch for the person sitting behind. Each passenger coach has just two doors, one each side, with a liquid crystal display on the outside giving the coach number and the train's destination. Waste from the toilets is held in 'retention' tanks beneath each carriage which are emptied at the end of each day, thus ensuring no effluent is discharged in the Tunnel. Externally the sleek lines of the train are breached only by the extra-deep windows which mark out the bar cars. Since 2001 Eurostar catering has been operated by Momentum Services, a joint venture between Cremonini of Italy and Compass plc.

The air-conditioned Eurostar cab is a grand affair, with the driving seat set centre with an undivided view of the track through a single, though not panoramic, windscreen. The cab's controls are based on those for the TGV-Atlantique, with a computer fault diagnostic panel and pre-selection 'cruise' speed control. A single driver controls each Eurostar throughout its entire inter-capital journey (there is a crew change at Lille or occasionally Chessy Marne-la-Vallée for ski trains running on to Bourg St-Maurice over SNCF metals). Through the Tunnel and over the TGV Nord-Europe, the trains operate under the same TVM430 cab-signalling and speed control system; in the tunnel itself Eurostars come under Eurotunnel's control centre and will be not be cleared for entry unless cab-to-control radio communications are functioning and power is available on all bogies. Eurostar cabs are also fitted with the standard BR, SNCF and SNCB warning systems for operation over conventional lines.

Eurostar's traction systems were based on the TGV, first examples of which went into service in 1981. Each train is driven by 12 bogies: two pairs of two on each power car, plus the first bogie of the carriage next to it. Eurostar's braking capacity is formidable; it can halt from its maximum speed of 300 kph in 3,500 m - just over two miles - or in good adhesive conditions 3,000 m. This is achieved by a combination of disc and regenerative electric brakes. The effectiveness of the trains' braking system was shown when the driver of the Eurostar derailed at high speed in June 2000 managed to halt it safely in less than 2 km. It can be witnessed daily by passengers awaiting their trains at Lille-Europe and Ashford International; the train seems certain to overshoot the platform until the full force of its brakes is applied.

Every Eurostar is equipped to operate under the 25kv AC systems powering the TGV network, the Tunnel, routes north of London, inside North Pole depot, the CTRL and the Belgian high-speed line, using the same pantographs despite differences in the overhead wiring. Eurostars also need to operate using the same pantographs on the Belgian domestic 3000v DC overhead system, though since completion of the Belgian high-speed line this facility is only needed on the approaches to Brussels Midi. The power output on Belgian lines, incidentally, is one-half that on the TGV routes and little more than that through Kent. All Eurostars were built with shoes for collecting 750v DC current from the third rail, with the added requirements of switching from overhead to third-rail power and vice versa at high speed, and being able to retract their pantographs within the British loading gauge when doing so. Eurostars also have to operate their pantographs at two different heights - 5.92 m above rail level in the Channel Tunnel, with its extra clearances to accommodate shuttle locomotives, and 5.08 m elsewhere. This is one reason for the neutral sections at either end of the tunnel, just south of Calais-Fréthun and 9 km inland from Cheriton; the Eurostar driver lowers his pantographs for the start of the section, coasts, then raises them to the new height at the end once both power cars have passed the break.

Gaps in the conductor rail and limitations to the power supply even after its augmentation to handle international trains restrict the output of Eurostars through Kent on the third rail to less than one-third of the 12kw maximum power it can generate in the Tunnel and on TGV lines, severely reducing their ability to accelerate over the hilly section between Orpington and Tonbridge. It is this deficiency in the power supply system as much as the CTRL's straighter alignment that has cut journey times for Eurostars using the high-speed link to London; with the first section of the link in use, Eurostars only need to draw third-rail current between Fawkham Junction and Waterloo, and on workings to North Pole. Special retractable lightweight shoegear was devised for the Eurostars, being tested on class '33' diesel No. 33115; this locomotive was fitted with Eurostar bogies and hauled 'dead' by a class '73' electro-diesel in a consist which also included a '4TC' rake of carriages so that the shoegear could be tested under realistic running conditions. It is likely that the shoes will be removed once the final stage of the CTRL comes into operation in 2007, unless a need to continue operating over third-rail routes in an emergency is identified.

Eight Eurostar rakes (Nos. 373 201/2, 373 203/4, 373 207/8, 373 209/10, 373 215/6, 373 223/4, 373 227/8 and 373 229/30) were also equipped for 1500v DC overhead operation, enabling them to run onto SNCF domestic routes off the TGV network. Originally this was done to permit the through operation of ski trains from Waterloo to the French Alps, but the conversions also enable spare units to operate on domestic services that do not entirely correspond to the TGV network, and three of the four-voltage units have now been debranded to operate purely on SNCF services.

Eurostar's designers had to accommodate the rigorous safety requirements imposed for working through the Tunnel. Most importantly, the train was designed to give 30-minute fire resistance, long enough to get it out of the tunnel in an emergency. In addition, the driver must be able to divide a train in mid-tunnel in case of breakdown or other emergency; automatic Scharfenberg couplings enable either power car to be separated, or the two rakes to be divided at mid-train. In addition, the Alstom traction equipment can operate at reduced power and temperature in the tunnel to reduce any risk of fire. In the carriages, inflatable door seals insulate passengers against sudden changes in air pressure as the train enters or leaves the tunnel at speed.

A further difference from the TGV stems from having to operate under British and Continental loading gauges and because TGV stock (even though small by European standards to allow maximum through running) is too wide below platform level to operate in Britain. Retractable footboards had to be installed at each doorway to offset the differing gaps between platform and coach on either side of the Channel, and also three different platform heights.

The first Eurostar rake rolled off the production line in January 1993, and on 20th June that year it transited the tunnel, hauled by a diesel locomotive, to begin trials with the second set on the TGV Nord-Europe; these commenced on 1st July and within a week they had reached 305 kph. The first production train was delivered to SNCF that September. Early in 1994 Eurostars successfully made the changeover from French to Belgian and French to third-rail current at speed. On 13th April a high-speed test run was made from Paris to Arras, and on 6th May a Eurostar carried the Queen from Waterloo through the tunnel to open it formally with President Mitterrand. The inaugural press run from London to Paris was made on 20th October after the embarrassing breakdown of the train allocated caused an hour's delay, but on 14th November commercial Eurostar services began without a hitch.

After a decade in service the 'Three Capitals' Eurostars internally were showing signs of wear, and late in 2001 the company announced a £25 million programme of refurbishment and restyling. The upgrade, which is taking two weeks for each set, is being overseen by Philippe Starck, who also designed the new first class lounges at Waterloo and the Gare du Nord, and should make the trains even more appealing for the accelerated service on offer as the CTRL is completed; the original hope had been that some of the refurbished sets would be ready for the opening of Phase One of the line, but the project slipped and it was 7th September, 2004 before the first refurbished train - Nos. 373 219/220 - entered passenger service on the 0813 Brussels-Waterloo. First in line for the new treatment at Hellemmes Works in Lille - which also includes provision of one premium-fare carriage in each 18-car train, new galley facilities, buffet counters and laptop power supplies, were the 13 class '373/2s' in SNCF ownership still used on tunnel services; the 11 British- and three Belgian-owned units still in front-line Eurostar service have followed and by early 2006 the programme was nearly complete. Starck's upgraded interior was put on show in the Champs Elysées in May-June 2003 for SNCF's 'Le Train Capitale' exhibition; the most obvious highlights were the more sophisticated wood-finished buffet with a longer counter, the leather-style business-class seating and the replacement of the distinctive mushroom-shaped table lights in first class with more conventional horizontal shades. However, Starck's mock-up was considered slightly too radical. The planned 'Premium Class' ninth carriage in each set with egg-shaped seats was abandoned. The layout of the buffet - though not the décor - has been left almost unchanged, and the first class seats now sport wrap-around headrests with an orange 'snooze-friendly' pillow. Standard class seats - now grey - have gained brown leather antimacassars to give them a 'BMW feel'. Sockets for laptops and mobile phones have been fitted in two standard class carriages as well as first class. The Starck refurbishment takes advantage of the fact that smoking has been banned on Eurostars since October 2001, making the interior of the carriages easier to keep clean and fresh. The new carpets are particularly welcome.

There is a variant of Eurostar train which until recently appeared a white elephant. Conventional Eurostar units are too long to operate on internal British routes, largely because of station platform lengths, so BR in addition to its allocation of standard 'Three Capitals' units ordered seven 14-car versions (in rakes of seven) at a cost of £24 million each for the 'North of London' services which were supposed to start running from 1995. Numbered in the (37)3 3xx series, these have four fewer trailers, with total seating down to 114 first class and 464 second class. Extra space was provided in coach 9 for customs and immigration staff to enable border checks to be carried out on board. Bizarrely, the class '373/3' power cars are not interchangeable with those on 'Three Capitals' units, a factor which has further reduced their utility.

The first short-formation Eurostar was delivered to European Passenger Services on 28th June, 1995, with expectations high that trains like it would soon start serving destinations on the East and West Coast Main Lines. But these hopes were managed downwards over a period as lower-than-expected passenger figures for the flagship service to Paris (and even lower to Brussels) brought traffic and revenue forecasts for Eurostar down with a bump.

This shortfall in patronage left not just the shortened regional sets but a number of 'Three Capitals' Eurostars short of work. The service did intensify, but not enough to justify the full quota of Eurostars that had been ordered at huge expense to operate it. So in due course alternative uses were found for some of the units on both sides of the Channel, without putting at risk Eurostar's ability to meet its timetable.

SNCF was first into the frame. In 1999 it diverted three 18-car Eurostar sets - Nos. 373 203/204, 227/228 and 223/224 as a spare - to non-tunnel services. Deprived of their Eurostar branding, with TGV-style coloured body panels to distinguish first- (pink) and second-class (blue-green) accommodation and the conductor shoes removed (to cover a temporary shortage of spares), they went into service at first on occasional Paris-Dunkerque workings and then, with the summer 1999 timetable, onto the 0925 Brussels-Nice and the 0924 return. This latter experiment was not a total success; SNCF drivers complained that the trains were underpowered on the gradients between Paris and Lyon compared with a TGV - a view disputed by some passengers - and passengers using the extra-low platforms on the Cote d'Azur found the step up too great: at Antibes the gap was 580 mm. From 28th November that year, the debranded Eurostars were taken off the Paris-Lyon-Marseille run for redeployment on winter ski trains from Continental cities to the Alps, and supplementing TGVs on the Brussels-Bordeaux service; since autumn 2000, they have concentrated on Paris-Lille TGV diagrams. In the exceptionally hot summer of 2003 they were temporarily restricted to 270 kph to conserve power for air conditioning.

The full complement of Eurostar sets (the pairs are very seldom split) is:

No.	Owner	Depot
3001/02	UK	NP
3003/04†	UK	NP
3005/06†	UK	NP
3007/08†	UK	NP
3009/10†	UK	NP
3011/12	UK	NP
3013/14†	UK	NP
3015/16	UK	NP
3017/18†	UK	NP
3019/20	UK	NP
3021/22	UK	NP

3101/02	SNCB	F	'Pool' set for any Eurostar operator
3103/04	SNCB	F	
3105/06†	SNCB	F	
3107/08†	SNCB	F	
3201/02#†	SNCF	LL*	
3203/04#	SNCF	LL	Debranded to TGV
3205/06†	SNCF	LL*	
3207/08#†	SNCF	LL*	
3209/10#	SNCF	LL*	
3211/12†	SNCF	LL*	
3213/14	SNCF	LL*	
3215/16#	SNCF	LL*	
3217/18	SNCF	LL*	
3219/20†	SNCF	LL*	
3221/22†	SNCF	LL*	
3223/24#	SNCF	LL*	
3225/26#	SNCF	LL	Debranded to TGV
3227/28#	SNCF	LL	Debranded to TGV
3229/30#†	SNCF	LL*	
3231/32†	SNCF	LL*	
3301/02	UK	NP	GNER livery
3303/04	UK	NP	GNER livery
3305/06	UK	NP	GNER livery
3307/08	UK	NP	Unused until autumn 2003, since raided for parts
3309/10	UK	NP	Used by GNER
3311/12	UK	NP	Used by GNER
3313/14	UK	NP	CTRL test train, occasionally used by GNER from Mar. 2004
3999	Spare power car		

*   All maintenance except the most major overhauls transferred to North Pole in 2003.
†   Refurbished by June 2005.
#   Four-voltage stock for use over SNCF classic lines.
NP - North Pole; F - Forest; LL - Le Landy

So far three Eurostars have been named Nos. 323 213/14 were named The *Entente Cordiale* by the Queen on 5th April, 2004, Nos. 323 207/08 *Michel Hollard*, after a hero of the Resistance, on 30th April, 2004, and Nos. 323 013/4 *London 2012* on 6th July, 2005, the day London pipped Paris for the right to host the 2012 Olympic Games.

Apart from the winter ski service to Bourg St-Maurice which operates twice each weekend (the overnight service being the only survivor of a grand ambition) and the equally successful summer Saturday service to Avignon begun in 2002, forays by Eurostars beyond Paris and Brussels on the Continental network have been rare. Floods on the TGV route southward in March 2001 did briefly bring the ski trains to the conventional main line via Dijon and Aix-les-Bains (and even a short section of the Paris 'Ceinture' near the Gare de Lyon), and this route has since been used quite frequently. A precedent for wider operation was set, however, on 16th September, 2000 when a Eurostar chartered by Hertfordshire Railtours (Nos. 373 201/2, from the batch equipped also for the SNCF's 1500v DC system) reached La Rochelle, on the west coast of France 1,020 km (or 632 miles) from Waterloo; a trial Eurostar run from Paris had been made some weeks previously. La Rochelle was an apt destination as some Eurostar bodyshells had been assembled in the Alstom factory there. A further railtour to Lyon, which the ski and Avignon trains bypass, was staged on 5th May, 2001.

On 23rd May, 2003 Eurostar itself put on a special from Waterloo to Bordeaux St Jean, travelling via the Nord Europe, Jonction and Atlantique TGV lines, plus a section of the Paris 'Grand Ceinture' between Villeneuve St Georges and Massy and the classic main line beyond Tours (the destination of a further excursion the following month). SNCF-owned four-voltage stock was used. The outward journey took 6 hrs 39 mins, the return on 26th May just over 9 hrs as it included a diversion to Gare du Nord for frontier clearance. Eurostar hoped to follow this first venture into south-western France with an excursion over new ground in the east to the Geneva, where the Swiss-administered Cornavin station, being outside the EU, already has customs facilities for passengers arriving from France. Ironically Calais-Ville was first reached by a railtour only in February 2006. In the other direction, special workings to London by four-voltage Eurostars operated by SNCF have originated from Tours, Orleans and Dijon.

In Britain, there was prolonged speculation that either Virgin, whose own inter-city fleet was ageing fast, or GNER, with severe overcrowding problems, might lease some of the seven regional Eurostars, which had lain unused save for very occasional London-Brussels duties early on and test runs over Railtrack metals. There was little urgency while Railtrack continued to remedy shortcomings in clearances and lineside circuits thrown up by continuing Eurostar tests on the East Coast (ECML) and West Coast Main Lines (WCML), one Eurostar sandwiched between two class '37' diesels, reached Glasgow on 3rd June, 1997, but eventually they were cleared to run as far north as York and over the Hertford loop. GNER then negotiated the hire of two regional Eurostar double sets, with two more as spares, to run four return trips each weekday from King's Cross to York with an extra down working between Peterborough and York. Limitations of power supply which initially ruled out their use south of Peterborough in the rush hours meant that full use could not be made of the hired-in stock when the first trains, redesignated 'White Rose', ran on 30th May, 2000. The two 14-car sets for regular use - Nos. 373 301/2 and 303/4 - were repainted in GNER colours but the others - Nos. 373 309/10 and 311/2 - remained initially in Eurostar livery. Modifications made at the time left these units, incidentally, uncleared to operate through the Channel Tunnel for which they were designed. Uncleared maybe, but still capable; in 2002 GNER-liveried Nos. 373 303/4 made an unpublicised and successful empty stock run from North Pole depot onto SNCF metals and back again, the East Coast operator was exploring the practicality, if no more, of through operation into France. From 29th May, 2002, the 'White Rose' service was switched from York to Leeds and a more intensive schedule introduced, the trains having proved very popular, if costly for GNER to lease. Units Nos. 373 305/6 were also now decked out in GNER livery to operate this service, making five in all. (Normally only two of the sets are in service at once.) From this point GNER drivers took over from the Eurostar men who had handled the York workings; GNER had provided the on-board staff from the start.

GNER's Eurostar were popular with the travelling public, but were costly to hire, were limited to 110 mph by pantograph problems and caused operational headaches. By late 2005 GNER's class '91' and type '4' carriage fleet was back to full strength after the 'Mallard' upgrade programme and there was a surplus of IC125 diesel sets which were able to run faster, were more economical to run and could carry almost as many passengers. Consequently GNER handed back the Eurostars, its final 'White Rose' services running on 10th December, 2005 after less than six years. They are likely to find new employment as the final stage of the CTRL is commissioned.

The final two regional Eurostar sets were raided for spares to get the GNER sets into operation, but one was reinstated before long and put back into use, test-running on Phase One of the CTRL; two carriages were converted to test vehicles to monitor track performance, electrical interference and the train's interaction with infrastructure. The long-stored set No. 373 313/4 made its first run over the CTRL, at 30 kph, between Ashford and Westenhanger on 13th April, 2003 to test clearances, and gradually increased both its speed and distance travelled; it was kept to 80 kph until the signalling system was fully commissioned, but accelerated from early July to test the line speed of 298 kph (186 mph), smashing the UK rail speed record in the process and finally setting a new standard of 305 kph (208 mph) on 30th July. It made its first revenue-earning trip with GNER the following year.

The final 'North of London' Eurostar set, rake No. 373 307/8, needed rather more work before it too could enter service; for the press run prior to the opening of the CTRL, No. 373 309/10 had to be borrowed back from GNER to provide a duplicate. No. 303 307 was repaired by the spring of 2003 as a spare for CTRL testing, but No. 373 308 had been so heavily stripped for spares at North Pole that it could not enter service until that November. Up to then the train had never carried passengers and had just 250 km on the clock.

In the run-up to the launch of Eurostar, it was imagined that traffic levels by, or soon after, the opening of the CTRL would leave the inaugural fleet fully stretched, and that it would need to be supplemented by a second generation of stock possibly modelled on the double-deck TGV, to take full advantage of the more generous clearances on the high-speed link. It was to accommodate and service this stock that plans for a second depot at Temple Mills to supplement North Pole were originally prepared. In the event, Eurostar has found itself with too much rolling stock rather than too little, and Temple Mills will now supplant North Pole as the more convenient of the two locations for a service solely operating from St Pancras. It is unlikely Eurostar will even address the issue of replacing its current fleet for another decade or more.

The third innovative form of traction commissioned for Channel Tunnel traffic was the class '92' Co-Co dual-voltage electric locomotive, built by Brush (though fabricated at Procor of Wakefield) with ABB traction equipment, which hauls all international freight trains through the tunnel, and increasingly over the British electrified network for what is now EWS. First of the class to leave the works, after problems over installing hotel power facilities for night services and TVM430 cab signalling, was No. 92002 on 10th December, 1993. After extensive testing on the Continent Railfreight Distribution (RfD) accepted its first '92', No. 92003, on 23rd March, 1994, 45 days before the official opening of the Tunnel. Tested in Britain on the Shepperton branch and the WCML near Carnforth and finally in the Tunnel itself, they entered service on 1st February, 1995.

Weighing in at 126 tonnes, the class '92s' have a bodyshell based on the class '60' diesel-electrics, though with more rounded cabs, and use similar bogies to the class '60', but with the wheelbase lengthened to accommodate the conductor shoes. Designed for a maximum speed of 140 kph, they also boast a maximum output of 6,700 hp 'under the wires', and have a tractive effort capable of hauling a 1,600-tonne train unaided not just between Willesden/Wembley and Calais but over Beattock. Indeed the emergency performance requirements for a class '92' include the ability to take a 1,600-tonne train northbound up Beattock on a 1 in 75 gradient from a dead stand, and hauling a train with a dead locomotive out of the Channel Tunnel.

The class '92s' livery is reminiscent of Eurostar's: yellow cab fronts and upper side trim, dark blue roofs, windscreen and cab window frames, and upper side panels of grey-blue and the lower ones of cream. The sides of each are adorned by three stainless steel rings, the largest just behind the front cab door, and by the BR or SNCF symbol also picked out in stainless steel.

Uniquely, the class '92s' were developed for use by SNCF as well as BR, though driver resistance has limited the locomotives' use to the section of the French network between Fréthun yard and the tunnel portal barely 2 km away. Indeed 16 of the locomotives operated between 1994 and 2003 exclusively on Eurotunnel metals and into the yards at Dollands Moor and Fréthun; having had their current collecting shoes removed and being prevented from running further into France, they were effectively stranded. When they needed repairs at Crewe, they had to be hauled dead over the third-rail network between Dollands Moor and the approaches to Wembley. In 2003 the safety cases for class '92s' on Eurotunnel metals and on Network Rail were bought into line, the tunnel-only locomotives adjusted and a single pool of 28 locomotives capable of operating anywhere was created, enabling through freight services to operate from Mossend and Wembley to Fréthun without a change of traction at Dollands Moor.

In the tunnel, class '92s' operate in pairs as a precaution against breakdown; generally, freight trains through the tunnel are double-headed, but had the planned international sleeper trains run, there would have been a locomotive at either end for the train to be pulled back out of the tunnel in case of emergency.

Numbered from 92001 and named after European cultural figures starting with *Victor Hugo* and *H G Wells*, 37 of the class were owned initially by BR and nine - Nos. 92006, 92010, 92014, 92018, 92023, 92028, 92033, 92038 and 92043 - by SNCF.

The class '92s' were developed not only to haul international freight trains but to head the sleeper trains that were expected to connect London and the regions with Continental cities through the tunnel and on the electrified portions of their journeys in Britain; they were to hand over to Continental traction at Calais. Seven of those allocated to BR were passed to Eurostar for operation of these night services between Fréthun, Waterloo and points north: 92020 *Milton*, 92021 *Purcell*, 92032 *César Franck*, 92040 *Goethe*, 92044 *Couperin*, 92045 *Chaucer* and 92046 *Sweelinck*. Yet they never hauled a passenger vehicle except on trials, and with the exception of No. 92040 which was out of traffic at the Brush works for three years from 1997, they settled into routine, if under-used, freight operation for EWS. All seven of the Eurostar class '92s' were put up for sale in June 2000; a proposed sale to EWS fell through and they are still on Eurostar's books, though a sale to Eurotunnel to operate its proposed through freight services between British and French locations was briefly mooted, before the tunnel operator opted for a completely SNCF-compatible new buy.

The class '92s' advanced electronics proved incompatible with lineside installations over much of the BR/Railtrack system, and it took five years after the tunnel opened for them to be accepted in full strength between the tunnel and Wembley via CTR2 and over the West Coast Main Line north of Crewe, where the class is maintained. The software fitted to some of the locomotives in the process made them incompatible with Eurotunnel's signalling systems, so these class '92s' are confined to use on domestic freight services.

In 1999 the class '92s' were at last cleared to operate between Wembley and Crewe, and from Carstairs via Edinburgh and the northern portion of the ECML to Doncaster; it took until 17th May, 2001, when No. 92013 hauled a Wakefield-Wembley service south of Doncaster, before they could use the full length of the ECML. With tunnel freight traffic well below expectations and the sleeper services shelved, they were even then far from fully used, at least 12 being out of traffic at any one time. They were still barred from the Tonbridge-Redhill route because of the cost of eliminating conflicts with trackside equipment. And the refusal of SNCF drivers to operate them on French domestic routes, with whose systems they can easily be made compatible, prevented their extending their range, as EWS would have liked, from Fréthun to La Delivérance yard in Lille; indeed the original hope had been to run them right through from Scotland to Lille. Ironically the SNCF class '92s' are now being modified to launch a Fret SNCF (SNCF's freight division) service through the tunnel to London.

The class '92' has proved itself a highly effective and reliable freight locomotive both 'under the wires' through the tunnel and in Britain, and on the third rail, and EWS has found it unexpectedly useful for hauling domestic freight trains over the WCML, notably its 'Enterprise' wagonload services. Except in rare emergencies and on railtours - for which the class '92' despite its limited route availability is very popular - the locomotives have not appeared on passenger services; it was September 2003 before one made it into King's Cross.

Delays in putting the highly-complex class '92s' into service proved even greater than those in opening the tunnel, so BR and SNCF were forced to find alternative traction to haul freight trains between Fréthun and Dollands Moor, supplementing those locomotives that had been delivered. And the choice fell on the SNCF's class '22200' B-B dual-voltage locomotives.

Introduced between 1976 and 1986, class '22200' was developed by Alsthom for traffic between Paris, Rennes and Nantes. Weighing 90 tonnes and with a maximum speed of 160 kph, they have two traction motors powering four driving axles and are rated at 3,780kW. Of the 202 built, nine were seconded to tunnel freight services from June 1994 to October 1995: Nos. 22379/80/99/22400-5. Modifications were carried out to suit them for the Eurotunnel system, though 22400/2/4 never received the TVM430 cab signalling they needed to head tunnel trains, and could only operate as the second double-heading locomotive.

The class '22200s' temporary stint on tunnel traffic embraced pre-opening duties, including haulage of test trains - for each of which four locomotives of this power rating were required - and scheduled freight services from northern France and Fréthun to Dollands Moor for well over a year after the tunnel had opened; indeed they double-headed the first commercial freight train through the tunnel on 1st June, 1994. They were not, however, used by Eurotunnel to haul test or service shuttle trains, though they had the capability to rescue a shuttle in an emergency.

For class '92'-hauled international freight trains through the tunnel, a number of new or improved types of wagon were developed, both to enable operation at high enough speeds to avoid delaying Eurostar and shuttle traffic and to ensure security of the cargo. Railfreight Distribution (RfD), SNCF and Intercontainer ordered 1,200 twin-wagon 'Multifret' sets from Arbel Fauvel capable of safe operation at 140 kph. With a deck 950 mm above rail level and a usable length of 15.8 m, they can carry both containers and swap-bodies for intermodal traffic. In addition RfD ordered a fleet of double-deck car carriers from Arbel Fauvel for international automotive traffic. The wagons are made up of articulated rakes of five, and almost totally enclosed by alloy hoods to protect them from vandalism away from the tunnel.

Three further batches of locomotives were allocated specifically for tunnel services or stock movements, though not for operation on Eurotunnel metals: the 12 class '37/6' Co-Co diesels, two class '73/1' Bo-Bo electro-diesels and one class '08' 0-6-0 diesel shunter transferred by BR to Eurostar. The former were intended primarily to haul Continental sleeper trains between Kensington Olympia, Plymouth and Swansea. Renumbered 37601 to 37612, they were converted from

Nos. 37501/2/4/6/7/8/11/12/14 and 37687/90/91, undergoing minor alterations to equip them for their new task. Six were sold to Direct Rail Services in 1997 once the plans for Nightstar trains had been abandoned, and three more followed in May 2002; while with Eurostar they saw occasional use hauling Eurostar units over de-energised sections of track, or on hire to other operators, principally EWS and Virgin. Just three class '37s' remain with Eurostar: Nos. 37601/4/5, leased from Angel Trains; they are generally stabled at Clapham Junction with a pair of match wagons in case of an emergency requiring a Eurostar to be towed, as when on 7th February, 2003 a Paris-bound train suffered a total brake pipe failure on the viaduct approaching Factory Junction and was towed back into Waterloo by a class '37' after a delay of five hours. The class '37s' also tow Eurostar units as required between North Pole and GNER's Ferme Park base over a circuitous route via the unelectrified Kew East curve and South Acton. Eurostar showed its commitment to its remaining class '37s' late in 2003 when it fitted them with TPWS and with new headlights and marker lights for operating over the CTRL . . . though not the link's TVM430 cab signalling. Since July 2005 the '37s' have been maintained by FM Rail, with major exams being undertaken at Derby.

The two class '73/1s' - Nos. 73118 and 73130 - were intended from the outset for rescuing Eurostars stranded on the former Southern Region's third-rail network and, if necessary, getting them home in the event of the power being switched off. They have seen only limited use, but Eurostar has no plans to dispose of them; occasionally they see other uses, such as hauling Network Rail test trains. The class '73s' are also used to maintain Eurostar drivers' knowledge of the 'classic' route to the tunnel via Tonbridge; a daily diagram, intermittently used, began on 28th September, 2003, the day the CTRL opened. These locomotives, too, are now maintained by FM Rail. The solitary class '08' - 08948 - is used on shunting duties at North Pole depot; embodying the *Entente Cordiale*, it bears a 'Le Landy' depot sticker. By contrast, rescue and shunting duties for Eurostar in France and Belgium are undertaken not by dedicated Eurostar locomotives, but by whatever motive power the national railway in question can supply at the time.

It was the final purpose-built stock acquired at great expense for Channel Tunnel services - the 'hotel on wheels' sleeper trains - that proved the greatest white elephant of the entire project: the 139 carriages of European night stock ordered by BR from Metro-Cammell in 1992 at approximately £1 million apiece never earned a penny in revenue in Britain or running through the tunnel. Owned initially by European Night Services (a consortium of BR, SNCF, NS and DB), they were intended to operate overnight trains between London and the regions, Paris, Brussels, Amsterdam, Frankfurt and Dortmund, but none of these services ever operated.

Even without a propulsion system of their own (they were to be hauled by class '92' electric locomotives except on non-electrified BR routes where Eurostar's class '37' diesels would do the honours, and by a variety of locomotives on the Continent) the night stock presented a severe technical challenge. They had to meet not only the fire survivability requirements of Eurotunnel and its safety authority, but the safety cases of BR and of the four national railways on the Continent over which they would operate. By virtue of the on-board 'hotel' services to be provided, they also carried highly complex electrical systems and no fewer than 17 different pipe and electrical connections were required between each carriage for these and haulage purposes. (One technical problem never resolved was that SNCB, which was not a partner in the Nightstar consortium but over whose metals a number of the sleeper services would have operated, realised at a late stage that it had no locomotives capable of powering the stock.)

Cleared for 200 kph operation and decked out in an attractive livery of twin shades of green, the 23 m-long 'Nightstar' carriages were marshalled in rakes of seven or eight, to operate in pairs on most services; a train of two rakes would carry around 400 people. The carriages are of three types: sleeping cars with 10 two-berth compartments, each with a toilet and six with their own shower; open carriages with 50 plinth-based reclining seats and three large toilet compartments, and buffet-bar cars with accommodation for disabled passengers, the train captain, customs and border control, and parcels.

One of the 'Nightstar' rakes saw service on test trains, principally over the West Coast Main Line, before the planned night services were shelved at the end of 1996. The trains were handed back to the makers, by now part of Alstom, when the economic case for these services evaporated - with the proviso that if they were resold for more than a 'threshold' price the taxpayer would receive a dividend.

Around 40 of the carriages were fully equipped and ready to take passengers, and nearly 60 more were put into storage without fitting-out having been completed; Alstom's Birmingham works housed many for a time, but a number were stored from the outset at Bicester army depot beside the Oxford-Bletchley line or at Kineton, the equally secure military site accessed from Fenny Compton on the Banbury-Leamington Spa line by the last vestige of the Stratford-upon-Avon and Midland Junction Railway, which also housed surplus class '92s' for a time.

Strenuous efforts were made to find another use for the night stock. Eurostar briefly considered using the seated carriages on class '92'-hauled day trains from Waterloo to Amsterdam or Cologne, and several train operating companies examined the same carriages with a view to easing the increasingly severe shortage of good-quality rolling stock. However the weight and high power consumption of the Nightstar stock, plus the fact that in the day carriages which were apparently most suitable for other uses, passengers would have to scramble up an uncomfortable step to reach their seats because of the amount of technical kit underneath, made them an unattractive proposition. With no domestic interest in prospect, Alstom sent three of the carriages to Morocco in 1999 with a view to their sale at a knock-down price, only for them to be returned. The following year a similar shipment - of a lounge car, a sleeping car and a seated carriage - was made to Canada where Via Rail had expressed an interest, and after the briefest of trials that company arranged to purchase all 139 carriages for £60 million; the first 10 carriages were shipped in March 2001, to enter service later that year on overnight services between Halifax, Montreal and Toronto. A political row understandably broke out in Britain when it was disclosed that while Via Rail valued the stock at £200 million, the 'threshold' had not been triggered and the taxpayer would not receive a penny of the purchase price. That was nothing, however, to the travails in Canada as getting further 'Nightstar' stock into service proved an even more costly and complex operation than had been foreseen. Via Rail knew it would have to modify the stock, and Bombardier in Canada was commissioned to turn it into a 'Renaissance' fleet by winterising it, adapting the electrical system, turning a bathroom in the crumple zone at the end of each carriage into luggage space, creating restaurant and baggage cars in sleeper bodyshells, installing heated retractable steps and removing immense espresso machines. Fourteen further modifications were ordered by the Canadian Transport Agency to make the trains accessible for all, bringing the cost of conversion for just three rakes to $C35 million (£13.5 million). The first of three 12-car rakes went into service over a year late on 23rd June, 2002, to a chorus of complaints about internal noise - 'a cross between Donald Duck and someone being choked to death' - said one passenger - and protruding compartment door handles. To add to Via's problems, the Council for Canadians with Disabilities in November 2003 forced further costly alterations after the stock was adjudged to be still not fully wheelchair-friendly. Meanwhile an indeterminate number of semi-completed 'Nightstar' carriages remains in Britain - at Kineton, Wolverton works, and other locations.

For the planned diesel-hauled 'Nightstar' services to Wales and the West, five surplus Mk III sleeping cars were converted to generator vans at Doncaster works and numbered 96371-96375 in the BR locomotive series. On the few occasions they were harnessed to test trains, they gave rise to almost as many technical problems as the night stock itself. After cancellation of the service, they were retained against the eventuality of the stock ever being hauled by motive power other than a class '92', but after several years in store at North Pole they were eventually put up for sale in 2000 . . . again at a very considerable discount. So far there have been no takers.

Eurostar fared better with the 10 barrier flat wagons it had converted from GUV vans - with their van bodies replaced by concrete ballast and air driers fitted to avoid moistening the Eurostar's sensitive braking system - before services through the tunnel began. Numbered 6380 to 6389, these again saw little use, but in March 2002 four of them (6386-9) were sold to Siemens for use as barrier vehicles with its Desiro electric multiple units, ordered by South West Trains (SWT) and First Great Eastern. Unfortunately, they were not to be used when the units were hauled to Britain through the Channel Tunnel, but for loco haulage over domestic metals; to this end two were based at Strawberry Hill – and later the new SWT depot at Northam - and Clacton respectively.

CTRL Domestic Services

The most recent procurement of Channel Tunnel-related motive power and stock concerns trains that will probably never transit the tunnel in revenue-earning service, but are nevertheless an integral part of the fabric of tunnel service: the trains to be used on domestic services over the CTRL. Provision of such services was essential to the financing of the CTRL, levering in sizeable Government funding for the project, though the viability of such services, not to mention the demand for them from Kent commuters whose destinations in the City are more conveniently served by existing terminals than by St Pancras, remains in doubt.

Coming up with a suitable train by the opening of Phase 2 of the CTRL in 2007 was a considerable challenge and one that will not be met. The stock needed to function over the CTRL and Network Rail infrastructure, with their different speeds, signalling systems and clearances, and coexist with other trains on both systems. It needed rapid acceleration and a top speed of 225 kph (140 mph), and also the high level of crashworthiness needed for a crowded train working at these speeds to satisfy the Health and Safety Executive.

It was always the stance of the Government and the Strategic Rail Authority (SRA) that new stock would be necessary, even though the likely cost at a time when Ministers were baulking at the rising cost of such to the taxpayer led some observers to suggest that no new trains would enter service. Alternatives using existing stock were canvassed by commentators: the use of surplus Eurostars on St Pancras-Ashford shuttles serving only Stratford International and Ebbsfleet and not penetrating further into Kent, or of mothballed class '92s' and driving van trailers with Mk 3 stock made redundant by the introduction of 'Pendolinos' on the West Coast Main Line. Porterbrook tried to interest the SRA in hiring its surplus Mk 3 sets on CTRL domestic services, and the SRA itself sounded out SNCF on running empty TGV stock through the Tunnel for a morning Ashford commuter service. But the powers that be stuck both to the goal of purpose-built stock, and also to the deadline of 2007, which led the UK trainbuilders Bombardier and Alstom, both desperate for orders, not to tender. Though Siemens was picking up many orders for conventional commuter stock, the field was left clear for Hitachi, which was eager to break into the European market and showed its desire to get things right by running a test train of combined 25kv AC and 750 DC stock, based on a class '310' unit, on routes in the South-East. This train demonstrated to Hitachi that its train would not conflict with Network Rail signalling systems, and near Ramsgate detected problems with icy conductor rails not experienced in Japan.

On 27th October, 2004, Transport Secretary Alistair Darling announced that Hitachi had been chosen as preferred bidder to supply the CTRL domestic stock: 30 six-car units based on the series 400 Shinkansen 'bullet train' operating so successfully in Japan, but with a distinctly Eurostar front end. Each unit, priced at around £34 million with the need for TVM cab signalling adding £500,000 per vehicle, would accommodate 300 to 350 passengers. The trains would be designed in the UK and Japan, be built at Kasado, near Hiroshima, and be maintained at a new purpose-built depot at Ashford for which up to 70 staff would be recruited, and taken to Japan for training. The sting in Mr Darling's announcement was in the tail: the first four units would not arrive until the Spring of 2009, with the rest being delivered during the year. This brought protests from Britain's trainmakers that if they had known they had an extra two years to come up with a train for the CTRL, they would have bid and filled a hole in their order books which in Alstom's case had brought the end of train manufacturing at Washwood Heath, where the night stock was constructed. After successful test runs on the CTRL, the £250 million contract for the Hitachi units, by now cut back to 28, was confirmed by the SRA in June 2005.

The way now seems clear for high-speed domestic traffic over the CTRL from St Pancras into Kent to get under way during 2009, with a 15 minute time to Ebbsfleet, a reduction in the headline journey time on the Ashford run from 67 to 34 minutes, and time savings, though maybe a less convenient journey to work, for commuters on the North Kent Line from the Medway towns and beyond Ashford (where they will use the domestic platforms) from Canterbury and Thanet. How extensive these services actually turn out to be remains to be seen; there are also capacity issues because of the £22.2 million estimated cost of extending platforms at Gravesend, Strood and Rochester. The Hitachi units will have a further important role in the summer of 2012: operating a 'Javelin' dedicated service for the London Olympics taking less than eight minutes between St Pancras and Stratford International, running on to Ebbsfleet to connect with outer suburban services and Eurostars, which will not serve Stratford during the Games.

Chapter Seven

Open at Last

The Channel Tunnel's first revenue-earning train made an incident-free transit on 19th May, 1994 - almost a year later than the target opening date of 15th June, 1993. Eurotunnel launched its HGV shuttle service on that date after receiving the first of the series of safety clearances it needed from the Inter-Governmental Commission to operate the full range of trains that would pass through the tunnel. Trains left simultaneously from each terminal; the very first lorry aboard at Cheriton was a Royal Mail truck carrying first-day commemorative covers for posting from Calais. Its driver, Ray Clementson from Meopham, Kent, joined 13 others for a fry-up or croissants *en route* as the inaugural freight shuttle set off carrying lorryloads of coiled metal for Switzerland, yoghurt for Paris and empty beer kegs for Germany. The verdict of the tunnel's first commercial users: quicker than the ferries, but not a knockout. And to date that remains the case, even though the HGV shuttles have proved by far the most successful of the tunnel rail services and their capacity had to be systematically increased before custom dipped from 2004.

Initially Eurotunnel operated just one HGV shuttle per hour on an 'invitation only' basis for the service to bed down; a 24-hour service with three departures an hour was promised within weeks. The need to build up services and capture demand rapidly was underlined a week after the running of the inaugural train when Eurotunnel completed the negotiation of £693 million of fresh loans with its bankers to give itself a breathing space; the deal was coupled with the announcement from Sir Alastair Morton that Eurotunnel's shareholders would be asked to subscribe a further £816 million through a rights issue. They stumped up a fair proportion of this, but some French shareholders later claimed that the company misled them about how soon its revenues would build up and at the turn of the millennium senior Eurotunnel executives were summoned before a French judge to justify the forecasts made all those years before. The legal process ground on, and in March 2003 the investigating magistrate, Dominique de Talance, declared that Sir Alastair and M. Bénard would have to stand trial on charges of publishing misleading information in the prospectus for the rights issue; in addition, two merchant bankers were charged with insider dealing. Sir Alastair was to die before the matter could be resolved.

For the first few days after the tunnel began receiving traffic, there was none other than the solitary hourly freight shuttle, but on 1st June, 1994 another landmark was achieved with the passage of the first international freight train: a service operated by BR's Railfreight Distribution from the West Midlands to Arluno, near Milan, carrying 250 Rover cars for export. As the class '92s' ordered for international freight services were in the early stages of delivery, the train was hauled to Dollands Moor by a class '47', and through the tunnel itself by two of the SNCF class '22200' electric locomotives hired to plug this gap. The first general freight service for containers and swapbodies to use the tunnel left Wembley for Milan late on 13th June, and a fortnight later the first two regular freight trains for the Continent from the Willesden terminal departed amid much razzmatazz. Though BR and Eurotunnel were eager for business, some categories of freight were barred from the tunnel by the Inter-Governmental Commission: gas and petroleum tankers, nuclear waste, explosives, dangerous chemicals and livestock; the risks of fire, explosion and nuclear leakages and the noxious effects of manure were the reasons cited.

Hopes for an early start to Eurostar services received a setback in June when a power short-circuit in the tunnel disrupted a full-scale evacuation drill involving a train carrying 800 people; after the current failed, it had to be towed out by a diesel resue locomotive. With eight weeks of endurance testing required once the IGC did declare evacuation arrangements successful, BR, SNCF and SNCB announced at the end of the month that Eurostar services would not commence until the autumn. However after a further, successful, drill, the IGC on 3rd August, 1994 gave Eurotunnel its licence to allow Eurostars and a limited car-carrying shuttle service through the tunnel.

Regular passenger-carrying shuttles did not start running until 29th September, late enough to mean that Eurotunnel had forfeited its expected £100 million share of that summer's cross-Channel holiday market because of delays in getting the tunnel open after its completion. Stock market nerves over the company's debts - now £8 billion and rising - had not been helped by a media report that pools of salt water had been found in the tunnel at the drier, English, end. Moreover, the initial Le Shuttle service for cars, which began operating on 13th July, 1994, was no more than a 10-day trial in which 'loyal customers' who had bought tickets for services earlier in the year that had never run were given a complimentary ride - regular fare-paying passengers would have to wait almost another three months. Even more frustratingly, Eurotunnel was still operating no more than a skeleton HGV shuttle service; though billed as 'normal' from 25th July, 1994, the full 24-hour service did not begin until 7th November.

The stage was, however, now set for the unveiling of Eurostar's prestige high-speed service between London, Paris and Brussels, which was confidently expected to be the precursor of equally-impressive links between Scotland, the English regions and the Continent and a network of night services stretching into the Netherlands and Germany. The preparations for a mid-Autumn start began smoothly. On 17th August staff of the three state railways that had developed Eurostar were given an introductory journey through the tunnel. Dover Marine station, one of that town's two boat train termini, was closed on 24th September in anticipation of an early switch of rail passengers from the ferries to Eurostar; the Dover-Ostend ferry, 30 per cent of whose passengers had gone by rail, had closed the previous December, vessels being diverted to less convenient Ramsgate. Dover Western Docks station also closed at the end of the 1994 summer timetable, but Folkestone Harbour, at the foot of the steepest branch on the BR/Railtrack network, remained in use until 2000 to connect with Hoverspeed's 'Seacat' for Boulogne and for 'specials', notably the Orient Express whose vintage Pullman stock would not satisfy tunnel safety regulations. Orient Express traffic to Folkestone Harbour resumed in 2003, but diesel-hauled after the de-energisation of the single remaining running line and with passengers now bused through the tunnel on shuttle trains instead of being conveyed to Boulogne by sea.

On 20th October, 1994, Eurostar 'went public' with a Press run from Waterloo to the Gare du Nord and back for 400 mainly British journalists. The event should have been a public relations triumph for the tunnel and the imminent launch of high-speed international passenger services through it, but the headlines the following day told a very different story. Despite the fact that a preview train for 200 SNCF staff the previous week had broken down, EPS management rejected the advice of their public relations team and decided not to have a back-up train standing by for the Press run. Inevitably, Murphy's law struck. The spotless Eurostar, crammed with liquid refreshment, that was due to convey the hacks and accompanying railway

personnel to Paris for the mother of all buffet lunches failed in its platform shortly
before its scheduled departure time. It took almost an hour before a replacement
unit, Nos. 3305/6, could be brought to Waterloo from North Pole fully prepared and
provisioned, and by the time it departed Eurostar's embarrassment appeared total.
Lunchtime media reports that the non-appearance of the train had caused chaos on
the BR network across Kent merely compounded the situation.

Eurostar managed to rescue something from the fiasco, for in a storming
performance the replacement train recovered 13 minutes of the time lost, setting an
impressive record with a start-to-stop run of 2 hours 49 minutes by the author's
watch; the comparable SNCF Press run which left Paris at 0807 hrs arrived on time 3
hours 3 minutes later. By contrast the only previous direct link, the Night Ferry, had
taken 10 hr 40 min. between Victoria and the Gare du Nord, although admittedly
there was no great pressure for speed. The Press train's rocket-like progress along the
TGV-Nord route was a revelation for those on board. But, just as significantly, units
373 305/6 shot through the tunnel in an impressive 19 minutes; to those on board
who had suffered the inconvenience of boat trains and ferries over the decades, the
trip was a psychological milestone. Moreover, almost everyone found the sub-
Channel portion of the journey almost mundane after the first few kilometres of
tunnel wall had slipped anonymously past. The return trip passed off without
incident, but sadly for Eurostar, the next morning's headlines had already been
written; 'Le Coq-Up' was one of the kinder to appear in the tabloids. Eurotunnel's
shares dipped further as the City concluded that the through rail services on whose
growth the company depended heavily would not be a success.

At the end of October the IGC lifted a ban on weekend operation of any trains in
the tunnel which had hampered preparations for starting a full timetable. And on
14th November, 1994 the first timetabled Eurostars - a 'Discovery' service of just two
trains a day each between Waterloo and Brussels in three hours dead, and Waterloo
and Paris in 3 hr 15 min., began to operate, with special promotional fares being
charged. First services out of Waterloo International were the 0823 to Paris and the
1023 to Brussels; this time there were no significant delays. Indeed the very first
revenue-earning train reached Paris almost three minutes ahead of schedule. It
completed the journey at an average speed of 104.1 mph (167.5 kph), but the contrast
between its performances on either side of the Channel spoke volumes: 55.4 mph
(89.13 kph) between Waterloo and the English portal and 152 mph (244.5 kph) from
the French portal to the Gare du Nord.

The start of Eurostar operations, coupled with the build-up of Le Shuttle, caught
the public imagination even if it did not produce a stampede for tickets. There was,
however, considerable confusion over which service did what. Quite a few car
drivers had to be turned away from Waterloo International after arriving in
expectation of loading their cars onto the train, and some foot passengers arrived at
the Cheriton terminal expecting that a train would whisk them straight to Paris.
Confusion over which services through the tunnel are operated by Eurotunnel and
which by Eurostar continues to this day, despite the efforts of both companies.

With around 12 million passengers forecast for the first full year of Eurostar
operation, it was planned to increase the service to 20 trains a day from Waterloo to
Paris by 1995 and 15 to Brussels. But it soom became evident that while Eurostar was
establishing itself as a brand, patronage was well below the levels predicted,
particularly on the Brussels route; promotional efforts were stepped up, but services
were increased more cautiously than had been planned. An extra Fridays-only
London-Paris train was introduced in December 1994, on 23rd January, 1995 the

Paris service was doubled to four trains daily, from 27th January this was increased to five and from 4th March to six, always with one train more on Fridays. By 3rd July nine trains a day (10 on Fridays) were operating between London and Paris, and five on the Brussels route.

Eurostar carried more than 200,000 passengers for the first time in the month of April - 11,000 on Easter Monday alone - and on May the service welcomed its millionth paying customer. The highest-profile among these was France's President Jacques Chirac, who for his arrival on a State visit to Britain on 14th May, 1995 forsook the traditional pomp associated with such occasions and simply booked two first-class Eurostar carriages for his entourage. From 23rd January that year a few Eurostars had called at Calais-Fréthun, carrying some domestic passengers over the TGV-Nord between there and Paris. SNCF also followed BR in withdrawing scheduled rail services to ferry ports in the expectation that traffic would switch *en bloc* to Eurostar; Boulogne Maritime and Calais Maritime stations were both closed on 21st January, 1995, but within three months continuing demand brought about their reopening on an experimental basis.

Throughout 1995 Eurostar's build-up continued; the two millionth passenger was carried on 31st August and the three millionth on 23rd December. From the start of the summer 1995 timetable, connecting domestic services enabled passengers from the East and West Coast main lines (by HST over the West London Line) and from Wales and the West (by class '158' dmu via Salisbury) direct access to Waterloo for transfer to Eurostar. Despite highly competitive fares, patronage was pitiful on most of these services and by the summer 1997 timetable only the western service survived, as still it does though now cut back to Bristol. Across the Channel, tracklaying on the Belgian high-speed line began on 3rd October. Hopes were also still high for an early start to North of London and night services: the first short-formation Eurostar rakes were delivered on 28th June, and on 27th July Railtrack approved the upgrading of the East Coast Main Line necessary for regional Eurostars to operate over it; when they eventually did, it would be as domestic trains in GNER colours.

On 8th January, 1996 Eurostar took an important step when trains began to call at Ashford International. Investment in the station had been heavy, and it was expected that within months over 5,000 people a day would be boarding or leaving international services there. In practice, this was far from the case - another indication that forecasts for the usage of Eurostar overall had been wildly optimistic - and it was three or four years before Ashford International really caught on. To begin with, the station's usefulness was limited by the service provided - only five of the 12 Monday-Friday trains now running daily to Paris stopped at Ashford, and four of the six Brussels services. Fares from Ashford to the Continent - apart from some initial promotional bargains - were not set at a level to attract custom: generally they were the same as from Waterloo, and for the short runs to Calais-Fréthun and to Lille this made them almost prohibitive. Against this, Connex anticipated the opening of an interchange enabling passengers from Sussex to board Eurostar in Kent by introducing an accelerated, through service from Brighton and Eastbourne via the 'Marshlink' line; this did not survive for long, though after the Strategic Rail Authority's rejection of the case for electrification it was reintroduced in December 2005 with new class '171' diesel units. Nevertheless when Ashford International was formally opened by the Duke of Kent that 8th February, hopes for its early success were still high.

Freight services, too, were intensifying, with continuing optimism that the target of 27 international trains through the tunnel each day would soon be reached. The range of cargoes and destinations was promising - the first trainload of steel slabs from Tinsley, Sheffield to Sweden ran on 21st December, 1994 - and by June 1995 over 10 trains a day were running, a quarter of them to Italy, a run on which the tunnel/rail combination offered particular time benefits. BR and SNCF marked the build-up in through tunnel freight services by withdrawing their Dover-Dunkerque train ferry in 1995; sadly this did not give rise to a straight transfer of traffic as a number of wagonload flows of chemicals and hydrocarbons fell foul of the ban on such cargoes through the tunnel and were lost to road.

Throughout this period the freight terminals developed in the UK for tunnel traffic began to come on stream, though the Scottish terminal at Mossend, in particular, took a disappointingly long time to start operations and disagreements over siting would delay the opening of the main terminal in South Wales for half a decade. Through freight services also suffered a setback toward the close of 1995 when a wave of strikes by SNCF staff severely disrupted tunnel traffic.

Even with Eurotunnel's bread and butter - its car and HGV shuttle services - it took a frustratingly long time to get the promised frequent service up and running. The trial car shuttle service operated for far longer than planned while bugs in the system were ironed out; one VIP test run on 22nd November, 1994 had to be aborted when a car being driven onto a shuttle train caught fire. But on 22nd December Le Shuttle for motorists was finally launched, and within a fortnight 40 car shuttles daily were being operated, around the clock. By Easter 1995 Eurotunnel was offering motorists a 'turn up and go' service, but with just four of the nine trains ordered in service, departures were still limited to little over one an hour and the Cheriton terminal, in particular, was jammed with drivers arriving 'on spec'. That April 96,375 cars were conveyed through the tunnel, a 30 per cent share of the Dover-Calais market, and by August 6,000 cars a day (143,577 during the month) were using the shuttles. The HGV shuttles attracted a similar market share, and from June 1995 four freight shuttles an hour, each able to carry 28 lorries, were run at peak times. From 26th June, Eurotunnel was also finally cleared to carry coaches and their passengers, these vehicles being accommodated with 4x4s and camper vans on single-deck carriages in the car shuttle trains; initially they were carried on one train per hour. Coach firms were offered a promotional £100-each-way fare in the hope of attracting valuable peak-season business.

One complicating factor as Eurotunnel and its partner railways strove to build up services through the tunnel was a rash of teething troubles that had not come to light even during the over-lengthy commissioning process demanded by the IGC. High on the list, though the company initially denied it, was the problem of salt water ingress that shorted the track circuits and led to 'ghost trains' showing up on the control room LED display, in turn triggering emergency stops by real trains in the tunnel. Water leaks - from underground strata, not the sea itself - at the English end of the tunnel were reported in September 1994, and by the following March TML had been called in to tackle ingress at five separate points, with a 4km stretch of roof near the French coast having to be resealed. These leakages had not only put bugs into the train control system; they also corroded wires supporting the electric catenary. In places, channels in the tunnel floor designed to let water flow away were failing to do their job because of a build-up of dust and 'gunge', and new courses for the water were drilled out using diamond cutters.

The reliability of the shuttle rolling stock was also tested more rigorously in commercial traffic, and on 20th February, 1995 the last wagon of a Coquelles-bound HGV train derailed just before entering the tunnel; a faulty wheel was blamed. Two months later, an emergency door from a car shuttle was found in the tunnel ripped from its hinges after a fault led to the train leaving with it unsecured. And on 21st June all traffic in the tunnel was halted for four hours because of a brake failure on a Cheriton-bound car shuttle train, which resulted in the first serious evacuation of the undersea system as more than 100 passengers were led via the cross-passages to another shuttle in the adjoining tunnel. This rare emergency took place as the contingent of 50 Kent firefighters who continually patrolled the service tunnel were complaining that there was nothing for them to do - 'not even a pole to slide down'. The morale of the 80-strong French firefighting team who carried out similar patrols was higher, as they were trained to tackle a broader range of civil emergencies and thus had more scope to exercise their skills.

Overall there were probably fewer bugs in the system than might have been expected given the complexity of both the tunnel itself and the technology of its rail system. But if the tunnel was starting to prove itself a success in transport terms, its finances remained a nightmare. By March 1995 the tunnel was covering its running costs, but it was light years away from being able to repay the interest on its debt, let alone the debt itself, and speculation grew that Sir Alastair Morton and his co-chairman Patrick Ponsolle would finally have to capitulate to the bankers. While business and market share were growing steadily, Eurotunnel still had a financial Everest to climb. The airlines had started trimming their London-Paris services as Eurostar picked up custom, but the ferries led by Stena Sealink and P&O embarked on a round of price-cutting which made the tunnel company's prospects even shakier; Eurotunnel had during construction based its revenue forcasts on the fares the ferries were charging in the late 1980s before price-cutting took hold, and the reductions made its rocky finances worse as it strove to compete.

The ferry operators complained that Eurotunnel was inflating its estimates of market share while at the same time discounting fares to a level it could not hope to sustain; Eurotunnel countered that the ferries were able to keep their fares low because of their lucrative on-board duty-free trade from which the tunnel's shuttles were excluded. Eurotunnel's terminals had, indeed, been designed without duty-free facilities because of European Union plans to scrap the facility from 1993; when Brussels agreed to a reprieve that was to postpone the end of duty-free for five years, Eurotunnel revised its plans and entered the market, but the company suffered through only being able to offer such goods at its terminals and not *en route*. In September 1995 Eurotunnel fractionally eased the financial pressures which could in theory have closed the tunnel at any moment, buying 18 months' breathing space to reschedule its debt.

Nor was all the traffic the tunnel was attracting necessarily the kind its promoters - or the authorities - wanted. Early in September 1995 customs officers made their first significant drugs seizure, discovering a quarter of a ton of cannabis worth £1 million in a cargo of dried yoghurt about to be driven onto a shuttle train at Coquelles.

Illegal immigration, too, proved an immediate headache, though initially on a small scale. From the moment Eurostar services began, trains through the tunnel became a new and attractive option to people trying to enter Britain illegally; 590 were sent back from Waterloo to Paris or Brussels in the first 10 months, usually unescorted. And in September 1995 an Algerian, Bonito Cobbola, managed to escape deportation by opening a train's emergency door and jumping out as it passed through Sandling at 70 kph on its way back to the tunnel.

At the same time, freight shippers and operators were becoming increasingly disenchanted at the hurdles to the swift movement of consignments via the tunnel erected by various organs of the UK Government. Freight below a certain weight was exempt from security measures, but for some time the Department of Transport refused on security grounds to tell shippers what that weight was. Anyone without security approval wanting to send freight through the tunnel had to give 20 hours' notice; installing the equipment to obtain security clearance could cost £250,000, and even then the process of clearing a consignment for departure took eight hours.

Nevertheless, the closing figures for 1995, the tunnel's first full year of operation, looked moderately healthy. Le Shuttle tourist had carried 1,222,713 cars, motorcycles, campers and caravans, and 23,383 coaches. The number of daily car shuttles each way had increased during the year from 35 to 55, compared with 20 departures a day offered by the (admittedly much more capacious) ferries. Le Shuttle freight had carried 390,975 trucks. Eurostar had attracted 2,920,309 passengers, and 1,349,802 tonnes of rail freight had been carried. Not the showstopper Eurotunnel had hoped for, but a sound start nevertheless.

On 29th February, 1996 John Major's Transport Secretary, Sir George Young, cleared the way both for the privatisation of Eurostar and construction of the Channel Tunnel Rail Link when he selected the London & Continental Railways (LCR) consortium to take over the service. It was the belief of Ministers and the consortium that the latter could be financed in part from the profits of the former, a calculation that would soon prove to be sadly adrift. Nevertheless the prospect of Eurostar coming under private sector management raised hopes for its commercial success and also heartened Sir Alastair Morton, who had grown increasingly irritated at the service's slow build-up. Shortly after LCR took over European Passenger Services on 1st June, 1996, he told the *Daily Telegraph*: 'Eurotunnel is complaining publicly and bitterly about the poor development of that service, since it adversely affects our revenues and, therefore, our relations with our bankers'.

LCR's shareholders were the American contractors and project managers Bechtel (18%), the merchant bank SBG Warburg (18%), the Virgin Group (17%), National Express (17%), Systra, the consulting subsidiary of SNCF (14%), London Electricity (12%), Sir William Halcrow and Partners, consulting engineers (2%), and Ove Arup, of whom more later (2%). The company's Chairman as it took over Eurostar was Sir Derek Hornby, a highly experienced businessman, former BR Board member and, incidentally, father of the author Nick Hornby (but no connection with Hornby Railways, despite the number of 00-gauge Eurostar sets he was presented with during his time at the company). Its chief executive was Adam Mills, an accountant with great entrepreneurial skills who had made his reputation with the National Bus Company.

LCR's takeover of EPS (it formally became Eurostar UK on 1st October, 1996) did give the service - and rail traffic through the tunnel - some impetus as Virgin, in particular, applied its marketing and public relations acumen. High-profile and witty commercials featuring (separately) the Manchester United footballer Eric Cantona and the 'Eurotrash' presenter Antoine de Caunes certainly got Eurostar talked about. There was, however, great resistance at the highest levels of the company to letting Richard Branson publicise Eurostar despite his stake in it. A boardroom belief that he would hijack it for his own purposes led to his being kept at arm's length, though in the aftermath of the fire on 18th November, 1996 Branson's appearance at Waterloo to reassure customers did much to maintain public faith in the tunnel as such; no other shareholder had thought of doing so. Before long an irreconcilable difference emerged between the philosophies of Virgin - eager to get more 'bums on seats' to popularise the service - and of National

Express, which was keen to raise the financial yield to stem the operation's losses. With tourists outnumbering business customers by four to one, the arguments on each side were cogent.

With professional money men now in charge, a serious look was also taken at the traffic projections for Eurostar; SNCF's original 16.5 million a year - Sir Alastair told the author - inflated to justify construction of the TGV-Nord, was looking increasingly hard to achieve, and Branson came in for heavy internal criticism for suggesting that, with aggressive marketing, 30 million could be reached.

Regional Eurostar services were still contemplated, though the inadequacies of the Railtrack infrastructure exposed by test runs was putting back the starting date again and again. Limited Eurostar services on both the East and West Coast main lines were by now being advertised in Railtrack's national rail timetables. One train was billed to run each way daily from Glasgow Central (dep. 0730) to the Gare du Nord (arr. 1753), with stops at Edinburgh, Newcastle, Darlington, York, Doncaster, Newark North Gate, Peterborough and Lille; the return journey leaving Paris at 1307 was due into Glasgow Central at 2130 on weekdays and 2155 on Sundays; the Saturday service was to run only to Edinburgh. The West Coast service consisted of two trains daily between Manchester Piccadilly and the Gare du Nord, one direct and the other via Birmingham, except on Sundays when there was only one southbound service, running direct. Stations to be served (some by only one train) were Stockport, Crewe, Stafford, Wolverhampton, Birmingham New Street, Birmingham International, Coventry, Rugby, Milton Keynes and Lille. Southbound there were departures from Manchester via Birmingham at 0600 (Saturdays) and 0612 (weekdays), and direct at 0754 (Sundays), 0907 (Saturdays) and 0927 (weekdays). Arrival times at the Gare du Nord were 1359 (via Birmingham) and 1629 (direct). Northbound a daily 1622 from Paris was timetabled, running by the direct route to reach Manchester at 2208 (2213 on Sundays, the only day it served Rugby). The West Midlands would be served by a 1743 daily from Paris, due into Manchester at 2340 (weekdays) and 2438 (Sundays). On Saturdays the train was to terminate at Birmingham New Street at 2151. With publicity for these services part of LCR's marketing build-up, hopes for an early start once the routes in question had been de-bugged were still high. It is probably a blessing for Britain's other train operators that they never did. Given the headaches caused for Thameslink on the Midland Main Line by delays caused on the Southern, the consequences of any regional Eurostar not passing through Brixton (the chosen anchor point for the timetable) at just the right time to avoid creating chaos on either the East or West Coast Main Line hardly bears thinking about. In addition, it is estimated that each Eurostar stopping at Milton Keynes would have blocked the modernised WCML for up to 12 miles behind it.

By the end of 1996, it was accepted within LCR that night passenger services through the tunnel would never run. Plans for the services were highly developed, and specimen times had been advertised and paths inserted in Railtrack's operational timetable: Glasgow dep. 1820, arr. Brussels 0650; Waterloo dep. 2123, arr. Amsterdam 0925; Swansea dep. 2000, arr. Paris 0650. However, the expenditure of £139 million on the night stock had coincided with a slump in sleeper traffic throughout the Continent and it was calculated that the trains would lose less in storage than they would in service. A solitary Nightstar service from Waterloo to Frankfurt/Dortmund or Amsterdam, splitting at Brussels, did, however, remain a 'runner' until that autumn. Soundings over the possibility of using the saloon and catering carriages from the Nightstar rakes on day services from Waterloo to these same destinations were also taken, but the idea was stillborn. The fiction that Nightstar services might yet operate was, however, maintained until February 2003 when the Rail Regulator, Tom Winsor, rejected an appeal by Eurostar against Network Rail's deletion of the sleeper trains from its working timetable.

Thoughout 1996 Eurostar's service build-up continued, though at a far slower rate than Eurotunnel or the service's planners would have expected. From 1st July the London-Paris service was boosted to 13 each weekday, including an 'early bird' 0453 from Waterloo (0615 from Ashford) giving an 0917 arrival. The slow running time of 3hrs 24 mins was explained by the train being pathed as far as Ashford immediately behind a domestic all-stations service (!); before long the Eurostar was given priority and a 20 minutes later departure from London.

On 1st July also, the Eurostar service to Disneyland Paris was launched, with a daily, though initially seasonal, departure from Waterloo throughout the summer of 0923 (0910 on Sundays) and a journey time (including a stop at Ashford) of just over three hours. This service terminates within sight of Disneyland Paris at Chessy Marne-la-Vallée station, on the loop around Paris by which TGVs also serve Charles de Gaulle Airport and access the rest of France's high-speed network. Eurostar ski trains also sometimes stop at Chessy Marne-la-Vallée for crewing purposes. Eurostar's new management also sought to maximise revenue by carrying Ashford commuters into Waterloo on the first morning train from Paris, which had plenty of seats to spare. This imaginative proposal would have greatly improved both the comfort and the journey times of an influential group of people who all too often had to watch the Eurostar pull up and leave half empty and on time while their own decrepit and overloaded BR/Connex train was running late. But it was vetoed by the customs and immigration authorities on security grounds. How a commuter boarding a London-bound train in the UK could pose a threat to the tunnel was never explained; nor were the authorities able to justify the ban when passengers on the line between Belfast and Dublin, the subject of repeated terrorist incidents, have never been subject to anything more than a visit from the ticket collector.

Hard commercial reality over services through the tunnel was also dawning at BR, which in the summer of 1996 wrote off £500 million from the accounts of Railfreight Distribution. BR acknowledged that in the tunnel's first full year of operation it had carried less than half the 6 million tonnes predicted. Having promised Eurotunnel £20 million a year for freight paths over 10 years, BR acknowledged that revenue was unlikely to make any contribution to these costs. In addition it wrote off £300 million in respect of locomotives, wagons and infrastructure, the bulk being the cost of its fleet of class '92s', which would be seriously under-utilised until conflicts between the locomotives' electronics and Railtrack's lineside circuits were resolved, and far from fully used thereafter. To add to BR's grief, the European Commission chose this moment to argue that the monopoly BR and SNCF enjoyed in commercial agreements with Eurotunnel which allowed them to use the half-share of paths through the tunnel not reserved for shuttles was illegal and that other operators must be allowed in.

On paper the tunnel was by now on course to meet its daily targets of first 27 and eventually 35 international freight trains each way. The working timetable for 8th August, 1996, at the start of what has become a traditionally quiet month for such traffic, did show 19 such trains each way, but of these six were light-engine workings so the number of revenue-earning trains was in fact only 13. Of the northbound freight trains, 10 were heading for Wembley (five from points in Italy, four from France and one Belgium), plus one from Calais to Corby, one from Silla in Spain to Dagenham and one from Arluno, Italy, for Longbridge. In the reverse direction the pattern was much the same. Most of the northbound trains transited the tunnel at night, just two being booked to leave Fréthun between 0334 and 1850; southbound, 11 of the 13 through freight workings left Cheriton between 2344 and 0734. Cars were the most conspicuous bulk cargo: Rovers for Italy and Fiats, Peugeots, Fords and Citroens bound for the UK. While the tunnel was under construction freight industry analysts had predicted that twice as much traffic would enter the UK via the tunnel as would leave it, but in practice the balance of flows has been more even.

The most obvious pain was still being felt at Eurotunnel, which reported a loss for 1995 of £925 million, or £1,759 a minute. With operations breaking even and Eurotunnel now claiming a market share of 45 per cent, this loss was entirely accounted for by the burden of the company's debts and the growing backlog of interest. But there were now some encouraging straws in the wind as shuttle, rail passenger and freight traffic at mid-1996 showed a 50 per cent increase on levels for the previous year. In February 1996 the former Conservative Cabinet Minister Lord Wakeham and the former French Justice Minister Robert Badinter were appointed by a Paris court as mediators - *mandataires ad hoc* - between Eurotunnel and the banks over the restructuring of its debt. An end to the price war between Eurotunnel and the ferries seemed in prospect when P&O and Stena Sealink applied to the UK Government to pool resources, but before this could be approved, Stena separated from the still-nationalised SeaFrance and a new round of price-cutting began.

Nevertheless Eurotunnel had managed, against considerable odds, to complete the transition from construction project to transport system, and at the end of October 1996 Sir Alastair Morton stepped down as co-Chairman, to be replaced by the less abrasive but highly experienced Sir Robert Malpas, a member of many boards after three decades at ICI. Sir Alastair would reappear on the railway scene early in 1999 as Chairman of the Shadow Strategic Rail Authority, exercising his powers pending the passage of legislation by virtue of chairing the almost-defunct British Railways Board. Sir Robert, prior to his appointment, had made his main impact on Eurotunnel by persuading Sir Alastair that he could not brand its shuttle services the 'V-train' because some Continental customers might be put off by its wartime connotations. At much the same time the French co-Chairman Andre Bénard also left, to be replaced by Patrick Ponsolle, who became Executive Chairman and the company's driving force.

During 1996 all forms of traffic through the tunnel increased steadily, if not spectacularly. Eurostar showed new energies in promotion and marketing, achieving solid bookings for the pre-Christmas period by selling the notion of holding your office Christmas lunch in Paris, and taking travel journalists on a 'preview' run to Bourg St-Maurice to advertise the ski trains that would operate from the 1997/98 winter season. Eurotunnel and the railway undertakings using the tunnel still had a mountain to climb, but some green shoots of confidence were starting to appear. By early November, car shuttle traffic was 87 per cent ahead of the 1995 level, coaches 239 per cent, HGVs 49 per cent, Eurostar passengers 69 per cent and rail freight up 65 per cent. Then, at 2045 UK time on 18th November, 1996, a northbound HGV shuttle train caught fire as it entered the tunnel.

Chapter Eight

Ordeal by Fire

Ever since a Channel Tunnel was first mooted, fears had been voiced - largely by groups with a vested interest in thwarting the project - that it was fatally susceptible to fire. The Flexilink consortium of ferry interests and the National Union of Seamen argued throughout the Parliamentary hearings into the project that a tunnel used by car-carrying trains would be inherently unsafe because of the risk of a petrol tank exploding. Rather more persuasively, the Fire Brigades Union and some - though not all - Chief Fire Officers voiced fears both that any tunnel with such traffic would be at serious risk from fire, and that Eurotunnel's plan to carry motorists through the tunnel in their cars would increase that risk. The ferry operators shared this concern, demanding once the scheme was approved that passengers be segregated from their vehicles - a procedure that would, conveniently for Eurotunnel's competitors, have added crucial minutes, and costs, to a tunnel transit. There were also concerns, accepted in part by the Inter-Governmental Safety Commission, that the virtually open-sided HGV shuttle vehicles ordered by Eurotunnel would not impede the spread of a fire; the design was modified before services began. By accommodating the HGV drivers in a club car, Eurotunnel was able to keep down the weight and cost of its shuttle wagons, which would otherwise have had to be fully enclosed and air-conditioned.

Once the tunnel was in operation, the Kent firemen patrolling it found the experience tedious rather than alarming. At the French end, the emergency teams had an ethos and a training that covered more than fighting fires, and this feeling was less pronounced. Nevertheless, by the time shuttles and through rail services had been running virtually without incident for a couple of years, the 'desktop exercises' carried out by Eurotunnel, Eurostar and other interested parties to test their emergency procedures looked increasingly unlikely to be put to the test. The prophets of doom fell strangely silent.

Then, around 2145 French time (2045 GMT) on Monday 18th November, 1996, two Eurotunnel security guards saw smoke coming from the rear of a shuttle train, No. 7539, carrying 27 HGVs and two vans, and headed by Tri-Bo No. 9006, as it headed into the Bessingue Trench three minutes out from Coquelles. They alerted the terminal's control room, which contacted the driver, who had entered the tunnel at 2149 after being slowed because the preceding shuttle was just ahead. He was just over 2 km into the tunnel when the message reached him, and was told to keep going and make for the emergency siding at Cheriton. This was standard emergency procedure; it makes more sense to fight an on-train fire in the open than in a confined space, and halting a train on fire may increase the risk to those on board. Eurotunnel's central control centre at Cheriton was, unaccountably, not notified by Coquelles control for a further 17 minutes, but controllers there were aware of the alert through a conversation with the train's French driver, who initially reported that he had no problems. Fire and smoke detectors in the tunnel, from the very first at 1km, indicated that the train was on fire and notified the control computer at Cheriton, but as the sensors did not actually catch fire the alarm was not technically 'confirmed' until the train reached sensors at the 5 km mark. At this point all signals for trains approaching the tunnel were automatically set at red, and the piston relief ducts between the running tunnels were sealed (though a few failed to shut, allowing smoke to escape into unaffected tunnels). Trains in the tunnel, save for those behind the afflicted shuttle, were ordered to continue their journeys at full speed . . . a sensible step which, however, handicapped the operation by creating pressure waves that prevented closure of the doors in the crossover chambers, enabling smoke to seep into the other tunnels.

The fire had broken out in a lorry carrying cornflakes from Belgium, in the fourth wagon of the rear rake, about 250 m behind the club car. Immediately behind it was a lorryload of pork fat, which was not only highly combustible but flowed when aflame, and in front of it trucks loaded with pineapples and cheese which, thankfully, slowed the spread of the fire as the moisture in them absorbed the heat. When salvage teams pored through the wreckage, they were still able to separate the cheese slices.

By now the driver had been alerted by a smoke alarm in the rear locomotive, and by the *chef de train* in the club car, but the train, travelling at 140 kph, went on to cover more than 17 km. It might even have made it to the English portal, had not an emergency light incorrectly indicated that a bridge plate on one of the shuttle wagons had shifted, forcing the driver to halt just after transiting the French crossover chamber. He made a controlled stop with the club car, in which all the HGV drivers were travelling, opposite a safety door to the service tunnel. He got down from his cab to check which of the many such doors his locomotive was opposite so that he could notify the firefighters, but was beaten back by smoke and returned to his cab. The fire crew from Coquelles worked out which door would be the right one - but were unaccountably sent on to the next by Cheriton control.

The driver was told by control to uncouple the locomotive and club car from the blazing shuttle train, and drive their occupants safely out of the tunnel. But before he could initiate the automatic uncoupling process from his cab, the power supply failed; the wagon in which the fire had begun had halted immediately beneath one of the motorised isolator switches that break the catenary into 1.2 km sections and melted the solder on the switch, causing a loss of power.

The lorry drivers in the club car feared the worst, one later describing the atmosphere as 'like a tomb'. The *chef de train*, Emile Grard, unwisely if understandably opened the carriage door to see what was happening; acrid smoke billowed in for 30 seconds before he could shut it again. M Grard himself inhaled a large amount of smoke because he could not wear a mask while he was on the intercom to the driver, as he was continually when not restraining truck drivers who wanted to smash the windows and get out.

With the train driver unable to detach the burning vehicles, the *chef de train* courageously evacuated the three train-crew and 31 passengers, while the driver with equal bravery remained in his cab for the firecrew to rescue him. The driver had stopped the train close to a safety door and luminous arrows on the tunnel wall should have marked the way to it, but at first the black smoke was too thick for these to be seen by the escapers. M. Grard led the drivers, clutching wet napkins to their noses for protection against the smoke, away from the fire until a blast of air caused by firemen opening one of the other safety doors made the arrows visible, and thence into the service tunnel. From here they were all transferred to a southbound passenger shuttle which had made a special stop; to prevent panic, tourists were moved to one end of the train and the evacuees accommodated in the other.

All the occupants of the fire-stricken shuttle were safely back at Coquelles within the 90-minute limit set by the IGC. All were suffering from smoke inhalation and were taken to hospitals in Calais, Boulogne and Lille. Eight, including a pregnant woman, were detained, but none suffered lasting ill-effects and there was immense relief that such a major fire had not claimed any lives.

At 2156 the French fire service had been alerted - though not the Kent brigade, whom the French fire chief had decided not to alert as the fire was seven miles closer to the French than the English portal. Fire crews from Coquelles were at the scene within 20 minutes. It took a further hour for Kent crews to be summoned from their base at the Folkestone terminal, and they arrived a full two hours after the alarm had first been raised. Although this delay did not affect the rescue operation which was well in hand before even the French crews arrived, it may well have ruled out a combined effort to contain the fire and limit the damage, and as such it featured prominently in post-mortems into the disaster. Under Eurotunnel's safety procedure it was up to the French duty controller - not the fire chief - to notify the English emergency services, and this did not happen. Eurotunnel later conceded that there had been 'avoidable delays' in responding to the blaze, and in any future emergency both sets of rescue services will be notified instantly as a matter of course. More damningly, it disclosed that an internal safety audit four months before the fire had identified 'underlying weaknesses' at the Cheriton control centre which had not subsequently been addressed.

Conditions in the tunnel were horrendous: the temperature reached 1000 degrees Celsius, causing the steel-reinforced concrete tunnel segments to behave like popcorn in a cooker and break into lumps. Closest to the seat of the fire, half the 400 mm thickness of the segments was reduced to dust. *New Civil Engineer* described the tunnel at this point as 'an unlined hole through the chalk', yet a safety door immediately adjacent remained undamaged and fully operable. Equally, despite the localised inferno the fire did not spread to engulf the entire train, the damage to all but the wagons closest to the seat of the fire being caused by heat and smoke.

The decision was taken to let the fire burn once all the occupants of the train had been rescued. Some experts reckon this course of action left the damage more extensive than it need have been, but in fact only two lorries were still ablaze when the first fire crews arrived. Fans which, incidentally, supplied oxygen to the fire were left on to clear the smoke and keep conditions bearable for the firefighters, and it was just after midnight before the nearest hydrant was turned on; within three more hours the blaze had been extinguished.

Eurotunnel's public response to the emergency was somewhat confused. It at first described the incident as a 'small fire' and predicted reopening of the tunnel within 24 hours. But as the tunnel cooled enough for the mangled wreckage to be inspected, it became clear that the damage was considerable; a lengthy closure of the section of bore affected, not to mention a stringent reassessment of fire precautions and emergency procedures, would be necessary. The extent to which traffic had already come to depend on the tunnel was emphasised as, shortly after the enforced closure, French lorry drivers began blockading the Channel ports and British truckers, not for the last time, found themselves stranded.

The lead locomotive and the wagons ahead of the fire, including the club car, were hauled to Cheriton, round the terminal loop there and back to Coquelles on 21st September by one of Eurotunnel's Schoma diesel-electric locomotives, which pending reopening were the only form of traction permitted in the tunnel. Those at the rear, together with locomotive No. 9030, blackened and with its electronics damaged beyond repair, were hauled back to Coquelles on 27th November; only its bogies were capable of re-use, having been shielded from the heat by falling concrete. As the last of these wagons was freed, sparks from an acetylene torch embarrassingly started a second, smaller fire at the same location as the first. The fire was this time put out by staff on the spot before fire crews could arrive. Five wagons at the seat of the blaze were left in place, covered with tarpaulins, as a *juge d'instruction* had designated it a 'crime scene', as is the case with any transport disaster in France, and increasingly with any incident on Britain's railways. It was early December before they were finally extracted.

The fire was an immense setback to Eurotunnel in terms of its finances as well as the image of the project; inevitably the blaze prompted massive coverage in the UK media, and considerably less in the French. Fortunately the company had taken out insurance to cover the cost of fire repairs (including the replacement of rolling stock), loss of revenue and penalty payments to train operators for non-availability of the tunnel. Damage to the tunnel and rolling stock covered by insurance was estimated at £56 million, and total loss of revenue £135 million - well within Eurotunnel's limits of cover. The company's share price slipped 10 per cent on the day after the fire, but as it had already lost most of its value during its successive financial crises and payment of a dividend was a good 10 years off, this was of little consequence.

At first there were suspicions that the fire might have been started deliberately by French Eurotunnel employees who had been on unofficial strike. The dispute had led to a build-up of traffic at Coquelles which had also, fortuitously, led to senior management being called in. But it soon became evident that the actual cause had been an overheating refrigeration unit in the lorry carrying cornflakes.

The section of the north running tunnel through which the stricken train had passed, between the French portal and crossover chamber, escaped with limited damage from fire and smoke and was repaired within 10 days. But 600 metres of the southern running tunnel just north of the French crossover had suffered considerable damage; half of this length was rated 'badly damaged' and almost 40 metres nearest the seat of the fire 'extensively damaged'.

Repairing the tunnel and making the damaged section stronger than ever was a six-month project. Concrete supports were rushed in to prevent the bore collapsing at the point of greatest damage. Tonnes of scrap metal, concrete lumps and dust and other debris had to be removed before any remedial work could begin, and the affected area sealed off from the rest of the tunnel where services were swiftly resumed.

It was 20th January, 1997 before contractors headed by the French firm Setec moved in to get the damaged section back into working order. The 17 most severely damaged segments near the seat of the fire had to be replaced; those further from the seat of the fire could be repaired by shotcreting. And with the tunnel itself reinstated, the complex task of installing and testing all over again the plethora of systems running through it needed to be undertaken.

Meanwhile, three inquiries were under way into the cause of the fire and the performance of Eurotunnel's staff and equipment: by the Safety Authority responsible to the IGC, by the French judiciary and by Eurotunnel itself. The IGC also had to be satisfied that loopholes in emergency procedures exposed by the fire had been closed, and that those procedures would work more smoothly in future. It was a cause for considerable concern that the first two of the three levels of the original safety plan - the hauling of a fire-affected train through the tunnel to safety and the uncoupling of the club car to protect the passengers - had proved impossible. The procedures were duly rewritten so that, in future, any HGV shuttle on which a fire was detected would make a controlled stop and disembark its passengers before any attempt was made to drive it out of the tunnel for the fire to be tackled. In addition, all the doors of the undersea crossovers are now kept shut except when trains need to pass through, to make sure they do not assist penetration of the system by smoke. Central monitoring of all fire sensors at Cheriton control was introduced, transponders were fitted to safety doors in the tunnel so that they can be instantly identified, and markers were placed on the tunnel walls enabling an HGV shuttle driver to halt with the door of the club car exactly opposite one of the cross-passages. Six fire control stations were built in each of the two running tunnels, equipped with all-round water jets to spray a burning train until firefighters could arrive. In addition, club cars were fitted with safety hoods in case of smoke ingress, with action also taken to plug as many leaks as possible in the bodywork; even after the door was shut a considerable amount of smoke entered through keyholes, the toilet and other weak points. Eurotunnel estimated that if all these precautions had been in place at the time of the fire, the drivers could have been got to safety 26 minutes earlier. In addition, a fire training unit was set up at Cheriton with a former BR Mk II carriage representing a club car, a mock-up of a passenger shuttle carriage and lineside equipment as is found in the tunnel, with the capacity to emit non-harmful smoke from a thin haze to a pea-souper. This has proved useful in training not only Eurotunnel personnel to deal with emergencies, but also staff from SNCF, SNCB, Connex, First Great Western and Lufthansa.

The fire led, naturally, to a renewed campaign by the Fire Brigades Union and other organisations for the HGV shuttle wagons to be totally enclosed, most practicably by fitting their sides with retractable shutters. Eurotunnel resisted this on ground of cost, of weight - heavier sides might have limited the shuttle to carrying 38-tonne lorries instead of the 44-tonners stipulated - and of practicality: when retracted, the shutters would have fouled the roof of a typical lorry. In the end, a new shuttle wagon design was adopted, the honeycomb pattern replaced by a more open but more robust framework.

There was no dispute that the undamaged portions of the tunnel remained safe for international trains and for passenger shuttles, subject to the constraint of having one 18 km section of running tunnel closed pending renovation work. Only a minimal amount of work was needed to get the rest of the system back into working order, and the Safety Authority quickly issued a certificate to allow empty Eurostars, international freight trains and a tourist shuttle for staff movements to operate.

The first through freight train since the fire ran at 0540 on 21st November - just 56 hours after the alarm was raised - and the backlog of freight bound for the Continent was cleared by the following day. It took longer to clear freight bound for the UK because of operational hiccups in various countries which had held back traffic that might otherwise have got through before the fire. On 26th November, 28 freight trains and seven light engines were run.

At first, international freight trains had the tunnel to themselves, save for the occasional Eurotunnel maintenance or staff movement. It took a few days for Eurostar to regroup and launch a timetable allowing for the blockage of one tunnel and slower transits through the other, but with ingenuity the company squeezed in 13 daily return trips between London and Paris - a loss of between one and three trains only a day - and seven on the Brussels run. This was only fractionally less than the timetable applying seven years later after the opening of the first phase of the CTRL. A successful trial evacuation of a Eurostar in the remaining serviceable running tunnel parallel with the seat of the fire was held on 1st December, 1996; it took two hours and five minutes to bring 491 people, including two in wheelchairs, 10 elderly and infirm and 20 babies and toddlers, to safety in the service tunnel.

The first scheduled Eurostar after the fire left Waterloo for Paris on 3rd December, 1996 unannounced and empty, gaining just four passengers *en route*. The first advertised working was the 0753 to Paris the following day; 23 passengers boarded the train, which took 30 minutes to transit the tunnel because of single-line working round the damaged section but still contrived to reach the Gare du Nord five minutes early. Customers quickly returned, and by the end of the 1996 Christmas holiday Eurostar was carrying half as many passengers again as the year before. On 7th May, 1997, the 10 millionth Eurostar passenger was carried.

Eurotunnel's car shuttle trains began running again on 10th December, 1996; confidence returned less rapidly, given the confusion in the public mind between tourist and HGV shuttles, but the loadings nevertheless soon averaged 3,000 cars a day despite being limited to three shuttles every two hours, half the previous level of service - a frequency boosted to twice hourly from 29th December. Within a month Le Shuttle had regained its position as market leader on the Dover-Calais route with a 36 per cent share of the tourist market.

Services through the tunnel built up steadily as work was undertaken on the damaged section, steadily better use being made of the undamaged capacity. Repair work was completed on 13th May, 1997 with very few mishaps, and after a short period of re-commissioning, full services were resumed: passenger shuttles and Eurostar - now offering 16 trains a day to Paris - on 1st June and the HGV shuttle on 15th June, after lengthy trials during which 11,000 lorries were carried. This service had to cope with one of the eight shuttles having been put out of commission by the fire; it was a further year before new HGV carriers already on order could enter service. This capacity problem was made worse by the IGC's initial insistence that the three wagons immediately behind the club car on each shuttle should be left empty. Eurotunnel also experienced problems with reliability of the HGV shuttle stock after nearly seven months out of use; cancellations reached 10 per cent of scheduled journeys at just the time when the company needed to regain users' confidence.

One further fire precaution for the HGV shuttles took a good eight years to implement: the addition to each train of a fire suppression vehicle immediately behind the club car. The first began tests in August 2003 but it was some time longer before they entered squadron service.

Eurotunnel's insurers had stumped up £93 million to cover lost revenue, and £9 million in respect of the lost locomotive and rolling stock. But it soon became clear that there would also be a considerable ongoing loss of projected income after the tunnel reopened, as planned expansion of services by Eurotunnel and rail operators was slowed or delayed. And this would not be covered by insurance.

Chapter Nine

Asylum and Fightback

The story of the Channel Tunnel between the fire and the opening of the CTRL was one first of consolidation, though with the volume of through rail traffic, especially freight, consistently disappointing, and then of havoc caused by the misuse of the tunnel as an illicit route into Britain by illegal immigrants and asylum-seekers from eastern Europe, the Near East and other areas of poverty and tension. The disruption caused by this clandestine traffic, which at times halted international freight trains and even, on a few occasions, all traffic through the tunnel, inflicted further damage on Eurotunnel's finances.

The fire, the ensuing disruption and the controversy surrounding it had obscured some important changes in the landscape. Eurotunnel's new management headed by Patrick Ponsolle and Sir Robert Malpas (who soon gave way to the non-executive Charles Mackay, though he stayed on the Board until 2000) had its hand strengthened by the identification of a number of shortcomings in the wake of the fire - some of them known about previously but not acted on. The changes at the top coincided with a firm shift in Eurotunnel's centre of gravity to the French side of the Channel, where most of the (increasingly disgruntled) shareholders were based; this reflected the fact that of the company's 3,114 staff at the time, 55 per cent worked in France - though there was a belief on the UK side that the Gallic operation was somewhat overmanned. The prospects for a restructuring of the company's debt had improved markedly by early 1997, despite the virtual shutdown; the banks agreed that February to give Eurotunnel an extra nine months to restructure its finances, and for the first half of the year the company, despite its difficulties, reported a £7 million operating surplus.

There were other apparent positives, too. The election that May of a Labour Government committed to greater use of the railways and an integrated transport policy under Deputy Prime Minister John Prescott offered some hopes of a modal shift that would benefit the tunnel. A start to work on the Channel Tunnel Rail Link under the stewardship of London & Continental appeared imminent. And Eurostar services to Brussels, the Cinderella of tunnel services to that point, looked set to benefit from the opening in stages of Belgium's high-speed link between Brussels and Lille.

The first 20 km stretch of that line from the French border to Antoing opened in June 1996, but it took the completion of a further 55 km to Lembeek in June 1997 for trains to be noticeably accelerated. The opening of the route through to Forest, almost within sight of Brussels-Midi, on 14th December, 1997 triggered a sharp acceleration in Eurostar schedules, as well as marking the start of Thalys services from Paris via the Belgian link to Brussels and Cologne. Half an hour was knocked off many Eurostar timings, the fastest Waterloo-Brussels time coming down to 2 hours 36 minutes. At the same time the number of Eurostars serving Brussels was stepped up from eight a day to ten. Increases in line speed as the new route bedded down shaved off five minutes more.

Services through the tunnel recovered - at differing rates - once it was fully back in operation, and during 1997 more than 15 million people passed through it, out of a total of 100 million crossing the Channel by all means. Eurostar came fastest out of the trap. Passengers carried rose from 4,886,566 in 1996 to 6,004,268 the following year (a 20 per cent increase) and in August 1997 681,653 passengers were carried. The year's total included the first users of the ski trains from Waterloo and Ashford to Moutiers and Bourg St Maurice, a daytime service operating each winter weekend from that December; Eurostar loadings also benefited from improved connections at Lille with TGV services as the SNCF's high-speed network expanded. Rail freight had only been briefly disrupted, and registered a 16 per cent increase to 2.9 million tonnes during 1997. The sale of Railfreight Distribution that November to English, Welsh and Scottish Railway marked the final instalment in the privatisation of BR; with EWS having pledged to double its business in five years, great things were expected, but in the short term the most noticeable effect was the use of the largely-idle class '92s' on some domestic freight services as they were cleared for a limited number of routes by Railtrack, and by 2003 for all 25kv AC main lines north of the Channel.

Throughout the tunnel's early years, high hopes for boosting rail freight through it were attached to the development in Britain of a spinal freight route with enhanced clearances for 'piggyback' trains, carrying road vehicles on rail wagons. The Piggyback Consortium promoting the idea had wide commercial support as well as backing from Eurotunnel, EWS, SNCF and, ambivalently, Railtrack. It was put together by Lord Berkeley, who as Tony Guterbock had been a prime mover in the Channel Tunnel from the outset and an invaluable figure in Eurotunnel during the construction period, liaising with local communities in Kent, politicians and the media. The Consortium campaigned vigorously during the mid- to late-1990s for an upgrade of the West Coast Main Line to link the tunnel and London with Manchester, Liverpool, Holyhead, Glasgow and Stranraer. Lord Berkeley and his backers were convinced that Piggyback operation would win crucial international traffic from the roads, benefiting both the tunnel and Britain's railways. The Consortium seemed around 1997 to have won the argument, but Railtrack effectively killed Piggyback by estimating that the upgrade would cost around £300 million - more than twice the Consortium's figure - and the campaign faded away; the amount saved by not pursuing Piggyback would in the event be dwarfed by the extraordinary escalation in the cost of the West Coast Route Mondernisation from £2.7 billion to a peak of around £12 billion between 1996 and 2003. The tunnel lost out by the rejection of Piggyback, but there were those in the industry who argued that this would not in any event have been the most effective way of boosting rail freight. (The other principal rail-based initiative to capitalise on the tunnel and get freight off Britain's roads - Central Railway - is discussed in Chapter Fifteen.)

Eurotunnel was pessimistic after the restart about Le Shuttle loadings, particularly for private cars, because of lingering consumer resistance as a result of the fire and, more significantly, the continuing price war with and between the ferry companies, which had driven fares 40 per cent below 1994 levels, pending decisions by the British Government and the European Commission on the P&O/Stena merger. The tie-up, which also relieved chronic over-capacity on the route, was finally approved on 19th November, 1997. Yet in the event it was the HGV rather than the car shuttles that took time to recover. The tourist shuttles carried 2,319,160 cars and 64,579 coaches in 1997, 11 per cent more than in 1996; up to four shuttles a day operated from that June, and a limited on-board refreshment service was introduced. But in contrast only 255,908 HGVs were carried, less than half the 1996 figure. The HGV shuttles had operated for barely half the year, but even so they were still carrying fewer lorries daily at the end of 1997 than they had been prior to the fire. Pressure on capacity at the busiest times eased a little during the year as 16 HGV shuttle wagons ordered before the fire went into operation and wagons that had survived it were used to reinforce other rakes.

Eurotunnel's medium-term survival was assured on 10th July, 1997 when shareholders' meetings in London and Paris approved a financial restructuring plan by overwhelming majorities. The plan involved a 40 per cent reduction in debt charges, conversion of part of the debt into shares, elimination of the 'snowball effect' of unpaid interest, extension of the debt repayment period by 20 years, plus opportunities for further relief in the future. To the company's relief, the package was accepted unanimously that November by its creditor banks.

A further easing of pressure came on 19th December, 1997 when the British and French Governments agreed to extend Eurotunnel's concession from 2052 to 2086 (the extension finally took effect on 30th June, 1999). While this decision had no immediate effect on the company's finances, it was of great importance long-term; the expectation had always been that the franchise would make most of its profits toward the end of the concession, and the extension of this period of maximum income by 34 years made Eurotunnel a much more bankable proposition. In recognition of this, the company had to promise to hand over 59 per cent of its pre-tax profits after 2052 to the two Governments, a considerably higher proportion than it had hoped.

On the same day as the concession was extended a number of outstanding disputes between Eurotunnel and TML were resolved. The settlement did not produce the large-scale compensation Sir Alastair Morton had been looking for, with TML paying Eurotunnel a total of £40 million and abandoning its own counter-claims. Yet although this was a moral victory for the contractors, it did free Eurotunnel's hands financially - and also left the tunnel company, rather than TML, managing contracts with suppliers which had been the cause of much friction. With relief, M Ponsolle stated: 'We have at last closed the construction phase of the tunnel' . . . three and a half years after the first trains had run.

For the full year 1997 Eurotunnel reported a £57 million operating profit, though this was still a drop in the ocean compared with its outstanding debts, which totalled £8,930 million of which £1,172 million was unpaid interest. Overall, the company registered a loss for the year of £611 million, down from £715 million in 1996.

The year 1998 was less than a month old when a fresh financial crisis hit the tunnel - this time involving not Eurotunnel but LCR. The company operating Eurostar and tasked with delivering the Channel Tunnel Rail Link had belatedly realised that its bid for the franchise had been highly optimistic. LCR had budgeted on using profits from Eurostar to meet part of the cost of constructing the line, but in practice traffic growth had fallen well below expectations (6 million passengers in 1997 against a projected 10 million) and the UK's share of the joint Eurostar operation with SNCF and SNCB was still losing £180 million a year. The result was that LCR had underestimated its financing needs by some £2 billion.

Sir Derek Hornby and Adam Mills, LCR's Chairman and Chief Executive, had tried to get in to see Conservative ministers and ask for extra Government money just before the May 1997 election, but left it too late. Late that summer, plans to float LCR on the stock exchange were pulled, and discussions began with Railtrack on involving the privatised company in financing construction of the Link. But Eurostar's losses continued to mount - partly because there was no practical way for a UK private-sector company to get its State-owned Continental partners to keep their costs down. And early in the new year a crestfallen Sir Derek and Adam Mills had to tell John Prescott that LCR could not deliver. They asked for an extra £1.2

billion of Government money, partly in guarantees, and were turned down flat. Late on 28th January Mr Prescott, in an emergency Commons statement, told MPs that unless a way through the crisis were found in 30 days, the operation of Eurostar would revert to British Rail.

In the event this did not happen; LCR hived off its interest in the CTRL to Railtrack - though remaining the promoter as a technicality to avoid undoing the legislative and EU grant structure for construction of the line - and then formed a new consortium to continue operating Eurostar: National Express, British Airways (BA), SNCF and SNCB. The most significant change here was the replacement of Virgin by BA; this was not only a moral and financial defeat for Richard Branson but a Pyrrhic victory for National Express, which had from the outset sought to neutralise Virgin's input to LCR. Several other shareholders lost their money, among them Ove Arup whose route for the CTRL had been adopted in the face of opposition from BR and who had taken an active interest in Eurostar, even proposing to the Sports Council (without the LCR Board's knowledge) that Eurostars could be operated through to Wembley Stadium on the Chiltern route for football internationals via the Willesden Junction-Neasden section of the Dudding Hill line which has not seen a scheduled passenger train for over a century. Ironically, when the World Cup was held in France in July/August 1998, Eurostar loadings fell by 7.4 per cent on the previous year.

The new Eurostar consortium, which took over operation of the services on 1st October, 1998, was eager to maximise use of the service and revenue from it, and was prudent about the scope for expanding the network. Given British Airways' involvement, it was no surprise that a study was launched into the practicalities of running an hourly Eurostar service from Heathrow to Paris by way of the West London Line and the Heathrow Express route; this foundered on the lack of any obvious demand, and on the cost of increasing clearances on the in-tunnel terminal loop at Heathrow and lengthening station platforms to take even a 14-car Eurostar train. However, the idea did generate a test run as far as Heathrow Terminals 1,2 and 3 on 10th October, 1998, when a North of London Eurostar set adorned with polyester blocks to check for clearances was hauled into the Heathrow Express tunnels late at night by one of Eurostar's class '37s', preceded by a man with a red flag. There was a lingering suspicion that the Heathrow service, firmly promised for 2001 when Eurostar was handed to the consortium, was in part a ploy to keep Virgin from hiring and operating regional Eurostar sets on the West Coast Main Line.

Eurostar's new management itself, at the Government's request, reviewed the prospects for the services from Glasgow and Manchester to Paris which still appeared in the Railtrack timetable and for which trains were still making test runs, but from the outset there was no enthusiasm. The trains needed to attract business passengers to cover their costs, and from most of the main centres to be served there was no way Eurostar could compete on time with the airlines, which were just starting to offer cut price fares which the railway could not hope to match. Virgin offered to take over the regional Eurostar stock and run the advertised services on a commercial basis, but the consortium was not keen, to put it mildly, and the only proposal that seemed to stack up economically was for some Eurostar services to start from the West Coast Main Line 'hub' at Watford Junction once the Channel Tunnel Rail Link and the head-on connection from it outside St Pancras to the WCML were completed.

The only Eurostar service improvement made in 1998, apart from some slight increases in frequency, was the introduction that December of an overnight weekend ski train from Waterloo to Bourg St Maurice to match the day service; of all the night services originally planned through the tunnel, this is the only one actually to have run. At the end of 1998 Eurostar could report only a 5 per cent increase in traffic, to 6.3 million passengers for the year; LCR's fears had been amply confirmed.

Rail freight fared little better, increasing during 1998 from 2.9 million tonnes to just 3.14 million. EWS's enterprising stance after taking over Railfreight Distribution and merging it with its domestic network was offset by complex clearing procedures in the UK, reluctance among hauliers and chartering companies to switch modes and the reluctance of some (though not all) State railways on the Continent to operate as businesses. A direct freight service to Germany through the tunnel did belatedly commence on 1st December, 1998, but the process of building traffic to Britain's main export market in Europe was hampered by DB's insistence on offering preferential charges to customers shipping freight via Germany's North Sea ports.

Eurotunnel's shuttles fared considerably better than the through rail traffic, helped by the P&O/Stena merger which finally took effect in March 1998, bringing a reduction in capacity to seven ferries from nine at the start of the year and 15 in 1996. Nearly 705,000 lorries were carried by Eurotunnel in 1998, easily a record and a sign that the dampening effect of the fire on traffic was over. Passenger shuttles also performed strongly: 3,351,348 cars and 96,234 coaches were carried. An overall profit of £63.8 million was recorded, thanks partly to financial adjustments stemming from the rescheduling of debt the previous year; without it there was an underlying loss of £194 million. A further bonus came from Eurotunnel's cross-Channel fibre optic network which had been opened up to outside customers and was starting to bring in revenue; during 1999 five contracts for installing commercial telecommunications through the tunnel would be signed. Profits were starting to come in, too, from four industrial estates developed in the Ashford area by Eurotunnel's property arm.

Otherwise 1999 was dominated by the ending on 30th June of sales of duty-free goods on international transport services (except for through trains) within the European Union. This dealt a serious blow to the ferry operators, who had been able to subsidise the cost of travel through duty-free sales on board and at their terminals. But it was also bad news for Eurotunnel, which like the ferries had handled a sizeable number of car passengers who were making their journey primarily to stock up with duty-frees and who also shopped duty-free at the Cheriton and Coquelles terminals. Indeed it was estimated that duty-free sales made up 40 per cent of Eurotunnel's turnover. Not only did Eurotunnel's car shuttle traffic take a downturn (17 per cent and 20 per cent for coaches) but BAA plc, whose 15-year contract to operate all Eurotunnel's retail outlets took effect the day after duty-free ended, found it had a commercial turkey on its hands; legal action followed. Even so, Eurotunnel's tourist shuttles carried 3,260,166 cars during 1999, a 54 per cent market share, and 82,074 coaches.

Better news for Eurotunnel was the increase in its HGV shuttle capacity as three new Arbel-constructed shuttle trains came into service, together with the first of 13 new Brush Tri-Bos numbered from 9101. The prototype wagons of the new design had been delivered in November 1997 for testing, and the first of the complete 32-wagon trains entered commercial service on 11th January, 1999; two more - the final one being a replacement for the fire-damaged shuttle - entered service by the end of the year, bringing the number in operation to ten. Two more freight shuttle trains were already on order, and with lorry traffic still surging, Eurotunnel that June announced the ordering of four more HGV trains from Arbel and seven more extra-powerful Tri-Bos from Brush for delivery by 2003, when up to seven trains an hour would be operating at peak times. To cope with the extra traffic, work began late in 1999 on installing two extra platform tracks at each terminal; maintenance facilities were also upgraded - for the second time in the tunnel's brief life - and extra toll lanes provided at each terminal, benefiting HGV and car traffic alike. For the calendar year 1999 Eurotunnel was able to report 838,776 HGVs carried, a 19 per cent increase on 1998 and a 39 per cent share of the market.

On 1st June, 1999 Eurotunnel and the rail freight operators celebrated five years in business as cross-Channel carriers. On that day a class '92'-hauled train exporting cars from Britain became the 33,110th commercial load to pass through. The figure sounds impressive, but in fact the anniversary coincided with a slump in rail freight through the tunnel. During the first half of the year shipments fell by 16.3 per cent, and just 2.87 million tonnes were carried during the whole of 1999, less than in 1997 and only 50 per cent more than the old train ferries had handled. By this stage, railway planners had expected the tunnel to be handling at least twice as much; much of the blame for the shortfall was placed on poor service quality on the Continent, particularly because of strikes and border delays, and the practice on some railways of holding up even express freight trains whenever a passenger working was due. EWS was also experiencing quality and reliability problems, and these did not help; neither did what rail operators considered unfair competition from corner-cutting road hauliers. On 28th August, 1999 John Prescott and the French Transport Minister Jean-Claude Gayssot agreed on the need for a major improvement of service quality to attract more cross-Channel freight to rail; EWS and SNCF were urged to shape up, and steps were taken to halve the 72-hour journey time for a freight train on the new EU-sponsored high-speed 'corridor' from the tunnel to Hungary by speeding up customs checks.

What seemed at the time to be the low point in tunnel rail freight coincided with - and may have contributed to - the boardroom coup at EWS's parent company Wisconsin Central, which saw the company's founder Ed Burkhardt forced out amid concerns over its spiralling share price and the failure of its UK subsidiary to deliver the traffic growth promised. But far worse for the company was to come.

Though rail freight traffic was sluggish during 1999, it did include two unusual workings. First came 42 EWS class '37' diesels, which were hired by SNCF for permanent way work on its TGV-Méditerranée route and were hauled through the tunnel in batches between June and September en route to their base at Eurre; they returned a year later, their job well done. In subsequent years, further surplus EWS locomotives of classes '37', '56' and '58' passed through en route to construction work on high-speed lines in Spain and Italy.

September 1999 saw an even more unlikely consist: the Kosovo 'Train For Life' bearing supplies for the former Yugoslav province which had just experienced ethnic cleansing and a NATO bombing campaign. The train, including three Direct Rail Services class '20s', was hauled by a circuitous route through the Balkans to Macedonia, whence after some argument it was allowed to proceed to the provincial capital of Pristina. The idea had been to use the class '20s' to help revive services on Kosovo's shattered railway system, and a dedicated British Army team put them to work, despite an absence of signalling. But after some vigorous handling by Italian army train crews they were judged surplus to requirements and returned to the UK by sea.

In the meantime the steady build-up of Eurostar passenger services was continuing, from the start of 1999 under a unified management instead of a coalition of three separate national owners. The summer 1999 timetable showed a core service of 16 weekday trains to and from Paris, with 22 on Fridays at the height of the tourist season, and 10 weekday services on the Brussels route. Traffic growth remained sluggish, however - 6.6 million passengers were carried during the year, an increase of just 4.5 per cent on 1998 despite very heavy marketing.

For the calendar year 1999 Eurotunnel, helped by a recovery in prices, reported an operating profit of £210 million, a net profit after restructuring of £202 million and an underlying loss of £139 million. Each of these results was significantly better than for the previous year, and during the first half of 2000 the improvement was continued. With its debt being traded at a heavy discount, the company was also able to reduce its potential burden of interest and repayment by cancelling £469 million of its debt at a cost of only £178 million.

Even with some traffics having under-performed, Eurotunnel by late 1999 was having to replace all the rails on its running lines. They had been expected to last for seven years, but in the event a full replacement programme proved necessary after five; high salinity in the tunnel atmosphere as well as the weight of tunnel trains was held responsible. The work was undertaken by Spie Drouard, with 600 or 900 metres of rail being replaced in each eight-hour overnight possession. Half the rails were replaced between November 1999 and March 2000, and the rest by March 2001.

The work was not before time, as 2000 brought a staggering 35 per cent increase in HGV shuttle traffic - pushing the tunnel's market share for HGVs up to 48 per cent - with the tunnel handling 1,133,146 lorries in the year, 116,104 in November alone. This surge was vital to Eurotunnel's finances as the abolition of duty-free cut its retail income by a staggering 59 per cent. With the delivery of two more freight shuttle trains - bringing the total to 12 - a fifth hourly service was operated at peak times from June 2000. The car shuttles, by contrast, slipped back 15 per cent from their pre-duty-free loadings to 2.8 million though the long term trend here, too, was upward. Significantly no new locomotives or wagons have yet needed to be ordered to cope with demand from cars and coaches; it is the lorry traffic that has been the tunnel's big success.

Rail freight through the tunnel showed a 3 per cent increase during 2000 to just 2,947,000 tonnes, a disappointing and ominous figure after a stronger start. Eurostar traffic also continued its slow increase, though near-stagnation on the Brussels run meant that the winter timetable on that route stayed in force throughout the year; this has since become standard practice. During the year 7.67 million passengers were carried, an increase of 9 per cent on 1999 and still the highest annual figure recorded. In the high season from 7th July to 3rd September, 134 Eurostars a week transited the tunnel in each direction, with 24 between London and Paris alone on Fridays. And from that autumn an earliest-ever 0550 departure from Waterloo for Brussels and a half-hourly weekday evening peak service from Paris were introduced to meet demand from business travellers. The chaos on the Railtrack network caused by emergency track relaying after the Hatfield disaster that autumn disrupted Eurostar services for a few weeks, but had only a minimal effect on traffic. However the Safety Authority's report on tunnel traffic during 2000 also recorded 59 unscheduled stops in the tunnel, two fires, three broken rails, three signals passed at danger and the high-speed derailment of a Eurostar at Arras in France on 16th June which, astoundingly, did not produce a single serious injury.

By 2000, however, the tunnel and the services using it were coming under another cloud, because of the upsurge in illegal immigration to Britain that produced tragic headlines when the bodies of 58 suffocated Chinese were found in a lorry leaving a ferry at Dover. As checks on HGV traffic using the ferries were tightened, the people-traffickers and individuals seeking a better or less hazardous life increasingly turned their attention to the tunnel. Despite the concerted efforts of Eurotunnel, SNCF and EWS, racketeers were able to use through international freight trains, in particular, as a means of smuggling their human cargo into - and even out of - the country, and on several occasions train operations through Cheriton had to be halted as 'illegals' leapt from trains emerging from the English portal. Some sustained injuries when they fell, and on 1st September, 2000 a major accident was narrowly averted when an EWS train that had been routed into the emergency siding after stowaways were seen jumping from it was ordered by Eurotunnel control to set back onto the main line, straight into the path of an approaching Eurostar. The passenger train managed to pull up with little over 100 metres to spare. The travails of EWS intensified when the Home Office extended to rail freight in March 2001 its £2,000-a-head penalty for carriers transporting illegal immigrants; within weeks the company was warning that it might have to halt its services through the tunnel as it stood to incur fines exceeding £5 million a year because of SNCF's inability or unwillingness to stop asylum-seekers boarding its trains at Fréthun. Increasingly the would-be stowaways were based in a Red Cross hostel sited at the former TML Sangatte construction site, which had opened in October 1999 and soon became part of the problem rather than the solution.

Illegal immigration via Eurostar also continued, and in May 2000 the Home Secretary Jack Straw and the French Interior Minister Jean-Pierre Chevènement concluded an agreement for British police officers to check Eurostar passengers boarding in France, with French police having similar rights at Waterloo and Ashford. Extraordinarily, on 2nd March, 2001 nine Romanians were found at Waterloo hidden inside cramped equipment boxes between the bogies of a Eurostar carriage, having apparently been locked in by accomplices in France.

The more orthodox potential of Eurostar was graphically illustrated on 16th September, 2000, when a 'Three Capitals' set hired by Hertfordshire Rail Tours made the 2,040 km round trip from Waterloo International to La Rochelle, all 766 seats having been sold in just over a week. The longest distance UK rail charter ever (and the longest single Eurostar journey until the Avignon service began), it took the Paris avoiding line, La Jonction, through Chessy Marne-la-Vallée (where a French customs and immigration team was picked up), the TGV Atlantique to Poitiers and then the classic route via Niort. An SNCF driver with encyclopaedic route knowledge took the train all the way from Lille to La Rochelle.

Despite this triumph for Eurostar's versatility, the shortfall in its promoters' expectations was reflected in a series of events during 2000: the launch on 30th May of the GNER 'White Rose' service between Kings Cross and York (subsequently Leeds) using surplus and rebranded regional Eurostar units, the SNCF's transfer of two Eurostar sets equipped for its domestic voltages to Brussels-Nice and Brussels-Bordeaux services, and the deletion from Railtrack's published winter timetable of the never-operated trains to the Continent from principal stations on the East Coast and West Coast Main Lines. A report to the UK Government in March 2000 from the consultants Arthur D. Little concluded that regional Eurostar services would not be financially viable even after the completion of the CTRL right through to St Pancras and the nearby head-on connection with the WCML. Ministers niftily passed the report on to Sir Alastair Morton's Strategic Rail Authority, which as successor to BR had a statutory duty under the Channel Tunnel Act to prepare a strategy for regional services through the tunnel . . . though Sir Alastair as a life president of Eurotunnel excused himself from the process.

Eurotunnel itself left behind its immediate post-construction phase in April 2001 when Patrick Ponsolle stepped down as the company's Chairman after seven years, having overseen the opening of the tunnel, the restructuring of the group and continued traffic growth despite the PR disaster of the fire of 1996. Charles Mackay was promoted to Chairman, with the executive power resting with Philippe Lazare, the 43-year-old Chief Executive the company had headhunted from a hotel and casino group; he had previously been with Air France. Almost the last corporate decision of the Ponsolle era was Eurostar's sale at the end of 2000 of its two telecommunications subsidiaries. M Lazare took charge after a three month run-in as Managing Director with Eurotunnel on course to cover its interest charges for the first time in 2002. The company's operating profit for 2000, despite the loss of duty free and the traffic attracted, was up £5 million to £208 million, and the underlying loss down £15 million to £124 million. The company, and the tunnel, looked almost out of the financial woods.

2001 was the year in which the disruption caused by asylum-seekers came to a head, although it would be the following year before a change of Government in France finally produced a political will to tackle it on that side of the Channel, as well as in Britain. Initially the source of the problem had been would-be migrants roaming the streets and parks of Calais, but once the Sangatte centre was up and running its existence served as a beacon to illegal migrants and those exploiting them, and soon Sangatte - ironically a building leased from Eurotunnel - had a rolling population of well over 1,000 people of 110 nationalities who tried daily to board trains through the tunnel, and were replaced by others when they succeeded; in one year 27,000 passed through. While some French politicians saw Sangatte as a 'British problem' caused by generous welfare benefits and the reluctance of supposedly desperate refugees from persecution to seek asylum in France, local residents were far from keen on its presence, not least the headlines had brought a slump in tourism and because the CRS riot police had repeatedly to be called in to quell fighting between Iraqis and Afghans who had supposedly had enough of that sort of thing back home.

The desperation of the asylum-seekers to reach Britain was now causing severe operational difficulties for Eurotunnel at Coquelles as the most determined got into the wire-fenced enclosure and at times roamed the tracks, causing trains to be halted. In December 2000 just 27 stowaways were detected on HGV shuttles arriving at Cheriton, but by the following May 563 people a month were being taken off the trains. The UK Government reacted by extending the £2,000-per-illegal penalty already applied to hauliers and to EWS to Eurotunnel.

By August 2001 four people had died and 175 been injured trying to jump onto moving freight or shuttle trains near Calais. Early that year Eurotunnel appealed to the British Government to send a detachment of Gurkhas to patrol the bounds of its French terminal because of the inability or unwillingness of the French authorities to take the problem seriously; any such action would have sparked a major diplomatic incident, and British Ministers wisely rejected the suggestion. Instead Eurotunnel spent £3 million on additional security measures to protect the 20-mile perimeter of the Coquelles terminal, and hired 98 extra security staff to patrol the site; later in 2001 the company appointed General Sir Roger Wheeler, who had just retired as a commander of Britain's land forces, to devise a strategy to keep the migrants out. Eurotunnel explained: 'We have been frustrated by the lack of action from the Government. This appointment is not designed to embarrass ministers, but simply to keep our services running'.

The General's strategy, involving the spending of millions more on razor wire, thermal imaging equipment and even tighter security, and deforesting 50 hectares of trees and shrubbery to deny the migrants cover, was successful up to a point, but it merely pushed the problem to other locations around Coquelles. The most dramatic example of this came on 30th August, 2001 when 44 Iraqis from Sangatte reached the French portal via a footbridge across the A16 motorway near Calais and penetrated six miles into the tunnel before they were apprehended; all tunnel services were suspended for two hours. The same month an increasingly desperate Eurotunnel tried in vain to take legal action against the French Government to reclaim the Sangatte building, but this came to nothing.

International freight trains operated by EWS were experiencing the most severe difficulties, with 'illegals' jumping from trains or being detected at the English tunnel portal or at Dollands Moor, at Willesden and Wembley and even further into the Railtrack network. Fines on EWS brought a 65 per cent decrease in the number of clandestine migrants detected at Dollands Moor, but lax security at the SNCF yard at Fréthun, and on yards as far away as Italy where people-smugglers would put 'illegals' aboard freight wagons, caused increasing problems as the year continued.

Matters came to a head on 29th October, 2001 when some 300 migrants stormed the Fréthun yard in the hope of stowing away on freight trains; more than 200 were arrested but the search for the rest closed the tunnel overnight. After further disruption SNCF - which up to now had neither taken nor sought continuous security cover, halted services altogether on 7th November out of concern for the safety of its staff. Some traffic was diverted to other routes and some lost to rail altogether, notably consignments from the Spanish shippers Transfesa which took the best part of three years to return; SNCF's action also left EWS locomotives and rolling stock out of place, causing yet further cancellations when a limited service resumed the following day.

Later in the month SNCF, having been offered police security cover for just four to six hours each night, banned all UK-bound freight trains between 0300 and 2100 hrs between Mondays and Fridays, reducing services to five trains per night instead of the previous 18; between 5th November and 3rd December just 119 trains ran, 17 short of the limit set by the French and a fraction of the 381 that would normally have operated. The European Commission threatened the French Government with heavy fines, Tony Blair wrote to his French Socialist counterpart, Lionel Jospin, demanding immediate restoration of the link and pointing out that 438 migrants had arrived on trains from Fréthun over the previous month, and Lord Berkeley, on behalf of the Rail Freight Group, echoed Eurotunnel's demand that British troops be sent to Calais. The French authorities responded with an offer to erect improved fencing around the terminal by the following April. All EWS could do was watch in dismay as its hard fought-for business evaporated, Scotch whisky exports being an early casualty.

Eurotunnel reckoned that its inability to keep migrants out of its French terminal cost it £25 million in lost revenue and extra security costs in 2001; the company's new Chief Executive Richard Shirrefs complained that of 54,000 trespassers at Coquelles, only six had been brought to court, but he also accused the British Government of 'cynically using the Channel Tunnel operators to block immigration', asking why people had to get to England before they could apply for asylum.

The asylum crisis, however, was not the only damper on the company's fortunes during 2001. The outbreak of foot-and-mouth disease that ravaged British agriculture from the Spring dealt a heavy blow to tourism to the UK, with coach traffic, in particular, hard hit, business traffic (especially on Eurostar) weakened as the global economy slowed down, and the devastating terrorist attacks on the United States on 11th September made Americans generally nervous of overseas travel. During 2001 rail freight through the tunnel fell 17 per cent to 2,447,432 tonnes and Eurostar passengers by 3 per cent to less than 7 million, car passengers also fell though HGV shuttle traffic, now the staple of the tunnel's finances, rose by 6 per cent to 1,197,771; a record 6,027 trucks were carried that 6th November. There was also an unexpected slump in Eurotunnel's telecoms business, for which high things had been forecast. The overall effect was that the company posted a £132 million net loss for 2001, with revenues down 6 per cent.

The year 2001 also saw continuing sporadic operational hiccups in the tunnel, notably an incident on 6th June when a car shuttle train split in two just before arriving at the French portal, and the forced evacuation of a Brussels-bound Eurostar on 16th October, 210 passengers having to detrain in mid-tunnel when a cardan shaft on the train failed.

The chaos at Fréthun continued to cause grief to Eurotunnel, EWS, UK exporters and freight handlers (with Tibbet and Britten forced to lay off workers at Daventry) and the British Government. On Christmas Day 2001, 150 Afghans stormed the French portal after breaking down four sets of fencing, one of them electrified. A few penetrated 10 km into the tunnel before they were caught. On 25th January, 2002 the ring-leaders of a Romanian gang who had been changing the signals at Hazebrouck to danger so that migrants could board UK-bound freight trains were arrested. Not all the lapses in security originated in France; one train was boarded by some 40 migrants near the French portal after the brake pipes were cut by a group of Romanians who had been smuggled on board in Italy.

The French authorities announced on 10th January - three days after freight services through the tunnel from Mossend had been terminated and with as few as two trains running on some nights - that they were starting to erect 4.5 km of double-skin security fencing at Fréthun; the work took eight months, during which time the incursions continued. All freight services were suspended once again for the first fortnight of March, before SNCF promised that normal services would resume on 2nd April, but only a limited service resumed, 80 extra gendarmes promised for the Fréthun site evaporating within days. On 8th April 100 stowaways were found at Dollands Moor despite their train having supposedly been checked by French security, and in the week ending 21st April a total of 137 were apprehended. In a new and frightening development for rail safety, the migrants were starting to arrive hanging from container trucks, and jumping from the trains in the tunnel mouth before they reached the security of Dollands Moor, where previously they had claimed asylum; 60 arrived in this fashion on 23rd April. The traffic continued unchecked into May, as rail freight through the tunnel for the first half of 2002 fell to half even of the disrupted level for the previous year.

EWS, which had by now lost £10 million as a result of the disruption on top of the access fees paid by the ongoing British Railways Board for trains that had not run, lodged a formal complaint with the European Commission accusing France of violating the Treaty of Rome by not tackling the disruption. But the company achieved rather more through a meeting at which the SNCF Chairman Louis Gallois promised EWS Chief Executive Philip Mengel that the French national railway was genuinely committed to expanding cross-Channel freight and to resolving the immediate problems.

The goings-on at Fréthun were filmed by one EWS train driver whose home video of asylum-seekers strolling around the sidings in search of an easy wagon to hide in caused a stir when shown on ITV News; it had an equal impact on Government Ministers who were shown the entire film, including footage in which those migrants who failed to board a train shinned up a grassy bank from the sidings to be taken back to Sangatte to lunch in French security vans.

The sticking-point, however, remained the French Government on whom the new Home Secretary David Blunkett was stepping up the pressure. He secured in May a promise that Sangatte would be closed in due course, but it took the defeat of Jospin's Government the following month and its replacement by a Centre-Right administration led by Jean-Paul Raffarin for action to be taken. The incoming Government recognised the Sangatte situation was causing not only chaos but resentment in that part of northern France, a needless irritation to relations with Britain and a powerful recruiting tool for Jean-Marie Le Pen's extremist National Front. Sixty gendarmes and 30 SNCF security guards were drafted in to Fréthun, though still not for 24-hour cover, SNCF promised a resumption of 'full' international freight services from 2nd September and the rundown of Sangatte began, resulting in closure on 14th December. Under a deal between Mr Blunkett and the French Interior Minister Nicolas Sarkozy, Britain took 1,000 Iraqi Kurds and 2,000 Afghans from Sangatte who already had families settled in Britain, and the remaining 3,600 people registered at Sangatte were given the choice of asylum in France or €2,000 to return home. Appropriately, the migrants admitted to Britain were taken by coach shuttle through the Channel Tunnel.

While the pledge of a full and disruption-free service from September 2002 did not fully materialise, EWS was able to report that by the end of October nearly 60 trains a week were running - twice the level for a year earlier - and that fewer than five stowaways a week were showing up on its trains.

The disruption had stripped EWS/SNCF freight traffic through the tunnel to its core, the strongest surviving traffic being with northern Italy. Intermodal traffic was still operating between Trafford Park and Daventry and Milan Smistamento, Hams Hall and Willesden and Milan Rogoredo, Hams Hall and Novara, Trafford Park and Willesden and Bari, Trafford Park and Daventry and Muizen in Belgium and between Silla (Spain) and Dagenham.

Automotive traffic between Saarlouis and Corby had survived, though not a second service from other points in France; china clay shipments between Exeter and Sezzadillo in Italy had also continued. Two wagonload services had also hung on: to Wembley from Somain in northern France and from Gremberg (Cologne). Resolution of the crisis had come just in time for Hams Hall, taken over by Associated British Ports when closure because of the disruption caused by asylum-seekers was staring it in the face, but services from Mossend, now thriving with domestic traffic, and from Wakefield did not resume. Services to and from terminals in France had been particularly hard hit, Paris Valenton, Paris Noisy, Lyon, Avignon and Perpignan all having lost their direct connections with the UK.

Shippers who had turned away from rail now began to return, starting with the paper maker Stora Enso which for a year had switched its trainloads of traffic to sea. In the spring of 2003 two of the logistics companies affected by the disruption, Environmental Freight Services and Road Track, sued SNCF for £2 million in respect of goods damaged by illegals who managed to board their trains; the nub of their case was that SNCF had done little to stop them.

Though trains continued to be delayed at Fréthun not only by seven-hour waits for inspection but by unaccountable shortages of SNCF staff and locomotives, by January 58 trains could operate each week out of the 76 there were paths for, against

45 in September, and services were also running with higher loadings. Operators stepped up the frequency of their services through the spring of 2003, with Interfrigo doubling its Milan-Daventry service to eight trains a week from then end of March; a new flow of steel between Ebange, north-east France, and Scunthorpe followed. One important new traffic was the delivery through the tunnel from Germany of Siemens' Desiro electric multiple units for South West Trains and First Great Eastern. With some 200 units on order and two paths each week available, this was a long-term traffic.

EWS was not the only tunnel operator looking to boost traffic after a grim period in public relations terms. Eurotunnel was far from satisfied with the level of enterprise shown by EWS and SNCF in building international rail freight services, and the moment the European Union approved the liberalisation of freight services on 15th March, 2003, Eurotunnel applied to the French Government to operate trains of its own over French metals. Alain Bertrand, Eurotunnel's director of railway services, said the new business had no desire to compete with existing operators, and had already discussed a partnership with SNCF and EWS. But the prospect was emerging of Eurotunnel freight services from Somain or beyond, through the tunnel to UK destinations, operated perhaps - though Eurotunnel denied it - by Eurostar's class '92' locomotives which were surplus to requirements since the cancellation of the planned night passenger services. At first a starting date of late 2004/early 2005 was posited for a service between Dourge (Lille) and Daventry; a rash of rail strikes in France, however, encouraged Eurotunnel to draw up a secondary plan 'using Belgian locomotives and Belgian drivers and turning left at Ghent', according to the company's veteran executive Bill Dix. By late 2003 the short-term alternative of Eurotunnel running intermodal trains from the Continent just as far as new dedicated sidings in its Cheriton terminal were being worked up, to strong reactions from EWS and SNCF and threats from French rail unions to blockade the tunnel; a start date of early 2005 was set, and Alstom Prima tri-voltage locomotives were ordered for the transit through France.

To reflect Eurotunnel's ambitions as a rail freight operator, the company was now split into three separate service divisions. Eurotunnel Shuttle Services, Railway Services, and Eurotunnel Freight Solutions. The service divisions were supported by three administrative divisions: Planning and Development, Technical, and Business Systems. Overall, Eurotunnel by now employed just over 4,000 staff, a slight majority in France reflecting the basing of most shuttle maintenance work at Coquelles.

Eurostar broke new ground in the summer of 2002 with a through service between Waterloo and Avignon, to which 45,000 through bookings a year were being made even with the need to change at Lille. Though it operated on only a few Saturdays between 20th July and 7th September the service took regular Eurostars into the south of France for the first time. With stops at Ashford International and (for crewing purposes only) Lille Europe and Marne-la-Vallée, the Avignon service was scheduled to cover the 1,150 km (719 miles) in 6 hrs 15 min. at an average speed of 184 kph, compared with 909 km in 8 hrs (114 kph) for the longest domestic distance from London, GNER's daily HST from Kings Cross to Inverness; it frequently did the journey in under six hours, thanks to generous recovery time on the TGV network. Southbound, the inaugural Avignon service followed the TGV-Mediterranée as far south as Lapalud, where it used a single-line bidirectional connection to the classic PLM main line for the final 50 km to Avignon Centre, which was preferred as a terminal to the more rudimentary stop on the TGV route itself.

Northbound, the service generally kept to the PLM main line as far as Valence because of pathing constraints on the high-speed route. The stock used for the service was drawn from the nine SNCF four-voltage Eurostar sets which are additionally equipped for 1500v DC overhead power, the system used on the PLM route. The Avignon service was an instant success, and for the 2003 season it was operated every Saturday from 24th May to 25th October, instead of just during peak season. Eurostar also marked the start of the 2003 tourist season with a pioneering one-off 'Bordeaux Express' at the end of May, giving passengers a Bank Holiday weekend in the French south-west, followed by a further special over the same route as far as Tours the following month.

Eurostar upped its game further by devising a 'Project Jupiter' to create a single entity in place of the previous structure where all decisions had to pass through the decision making process of the various shareholders in the UK, France and Belgium. Promoted in the face of opposition from the French unions who saw it as 'privatisation' of part of SNCF, Project Jupiter was accompanied by a shake-up in Eurostar's management. Guillaume Pépy, previously SNCF Vice-President, took over as Chairman of Eurostar from David Azéma, who left to join the airport group Vinci and before long turned up as dissident French shareholders' nominee for a seat on the Eurotunnel Board. Richard Brown, who had taken Midland Mainline through privatisation and had most recently been Commercial Director of National Express, became Chief Executive of Eurostar UK and the Eurostar Group. A scathing critic of the time it had taken to develop the CTRL, his priority was to work up in less than 12 months an aggressive marketing campaign to coincide with the opening of Phase One.

Eurotunnel, too, was gearing up for growth as the repercussions of the Sangatte crisis subsided. On 21st October, 2002 the pairs of new platforms for HGV shuttles that it had constructed at Coquelles and Cheriton were inaugurated, and by now the more powerful class '97xx' shuttle locomotives were coming into service; uprating of the earlier models of shuttle locomotive began the following spring. Service planners freed up capacity for the 15th and 16th HGV shuttle trains, which came into use in 2003, by reorganising train paths through the tunnel to reflect the preponderance of shuttle traffic. The company also eased some of its financial pressures by paying over £345 million to Abbey National bank for its aircraft and water-plant leasing business; the deal benefited Eurotunnel by enabling it to refinance part of its debt, and by bringing in £28 million in cash which further eased the debt situation.

At the close of 2002, Eurotunnel was able to report that it had achieved its objective of cash breakeven, reducing its underlying loss from £147 million to £105 million; operating profit rose to £194 million. Each day 39,000 people (19,000 on Eurostar), 5,000 cars, 3,000 lorries and 400 rail freight wagons in each direction were transiting the tunnel. Truck shuttle traffic was 3 per cent up over the year; in the week prior to Christmas 2002, a record 29,000 lorries were carried. Other traffics were less healthy: car shuttle traffic down 2 per cent, Eurostar a further 5 per cent down to 6,602,817 and freight tonnage (predictably) 40 per cent down over the year to 1,463,000 tonnes. But the mood overall was optimistic.

Operationally, however, the tunnel and its users were going through a difficult time. The tunnel had to be closed altogether for two days from 27th October, 2002 after storm and salt damage knocked out power lines near Calais, halting some Eurostars in their tracks and also impeding shuttle operation. The situation was exacerbated when a helicopter crashed onto high-voltage power supply lines near the French portal. Ice again caused problems on 4th January, 2003, when a thaw

Chapter Ten

Tunnel-Connected Railway Improvements in Britain

For the successful operation of international trains through the tunnel the SNCF promoted a high-speed TGV line from Paris to Fréthun, close to the French tunnel portal, and the Belgians a connecting route of their own which would also accommodate TGV traffic. Details of these new high-speed routes are given in Chapter Thirteen. British Rail - opting initially to improve existing routes - had to deliver a new international terminus in central London and an intermediate station at Ashford, and upgrade, resignal and where necessary electrify existing lines through Kent and south London to handle tunnel trains. BR and its Continental partners also needed to acquire compatible high-speed multiple-unit and coaching stock necessary to operate through day and night services, and specialised motive power for freight.

BR faced considerably greater headaches in preparing for the tunnel than did its French counterpart. A high-speed line such as the French were to build had been ruled out when the tunnel was promoted for the simple reason that had the environmental controversy about such a link in the mid-1970s been revived at that stage, the Channel Tunnel Bill would almost certainly not have got through Parliament. Indeed specific undertakings were given to the Select Committees which considered the Bill in both Houses that no such link was envisaged. Consequently BR faced the challenge of having to graft a high-speed international service onto a commuter network which still depended in places on Victorian technology and was operating close to capacity in the peak hours. Moreover, SNCF had ample experience both of building TGV routes for prestige services and of developing ultra high-speed stock for them; BR, after its nightmare experience with the pioneering and cancelled Advanced Passenger Train, knew that the stock ordered for tunnel services would need to be a mini-TGV (because of the tighter British loading gauge) capable of operating over the Southern Region's third-rail electrified tracks with their sharp curves, steep gradients, tight clearances, speed restrictions and (even) manually-operated level crossings. In the absence of a high-speed link, such trains would sprint across France and then, as President Mitterrand cruelly but aptly put it, give passengers the chance to enjoy the English countryside.

The challenge of devising a successful international train impacted heavily on the infrastructure. Before a single Eurostar could run between London and the tunnel portal, a massive upgrading operation was needed not only to cope with longer and heavier trains but to boost electricity supply on the routes to be used - foreshadowing the £800 million exercise required for power upgrades for the rest of the Southern Region when new-generation electric multiple units (emus) were introduced in the early 2000s. Without a power upgrade the trains, had they shifted at all, would have covered the English section of the route at an even more embarrassing crawl than the speeds at which they eventually operated. Extra substations were constructed along the 750v DC Southern Region line to make sure the power supply was adequate for a combination of Eurostar, domestic passenger and international freight services. But as late as December 1993, BR was forced to spend £30 million on replacing up to 900 lineside circuits to prevent arcing when Eurostars passed over gaps in the conductor rail.

The total budgeted cost of preparing the routes from London to the Cheriton tunnel portal and providing suitable station, freight and depot facilities, locomotives and rolling stock for the new services was £1.7 billion; some of the expenditure has proved well justified, other items much less so.

Waterloo International and Approaches

The highest-profile BR project connected with tunnel rail services was unquestionably its Waterloo International terminal: five platforms squeezed onto the north-western side of the station between the Windsor lines and York Road, with a space-age concourse on three levels beneath a spectacular and award-winning roof designed by Nicholas Grimshaw. Sadly this roof has had its problems; at the end of 1999 Eurostar sued the architects and contractors for £120 million after having to shroud the glass panels in tarpaulin for fear that they would 'explode' on top of passengers. One press report attributed the damage to a reindeer whose severed leg had been found on the roof!

The decision to run international trains into Waterloo was not, as some claimed, a dig at the French over the collapse of Napoleon's imperial dream but was born of a belief that none of the alternatives considered - Victoria, Bricklayers' Arms, King's Cross, White City or several others - either could cope with the volume of traffic passing through or would be convenient for the bulk of travellers. A central position, excellent Tube connections especially to the City and bearable approaches by road all gave Waterloo the edge. This did not, however, prevent Eurostar deciding in November 2004, for a variety of operational and economy reasons, not to continue a limited service from Waterloo after the CTRL is open right through to St Pancras - which it insists has even better rail connections especially to the Midlands and North - in 2007. In consequence, Waterloo's international service will come to an end after just 13 years. This should be good news for South West Trains and possibly South Eastern or even Great Western, who stand to gain valuable extra terminal capacity for their commuter services, with platforms for longer trains and paths freed up on the station approaches; South West Trains' first reaction, however, was that the changeover would cost £100 million which it could not afford. After speculation that the terminal would become a shopping centre, the SRA and SWT got down to work on what would be needed for it to enhance the capacity of the domestic station. Initial thoughts were that a flyover and new and extended platforms at Clapham Junction would also be necessary. Whether Eurostar's switch to St Pancras also erodes its present strong customer base in south-west London and revives the attractions of Heathrow remains to be seen.

Space was found for London's original Eurostar terminal on a twisting three-hectare site within the confines of Waterloo station, freed up by eliminating four existing platforms (the Reading lines 18-21, two of them being replaced by converting the taxi road into new platforms) and a number of carriage sidings. Into this space, accessed by escalators down from the main station concourse and up from the Underground, were inserted five platform lines, numbered 20 to 24 and served by three platforms 400 metres long, two of them islands.

The whole of the platform is covered by a one-hectare ribbed glass and steel roof supported by 37 bowstring arches, likened by *La Vie du Rail* in a highly complimentary review to a gigantic reptile. Beneath the elevated platforms are three lower levels, first the departure level with a full range of catering and shopping facilities, beneath it one for arrivals with customs and immigration facilities and exits to the main station with a taxi rank to the side, and lower still a basement car park and stores. One novel feature of the terminal is that whenever a train is due, a shoal of 10 steel fish by the French sculptor Jean-Luc Vilmouth suspended over the concourse starts to wiggle.

Major improvements were also required to Waterloo underground station to handle the expected influx of international passengers. Apart from the provision of an escalator direct to the Eurostar concourse from the Underground booking hall, new interchange tunnels between the Bakerloo, Northern and Waterloo and City lines were excavated, though these owed at least as much to the Jubilee Line extension between Green Park and Stratford which would increase the pressure on Waterloo considerably more than the advent of Eurostar. It was, however, September 1999 before Jubilee trains finally served the station.

Waterloo International was designed to handle 6,000 arriving and departing passengers each hour, and to this end inward and outward passengers are totally segregated and each platform is accessed from below by a series of escalators serving different portions of an 18-coach Eurostar train. Although traffic growth has fallen well below projections, the Waterloo-Paris flow alone (over 5 million passengers a year), is greater than that between Euston and Manchester, and the capacity of the terminal can come under severe strain when more than one train is due to depart. Passengers gather in a fairly confined concourse between the Eurostar ticket office and the automatic gates which read their tickets; the lack of space is exaggerated by the fact that this area is open to Waterloo's overall roof.

At busy times this concourse is packed, the congestion being all the greater because the security screening machines are only a few metres beyond the automatic gates and a delay at one feeds through to the other. The situation was worst on winter Saturday mornings when trains to Disney and Bourg St Maurice left four minutes apart; getting 500 skiers' luggage through three security machines brought the system to a near-standstill, especially during times of terrorist alert, and could delay the train's departure; stretching the gap between departures to nine minutes after the opening of the CTRL did little to help. The staff operating the machines do not appear well organised, but Eurostar suffers the huge disadvantage compared with the airlines that every piece of baggage - and not just hand luggage - has to be processed and much of it is too bulky to go through the machines. Nevertheless there is scope to move the security portals a little further into the terminal, and it is surprising this has not been done. Congestion in the eel-like passenger lounge beyond the security machines is less acute, but at busy times there is little space to spare; business passengers have benefited from the expansion of the dedicated lounges for them from 60 to 180 seats in 2002 as part of a redesign by Philippe Starck, though it is still easier for a camel to get through the eye of a needle than for a passenger with a discounted business class ticket to get into the lounge.

Work on the terminal began under the auspices of BR in December 1990, and the £130 million station was officially opened on 6th May, 1993 - the originally-projected opening date for the tunnel. Seventeen frustrating months supervened before the first revenue-earning trains finally ran; in the interim European Passenger Services, who had now taken over the terminal along with the planned Eurostar and sleeper operations, made it available for parties and concerts.

Eurostar traffic into and out of Waterloo had to coexist at its inception with 149 incoming commuter trains between 0700 and 1000, and 132 leaving between 1600 and 1900. To prevent conflicts, extra capacity was created in the station throat by widening the existing brick arched viaduct to accommodate more running lines to prevent movement conflicts between Eurostar and commuter trains. Beyond the throat on the busy section of line toward Clapham Junction, the most northerly of the four pairs of tracks was rededicated to tunnel traffic: Eurostars for Paris and Brussels, empty stock workings to North Pole depot and the projected international sleeper trains both for points beyond North Pole and for Plymouth, down the old London & South Western main line. Each Eurostar track is equipped for bi-directional running; domestic services also make use of them, especially the down line, and outgoing Eurostars also use the first of the other six tracks. Despite the otherwise total segregation of domestic and international traffic, the limited capacities of the power supply mean that departing (and arriving) Eurostars are comfortably outpaced by suburban trains on parallel tracks.

The first major engineering work on the route to the tunnel was undertaken from the 2.4 km mark beyond Vauxhall, the first station out of Waterloo. Here a 1.15 km double-track concrete viaduct of more than 40 spans incorporating a 90-degree bend was constructed so that international trains could rise from a new Nine Elms Junction to swing southward over the domestic lines between both Waterloo and Victoria and Clapham Junction, then south-east to meet the South London Line out of Victoria at Linford Street Junction, as it approached the diminutive (and then little-used) Clapham High Street station. The Stewarts Lane chord (named after the locomotive depot visible below Linford Street Junction) that makes the connection is long enough to hold a Eurostar train should the line out of Victoria be occupied, a fact that turned into a blessing when, on 7th February, 2003, an outward-bound Eurostar was stranded on the viaduct for more than five hours in the evening peak. This section of track carries no domestic or freight traffic (an exception being a Hastings-Alresford railtour in 2005) and was the only entirely new line constructed in Britain to serve the tunnel when it opened, save for the tracks entering the Cheriton terminal and North Pole Depot.

North Pole and the West London Line

Were its location as central as Waterloo International, Eurostar's North Pole depot, which Eurostar is also abandoning in 2007, would have made almost as great a visual impact. The depot is 3 km long, and its maintenance shed is claimed to be the largest railway servicing structure in the United Kingdom. The £80 million facility is as remote as its name suggests even though the title comes from a neighbouring pub rather than an Arctic waste; North Pole straddles three London boroughs on a bleak site bordered by Wormwood Scrubs and the Great Western main line and Parliament only approved construction of the depot under the Channel Tunnel Act after ensuring the protection of a nearby wildlife site.

Instead of taking the new Continental main line from Queenstown Road Junction, Eurostar stock for North Pole remains on a single track on the pre-existing formation which passes through the disused most westerly platform at Queenstown Road station before eventually diverging from the main South-Western route about a mile short of Clapham Junction. This reinstated line - the Sheepcote chord - was needed to enable empty Eurostar stock from Waterloo International to run direct to North Pole (and permit sleeper trains - which, it was planned, would change locomotives at the terminal station - to gain the West London Line). The chord was in fact a reinstated and electrified version of a little-used stretch of line removed in the 1950s when Waterloo was not in the frame as a potential tunnel terminal. The only revenue-earning services to have used this connection were the short-lived HST services from Newcastle and Manchester which between 1995 and 1997 offered Eurostar passengers an easy connection at Waterloo, the Great Western sleeper to Penzance, which was diverted briefly from Paddington to Waterloo in the mid-1990s to provide a connection with Eurostar, a daily train to and from Cardiff, very occasional diverted Eurostars, railtours and steam specials. When the Cardiff train was suspended in April

2004, the curve was finally proposed for closure to passenger service and a minibus service was laid on by the SRA between Waterloo and Clapham Junction while the formalities were gone through. The train it replaced - the 0300 from Reading to Waterloo - had attracted six passengers a day and the returning 0505 just two but rail enthusiasts with a masochistic streak flocked to travel on the minibus until the Secretary of State eventually gave his consent at the end of the year.

Access to the North Pole depot is from the West London line at North Pole Junction, two-thirds of the way between Kensington Olympia and Willesden Junction. There are two connections with this through route: in, forking left (west) off the West London Line into reception sidings, and out along what used to be a through chord giving direct access for inter-Regional traffic to the GW fast lines. The severing of this link when the depot was constructed required the infrequent Brighton-Kensington Olympia-Reading-Manchester service to make a 15-minute detour at snail's pace through Old Oak Sidings. Although the West London Line at North Pole Junction is electrified at 25kv AC and trains diverge for the depot 'under the wires', the four reception sidings to the west of that line through which they normally enter it are electrified third-rail at 750v DC. Inside the depot itself electrification is again overhead; a short section can be energised at 3000v DC to test trains for operation in Belgium.

North Pole depot was planned as the base for 11 of the 'Three Capitals' 18-coach Eurostars and of all seven 'North of London' sets which are four carriages shorter, and also as a maintenance base for class '92' tunnel freight locomotives. During 2003 it took on responsibility additionally for servicing 13 of the SNCF-allocated Eurostars previously maintained at Le Landy, except for the very heaviest overhauls; 30 extra staff were recruited, bringing North Pole's total workforce to 294. North Pole was intended as the permanent base for the Eurostar fleet, with a supplementary facility at Temple Mills opening after completion of the CTRL in 2007 to handle sets using St Pancras, which it was estimated would be stock of a new generation required because of booming traffic. The reality will be rather different, it was decided in November 2004 not only to run all services from St Pancras once the CTRL was finished, but to close North Pole then and shift all its work to Temple Mills because the North London line was too congested to handle empty stock workings between North Pole and St Pancras. The depot with its excellent facilities will be offered to other operators; Crossrail would be a possibility but for uncertainties over when, if ever, the scheme will be implemented.

The site comprises two elongated maintenance facilities linked by a single rail track (and a roadway which employees traverse on company-provided bicycles). North Pole also houses Eurostar's central store of components, and five training suites for the company's staff. Work on the depot began in May 1990 and it was officially opened by the BR Chairman Sir Bob Reid on 11th November, 1992, in good time for the arrival of the first half Eurostar unit in June 1993.

The eastern site at North Pole comprises the workshop where heavy maintenance is undertaken: an exam every 37 days (*Autre Travail Systematique* or ATS, and steadily heavier servicing every three months (ATS 2), six months (*Visite Limitée*), 12 months (*Visite Générale*) and two years (*Grande Visite Générale* or GVG). A GVG can be ordered at 240,000 km if this milestone is reached within two years. North Pole has also come in recent years to specialise in maintaining the 'common block' traction units of the entire class of units. Although this workshop is 700 m long, it will not hold an entire Eurostar train, so 18-car sets have to be split in two for servicing there. Where trains cannot travel in the maintenance area under their own power - until 2003 only two of the four tracks in the maintenance building were electrified - they are propelled by Eurostar's class '08' shunter or class '73' electro-diesels, all of which have retractable Scharfenberg couplings. The depot's eastern extremity became a nationally-recognised sight as the backdrop for the Ladbroke Grove disaster of October 1999.

The western site consists of a servicing shed 413 m long, where Eurostars (the facility can handle 13 a night and normally tackles 11) get a two-hour technical checkup at the end of a day in service while their interiors are cleaned; every 4,000 km they receive a light A-exam, and this is being stretched to 5,000 km with the opening of the CTRL as proportionately more time will be needed on the overhead power collection equipment and less on the third-rail system. Before reversing to enter the six-track servicing shed, each train is washed, put through the lavatory discharge area and has its track-train communications system tested. Also during the nightly service, underfloor equipment compartment doors are checked in case the voids have been occupied or damaged by illegal migrants who have travelled in them, as has sometimes been the case.

The siting of the depot at North Pole fitted in neatly with long-term plans for the development of Channel Tunnel services, as the West London Line was earmarked as a route for regional Eurostar traffic to the West Coast and East Coast main lines and for international sleeping car trains, as well as tunnel freight. Consequently the upgrading of the line for the opening of the tunnel killed a number of birds with one stone. Some of the tunnel-connected services never materialised, but the capacity created enabled Silverlink to upgrade its local service on the route from Clapham Junction-Olympia to a through facility to Willesden Junction with extra stops now planned *en route* at Imperial Wharf and Shepherds Bush, and Connex South Central to launch its hourly service between Gatwick Airport and Rugby, now cut back to Watford Junction through lack of capacity on the WCML.

On the West London line itself, the principal tunnel-connected work was electrification of the 11 km route, though it also had to be resignalled and the track upgraded to keep down noise. The portion from a point just south of North Pole Junction to Willesden Junction was electrified on 25kv AC overhead, easing the blockage at Mitre Bridge Junction when inter-regional passenger and freight trains had halted to change locomotives or voltages, and providing electrified access to North Pole. The 1,100 metres south from the junction to the elevated A40(M) were electrified on both systems, just long enough for a Eurostar to exit the depot 'under the wires', clear the junction and then reverse northward without needing to lower its pantographs. Network Rail has been considering extending the overhead a little further south to the new station at Shepherds Bush to permit locomotive and voltage changes to take place there, freeing up a couple of extra train paths each hour but this depends on work to immunise the signalling on London Underground's Central Line.

From the end of the overhead wiring south to Clapham Junction (just before which the line splits to serve each extremity of the 17-platform station) third-rail electrification was installed to enable diesel stock on existing local services to be phased out, permit the operation of electrically-hauled international freight to the tunnel from Willesden and Wembley yards and, of course, give Eurostar stock access to Waterloo. The 1.8 km section of track between Latchmere Junction and Factory Junction, which took inter-regional freight trains and a handful of Inter-City services from the West London Line onto the new route from Waterloo where it joined the lines out of Victoria at Stewarts Lane, was also electrified with both class '92'-hauled tunnel freight and direct Eurostar services to the regions in mind.

Kensington Olympia station was supposed to play an important role for night services through the tunnel; diesel-hauled sets from Plymouth and Swansea respectively would be marshalled there for attachment to the rakes arriving from Glasgow and Edinburgh with class '92' haulage, for onward passage as single trains to Paris and Brussels. Accommodation was provided at Olympia where Eurostar staff waited for several years for night services and through Eurostars to the regions to commence; recruited to supervise stops for marshalling, crew changes and border control, they were withdrawn in 1997. The following year Olympia played host to an in-service Eurostar for the first time, when a cable fire closed Waterloo and an incoming train from Brussels was diverted to unload there. Eurostars were also diverted via Kensington Olympia during the five-hour blockage of the Stewarts Lane viaduct on 7th February, 2003, but passengers were boarded and disembarked at Waterloo as normal and the trains simply reversed at Olympia to complete two sides of an avoiding triangle via the Latchmere and Sheepcote chords. Reinstatement of the southbound loop at Olympia for international freight trains is now being considered.

The other preparatory work on the West London line itself for tunnel traffic was strengthening of the weak Chelsea River Bridge over the Thames to enable heavier trains to cross it and the speed limit to be raised from 24 to 64 kph; a further improvement to 80 kph is planned.

To ensure access to North Pole and keep international freight moving in the event of the West London Line and its approaches being blocked, BR also eased clearances – though not filling a gap in the third rail - to provide an alternative route, over which tunnel stock is hauled by Eurostar's dedicated class '37' diesels. From the depot, trains head north to Mitre Bridge Junction, then skirt Willesden Junction to join the North London Line at Acton Wells Junction, then diverge at Kew East Junction to access Clapham Junction via Barnes and Putney; from there Eurostar stock can run direct to Waterloo, and freight joins the route to the tunnel at Factory Junction. The route has occasionally been used because of engineering work, for stock transfers or to keep up drivers' knowledge, but it involves freight trains reversing at Olympia.

En route to Cheriton

From the outset it was envisaged that passenger trains between London and the tunnel portal would travel by the two routes traditionally traversed by Southern Region boat trains for Folkestone and Dover, and known in consequence as BTR (Boat Train Route)1 and BTR2; with the opening of the tunnel these were redesignated CTR (Channel Tunnel Route)1 and CTR2. Route CTR1 takes trains to the tunnel by the classic 'main' line through Herne Hill and Sevenoaks; CTR2 goes by way of the Catford loop and Maidstone East. The two routes diverge at Brixton and rejoin from Shortlands to the grade-separated junctions east of Bickley; Eurostars continue now via Swanley to the CTRL, but they formerly - and now if the high-speed route is closed - proceeded via Tonbridge or Maidstone to combine finally at Ashford for the final stretch to Cheriton. There is also a facility for international trains to switch from CTR2 to CTR1 using the 5 km connection between Otford and Sevenoaks via Bat & Ball, which otherwise sees purely local traffic.

Of the two routes CTR1 is hillier (no small consideration given the power needed to shift a Eurostar) and more densely-trafficked, but it also includes a 42 km dead straight between Tonbridge and Ashford along most of which Eurostars can sustain 160 kph.

CTR2 has a slower line speed and is 4 km longer, but is less severely graded; between 1994 and 2003 it handled on a weekday two out of a maximum 31 Eurostars in each direction (two inward in the morning peak, two outward in the evening) plus some seasonal ski trains and Disney services, and the bulk of tunnel freight. For several days in October 2000 it had to handle the entire Eurostar and tunnel freight service, not to mention a large volume of domestic traffic, after floods near Pluckley breached the Tonbridge-Ashford line. Both routes were needed to provide enough paths for international traffic if construction of a completely new line were to be avoided, and to allow for flexibility in the event of engineering work or signal or points failures. With the opening of the CTRL Eurostars - but not tunnel freight - have vanished from CTR2 east of Swanley, but engineering work still brings them occasionally to CTR1. Such traffic will end when services switch to St Pancras.

Considerable improvements were made to each route before such traffic could operate. Clearances had to be improved to make sure Eurostars did not foul platforms or bridges or infringe the kinetic envelopes of other trains. Track was upgraded, and though the French disdainfully note that the nostalgic clicking of rail joints can still be heard on the English side of the Channel, both routes were very largely relaid with continuous welded rail - including the entire 27 km between a point west of Ashford and Continental Junction, where the line for the tunnel diverges from the route to Folkestone and Dover parallel to Dollands Moor freight yard. But while high-speed turnouts were installed at some junctions, it was not possible within budget and without a controversial land take also to iron out the worst bends, notably that at the west end of Tonbridge station where the London-bound line veers sharply to the north and Eurostar's fairly rapid progress across Kent ends abruptly in a severe speed restriction.

Signalling had to be modernised too, to cater for greater traffic, higher train speeds and, in places, improved track layout - notably the loops for tunnel freight trains which will be described later. The opportunity was taken to upgrade signalling for domestic traffic between Chislehurst and Folkestone, and a new Integrated Electronic Control Centre was opened at Ashford to handle the routes to the tunnel, among others. One phenomenon that remained, however - to the delight of the French - was a manually-operated level crossing at Willesborough, on the eastern fringe of Ashford, complete with crossing keeper's hut; it was not finally dispensed with until April 2001.

One major improvement affecting CTR1 and CTR2 was not even considered in the original planning for Channel Tunnel services, and only came into being just before the opening of the first phase of the CTRL: the £60 million burrowing junction at Shortlands to enable London-bound Eurostar and freight traffic to branch onto the Catford Loop (CTR2) without impeding trains on CTR1 heading for the Continent. Plans for the separation of the running tracks just west of Shortlands station and for an underpass in a box tunnel taking Catford Loop traffic under the main lines to a point just short of Ravensbourne station were not mooted until 1999 in the light of operational experience, and the first trains used it in May 2003, improving punctuality for all services in advance of the opening of the CTRL. With Eurostars heading for Fawkham Junction rather than Tonbridge, it now makes sense for them to use the former Chatham slow – rather than fast - lines between Shortlands and Bickley, and the remodelling at Shortlands enables them to do this. Once the CTRL is completed, taking the bulk of Eurostars to St Pancras, the underpass will have a continued role in segregating from commuter traffic the tunnel freight trains which will continue to use the classic routes.

Quite apart from upgrading the classic route, BR (or rather European Passenger services, the body set up in 1991, initially as part of the state railway, to operate Eurostar) was required under the Channel Tunnel Act to construct an intermediate station for international trains in the historic railway town of Ashford. The purpose of the station, sharing a site with the existing interchange for domestic services, was to give the people of east and central Kent (and, via the still-unelectrified Hastings line, those of east Sussex) direct access to tunnel services instead of having to travel via London.

Plans for this £100 million development, undertaken by a Public-Private Partnership to which Eurostar pays a 'user tax' for every passenger - took shape later than those for the tunnel, BR holding back for a time in the hope that they could go before Parliament in the Bill for the CTRL. Late in 1990 this aim was abandoned and a separate Bill promoted. During its passage sensitivities surfaced locally over the precise location of the international tracks and platforms, and uncertainties over how rigidly tunnel and domestic passengers would be segregated and what facilities customs and immigration would demand. It has been a sore point with Eurostar that its London-bound trains in the morning rush hour, which have spare capacity, cannot pick up commuters at Ashford because of theological objections by the Home Office and the Customs and Excise to domestic passengers using international trains. Equally, international passengers have been disgruntled that it has often been no cheaper to travel from Ashford than from Waterloo, despite the shorter distance and journey time to Paris or even Calais.

The new international platforms - 3 and 4 - were shoehorned into the centre of the station, the island platforms on either side being extended to 400 m to cater for Eurostars. The facilities were designed to handle 2 million passengers a year; although Ashford International caught on well after a very slow start (in 2001 550,000 Eurostar passengers used the station), this design capacity, like that at Waterloo International, has yet to be tested. Segregation of arriving and departing passengers was complete: those arriving leave the platforms by a subway, while those beginning their journeys use a footbridge. Above the platforms is a check-in area and departure hall for 800 passengers with catering facilities; passengers enter and leave the international station at ground-floor level, where the concourse provides a link with local services, or by a walkway to a multi-storey park for nearly 2,000 cars. To make way for tunnel trains, a new island platform was constructed on the north side of the station to take some domestic services; connections from the BR tracks to the international platform roads were said to be 'temporary'.

Work on Ashford International began under BR auspices in October 1993 but the project was completed by Railtrack; the new domestic station was opened by the Duke of Kent on 6th September, 1995, but it was 8th January, 1996 before the first Eurostars called there, bringing Ashford within two hours of the Gare du Nord. Work on the CTRL has positioned two elevated lines immediately to the north of Ashford International station, with tunnel trains stopping there slipping under them to gain the Eurostar platforms, each of whose tracks (plus two domestic lines as back-up) is now electrified with 25kv AC overhead as well as the extant third rail. Infuriatingly, the Beaver Road bridge over the station complex, which was raised to accommodate Eurostar clearances during construction of Ashford International, had to be raised a second time during work on the CTRL to allow the erection of overhead catenary for international trains making a stop there.

Specifically for Freight

BR's planning of freight routes and facilities to serve the tunnel was based on high hopes - widely shared - of a boom in international rail freight once it was opened. It also took into account the very different routeing requirements of freight trains from Eurostars, for which speed was of the essence, while nevertheless creating the scope to operate more and heavier goods trains at higher speeds over an already-crowded domestic network.

The basis of BR's planning was that international freight trains would line up to join the Eurotunnel system at a new yard at Dollands Moor, beside Continental Junction, and that while a few might reach there by other routes - china clay traffic from Cornwall, for instance - the vast majority would travel down from London, where a further new yard specifically for tunnel trains was created at Wembley.

Between those points, international freight trains would be electrically-hauled and travel either by CTR2 from the West London Line through Maidstone East or by a more southerly route, CTR3, via Clapham Junction and the Brighton line to Redhill, joining CTR1 at Tonbridge. A total of 35 paths each day in each direction were reserved until 2052 for tunnel freight trains, way in excess of demand to date. To prevent conflicts with far speedier Eurostars, passing loops 1 km long were installed at Hollingbourne on CTR2, and at Headcorn on CTR1 where Eurostar's highest speeds in England would be reached, and which would be shared by freight trains using CTR3. At Headcorn, the loop on the up side of the station eliminated the last traces there of the Kent and East Sussex Railway, whose northern terminus the station's bay platform had been until 1954; the loop on the down side is 1 km toward London. There is also a loop from the up line on CTR2 just south of Otford which, from the style of fencing, appears to have been constructed at the same time as Headcorn's; this has been used to loop not only freight trains but stopping domestic passenger trains to enable Eurostars to pass.

At no time was use of CTR3 by Eurostars envisaged, even in an emergency, despite the potential of the dead straight and lightly used Redhill-Tonbridge section for high speeds; limited clearances on the main Brighton line through East Croydon would not permit it. However preparing CTR3 simply to handle international freight required the electrification of almost 34 km between Tonbridge and Redhill, enabling Network South-East to upgrade its local service by ending diesel traction. Up till then 'heritage' diesel stock had operated a stopping service all the way from Tonbridge to Reading; with electrification this was accelerated, split and more profitably diverted at Redhill to serve Gatwick Airport. The Redhill-Tonbridge electrification proved in the short term a white elephant, as the electronics of the class '92' locomotives acquired to haul tunnel freight trains proved incompatible with the signalling on that route and the Brighton line; only those international trains powered by class '47' diesels, and later class '66s', have been permitted to use the line, and its use was fairly infrequent until completion of Phase One of the CTRL when a conscious decision was taken to divert some international freight via Redhill. How rarely trains previously transited the route was demonstrated on 5th October, 2002 when the 0307 Trafford Park-Dollands Moor headed by No. 66063 had to be halted at Latchmere Junction when the driver revealed that he had no route knowledge via Redhill; the southbound West London Line was blocked for some considerable time until another driver could be found, and single-line working was imposed. The benefits of electrification between Redhill and Tonbridge were confined to local commuters, and users of new through services from Gatwick via Tonbridge to Maidstone West, and from Tonbridge via Redhill to Victoria.

The limited extent to which tunnel freight was able to rely on class '92' traction (the class was not, at first, cleared by Railtrack to operate on any route to the tunnel because as introduced it interfered universally with signalling and lineside circuits) gave the yard at Dollands Moor even greater importance than it would otherwise have had. The yard was intended primarily as a 'stacking area' where freight trains about to transit the tunnel or newly out of it could undergo inspection and await the availability of a path. Class '92s' were supposed to bring a train in from the tunnel 'under the wires', then set out onto the BR system using the third rail which began at the western end of each road. But in the tunnel's first years of operation the yard, despite not having been designed for diesel haulage, was pressed into service as the point where class '47s' from throughout the BR system delivered international freight trains for class '92s' to take on through the tunnel, where they were welcome from the outset, and collected incoming freight for haulage to Wembley or beyond. Equally unforeseen was the extent to which customs officials scanning the sides and underneaths of the trains had to be joined by immigration staff detecting a growing number of asylum-seekers who had stowed away at Fréthun or even further afield. As through freight traffic fell short of expectations, passengers on passing Eurostars were more often treated to the sight of rows of class '47s' and '92s' standing by for a handover than to a yard packed with freight trains in transit. Once the class '92s' were finally passed for operation to Wembley and then up the West Coast Main Line, non-stop haulage by this class from Fréthun to Wembley, or even through running to or from Mossend, became an option.

Dollands Moor yard lies to the north side of the main line from London and Ashford to the tunnel, skirted on its north side by the Channel Tunnel Rail Link's southbound track and to the south by the traditional Folkestone-Ashford line. Electrified overhead throughout save for the locomotive inspection shed at its western extremity, its trackwork begins not far from the eastern mouth of Saltwood tunnel with a neck passing that shed, and lines from it rejoin the classic route to the tunnel 1.5 km further east, short of the Cheriton terminal and still over 3 km from the tunnel portal. The nine-road yard was laid out for safety and security; sturdy fences surround it and between each pair of tracks is an island platform for rail and customs personnel, accessed by a subway.

BR commissioned four dedicated terminals for Channel Tunnel freight: at Willesden, Mossend (Lanarkshire), Trafford Park and Wakefield; existing rail container terminals at Birmingham Landor Street and Liverpool Seaforth were converted for intermodal use, but attracted little business. A further terminal at Stratford, planned as a supplement to Willesden, was never built. Each was planned as a railhead for international freight, with road access, impressive lifting gear for swap-bodies and containers and plenty of space for storage.

The Willesden terminal lies immediately to the south of the West Coast Main Line parallel with Willesden Junction station on a site previously used to load Freightliner trains; trains from the Channel Tunnel continue up the West London Line from North Pole Junction to fork left into it. Used from the moment the tunnel opened to freight in the spring of 1994, Willesden is the principal customs clearance point for tunnel freight - and was the only one until 2000, when the Customs and Excise dropped its refusal to clear international freight trains at their final destination which had caused delays of up to 24 hours and greatly reduced the competitiveness of rail.

Separate from the Willesden terminal, 2 km to its north on the other side of the WCML, is Wembley yard, brought into use specifically for tunnel traffic but now a general-user freight yard for international wagonload and domestic traffic only. This large and busy yard was where international freight trains originally changed locomotives and intermodal services from the tunnel for the East and West Coast main lines were split. But although Wembley was planned for tunnel traffic, it proved difficult to work as there have been far fewer block trains and simple splits than expected, and more wagonload traffic. In consequence Wembley had to be used as a flat shunt yard, which is not what it was designed for, and in the summer of 2001 all intermodal shunting was concentrated on Willesden and Daventry. Wembley does, however, have plenty of room for locomotive stabling, which came in handy during the years until 1999 when class '92' use was severely limited and many switches to and from class '47' haulage had to be made there, and for wagons spare or awaiting transit.

The best known of the originally-planned tunnel freight terminals north of London is at Mossend, beside the yard on the Motherwell-Cumbernauld route where Inter-City trains from the WCML avoiding Glasgow to travel further north used to switch from electric to diesel traction. The promotion of Mossend was a political totem, concrete proof that the Channel Tunnel would be of benefit for Scotland, but it did not open until a year or so after the tunnel was finished, international traffic volumes were slow to build and much traffic was lost during the chaos over asylum-seekers to the point where direct services to the Continent were withdrawn. It has, however, thrived as a domestic terminal and tunnel freight there is now reviving.

The most commercially successful tunnel freight terminal north of London has been the Daventry International Rail Freight Terminal (or DIRFT) on the WCML's Northampton loop. Though DIRFT struggled to retain its Continental traffic during the disruption over asylum-seekers, its increasingly strong base in domestic rail freight saw it through and it came out of the crisis still handling 10 intermodal tunnel trains each week; the volume has risen again since.

Intermodal traffic has also kept flowing from Trafford Park, on the old Cheshire Lines route out of Manchester to Warrington and Liverpool. Events have not borne out the forecasts of 100,000 containers and swapbodies a year bound for the Continent which led to £11million being invested and freight traffic to the neighbouring industrial estate has ceased altogether. But like Daventry the 20-acre terminal with five parallel sidings handles 10 intermodal trains a week, rating itself Britain's busiest source of tunnel traffic. The thrice-weekly service from Bari, in southern Italy, to Trafford Park makes the longest journey of any train using the tunnel. The Manchester-Bari service is, indeed, almost unmatched in Europe, taking a highly competitive 50 hours southbound and running via Willesden, Hazebrouck, Paris Valenton, Dijon, Chambéry, Turin, Piacenza and Rimini.

The final British intermodal terminal now handling tunnel traffic is at Hams Hall, on the site of a former power station abutting the old Midland route between Birmingham and Nuneaton. Survival of this terminal was touch and go until Associated British Ports took it over, but as EWS services returned to normal during the winter of 2002/03, nine trains a week were operating for Milan Rogoredo and Novara.

EWS continues to operate automotive trains to and from Corby, Tyne Yard and Dagenham (also now intermodal), and also to canvass business for European freight from and for Birmingham, Manchester, Longport, Rotherham, Wakefield, Walsall and Wolverhampton. At the time of writing, however, traffic from Wakefield, on the site of the former Kirkgate locomotive depot, and also from Doncaster has fizzled out; a further terminal for South Wales, constructed at Wentloog, east of Cardiff, has yet to handle any tunnel traffic. Tunnel freight traffic has also been handled at Hull,

Immingham, Newport and Teesport, and at small private railheads at Blackburn, Ely, Selby and Widnes, among others. Dalry, Hartlepool, Middlesbrough, Scunthorpe, Stapleford, Blackburn, Knowsley, Burton-on-Trent, Bloxwich, Birch Coppice, Neasden, Cricklewood, Hoo Junction, Paddock Wood, Eastleigh, Barry, Port Talbot, Trostre, Avonmouth, Bridgwater and various china clay terminals in Cornwall have also either generated tunnel freight traffic, or are seen as potential sources.

Regional Eurostar improvements

Nowhere were hopes for the Channel Tunnel to generate new international rail traffic flows more cruelly dashed than in the field of passenger services to and from regions of Britain beyond London, both by Eurostar and by sleeper. BR regarded both these traffics as integral to the commercial success of the project, and as politically essential also. The provision of through trains to and from Scotland, Wales and the English regions had been a *quid pro quo* with regional MPs for the passage of the Channel Tunnel Act, and the revival of proposals for a high-speed link between London and the tunnel once boring had begun only heightened their expectations.

In this climate BR, despite its tight budget, was required by the Government to invest heavily not only in rolling stock for the projected services but in major improvements to the domestic system to cater even for the sparse Eurostar service that was envisaged up the East and West Coast main lines. (Few improvements to the infrastructure apart from some strengthening of the track formation and easing of clearances were needed to accommodate trains of Nightstar stock which were in addition to serve South Wales and the West Country, as they would be hauled on those routes by venerable class '37' diesels.)

Regional Eurostar services were projected to follow routes CTR1 or CTR2 to Stewarts Lane, then use the same route as Channel Tunnel freight to avoid Waterloo and gain the West London line, from whose electrification and upgrading they would benefit. After a stop for a crew change at Olympia the trains were to pass North Pole and return to overhead traction before diverging as they neared the WCML. More than half the trains would thread their way onto the main line for Birmingham or Manchester; a smaller number would follow the North London Line round through Willesden Junction (High Level) to gain the ECML by a previously freight-only chord at Maiden Lane, just north of Kings Cross. From there they would head for York, Newcastle, Edinburgh (and in the case of one train a day) Glasgow. Plans for Regional Eurostar also to serve Glasgow via the WCML were dropped early on. A projected service to Leeds via the ECML also foundered because of short platforms and acute congestion at the Yorkshire terminal; these shortcomings have now been remedied and class '373' Eurostars operated by GNER on domestic services began serving Leeds in 2002.

To enable North-of-London services to run, four main tasks had to be undertaken: wholesale reconstruction of the stretch of the North London Line through Hampstead Heath tunnel where clearances were inadequate, immunisation of signalling and trackside circuits on both main routes against Eurostars' electronics, general work on clearances, and provision of depot facilities for Eurostar and night stock at Glasgow and Manchester and (for night stock only) at Plymouth. The most costly of these projects was the £148 million upgrade of the North London Line, which was closed for several months between Willesden Junction and Gospel Oak while track in the offending tunnel was lowered and relaid, drainage improved and the opportunity taken to strip out the third rail and convert that section of route to overhead current. The main beneficiaries in the event were inter-regional domestic freight, which could now use 25kv AC haulage between Willesden and Stratford instead of having to change locomotives, and commuters on the North London Line who got a smoother and fractionally quicker ride. But once it became clear Regional Eurostar services would not start with the opening of the tunnel, if at all, spending on such a scale when other portions of the BR network were being starved of investment came in question; the questioning became all the fiercer when it was discovered that even the upgraded Hampstead Heath tunnel was still too small to handle 'Piggyback' intermodal traffic without further costly work involving yet another closure, and that once the St Pancras Eurostar terminal came into use class '373s' could not access it from North Pole without still more improvements to the route - one reason for the decision to switch from North Pole to Temple Mills.

Considerable improvements were carried out on both the East and West Coast main lines in anticipation of Regional Eurostar services: upgrading of the power supply, improved signalling and minor but important changes to bridges and station platforms to accommodate the loading gauge of tunnel stock which pushed the kinetic envelope to its limit. Yet when testing of Regional Eurostar and Nightstar trains on these routes eventually began, Railtrack managers were shocked to discover that the electronics of both played havoc with lineside circuits just as the class '92s' to haul them were doing; the problem was the greater on the East Coast Main Line because in the tunnel's first years of operation, class '92s' were not scheduled to operate along it and it was the Regional Eurostar sets under test that triggered the lineside problems for the first time. Despite the repeated postponement of the start of regional services, both the tests and the improvements continued. The WCML to Manchester (via Birmingham and direct) was pretty well clear by mid-1997, but on the ECML serious problems remained. When in 2000 GNER hired surplus Eurostar regional sets to cope with booming traffic volumes, it was forced to start with only a shuttle service between Kings Cross - where only two platforms were long enough to accommodate even a Eurostar of reduced length - and York. Edinburgh was out as a destination because the curved platforms at Newcastle would have required wholesale reconstruction to handle a Eurostar, but the restructuring and expansion of Leeds station did permit a start to 'White Rose' services, as the Eurostars were rebranded, to the West Riding city from May 2002.

Despite the lavish expenditure on North Pole and the range of facilities on offer, regional depots were also needed for stabling and maintenance of Regional Eurostar and night stock. At Manchester International (Longsight) and Glasgow Polmadie, sidings and covered accommodation were provided to stable one 14-car Eurostar overnight and service one train of night stock by day. Facilities were provided at Plymouth Laira to service night stock on the Wales/West Country run. The new millennium dawned, however, without either of Eurostar's purpose-built regional depots having seen anything more than a test train. Servicing of Regional Eurostars on test was routinely carried out at Manchester International - on the side of which a banner reading 'L'Eurostar habite ici' (Eurostar lives here) was prematurely hoisted, remaining there until 2000 when West Coast Train Care, who had taken over the running of the depot, decided the embarrassment was too great and had it removed. The depot was most recently used to house Channel Tunnel trains of a kind ... Siemens class '185' diesel units brought from the Continent for Trans-Pennine Express. Eurostar's servicing facilities at Polmadie were never used, and were eventually leased out to Virgin which in 2003 used it to stable 'Pendolino' sets unable to enter service on the WCML because upgrading work was well behind schedule.

Chapter Eleven

The Channel Tunnel Rail Link

When the shambolic history of decision-making in Britain on major infrastructure projects comes to be written, the Channel Tunnel Rail Link will come a close second to the tunnel itself in terms of time and money wasted, and of false starts made by nervous officialdom. Nevertheless the 109 km (67.8 mile) link is now well on the way to fruition, with the first stage from Cheriton to Fawkham Junction on the Victoria-Chatham line having opened to schedule on 28th September, 2003. The benefits in faster journey times and operation clear of congested commuter lines are already apparent, and there is every likelihood that Phase Two through to the long-designated Eurostar terminal at St Pancras will be completed on time, if not to budget, in 2007. Barring some last-minute hiccup, the line will enter service 19 years after the first route for it was proposed, and 35 years after a high-speed link was first mooted.

Phase One of the link has knocked 3 km and 20 minutes off journeys between London and Eurostar's Continental destinations; a greater benefit will be felt when it opens through to St Pancras and a further similar saving is made to bring Paris within 2 hrs 15 min from London, and Brussels attainable in two hours dead. For commuters - with paths available for eight trains an hour with a maximum speed of 200 kph at peak times - there is the prospect of a 37-minute timing between St Pancras and Ashford and half an hour to the Medway Towns, with knock-on benefits right across east Kent. (No commuter trains are expected to use the link for two years after it reaches St Pancras, though reliability and some service frequencies have already benefited from the removal of Eurostars from classic lines across Kent.)

With a maximum line speed of 300 kph (186 mph) and operating under the same TVM430 cab signalling as is used in the Channel Tunnel itself, Eurostars will take just 32 minutes from St Pancras to the Cheriton portal despite line gradients as steep as 1 in 40 which rule out the line's use for heavier forms of freight. Some high-value goods will probably be carried, most likely only at night, at a maximum speed of 140 kph, and two sets of freight passing loops have been included in Phase One to make sure Eurostar services are not impeded, yet freight on the CTRL will always be of secondary importance, not least because the cant on the curves to handle high-speed trains will lead to exceptional wear and tear being caused by slower heavy traffic. No freight is likely to be handled on the CTRL north of Ashford in any event until the connection to Network Rail north of the Thames at Ripple Lane opens with Phase Two.

The route now open, and indeed the entire CTRL into St Pancras (apart from the Midland platforms which will still be controlled from West Hampstead), is regulated from a control centre at Ashford. The line is being signalled bidirectionally throughout, with a handful of crossing places, to allow services to be maintained during engineering possessions. Only serious or unforeseen disruption now requires Eurostars to use route CTR1 through rural Kent. The route of the CTRL boasts the same blue and yellow 'flag' markers for block section boundaries as one sees in the tunnel and on the TGV network. The shunt markers, however, replicate those on the Belgian high-speed line. The 'cab secure' system enabling positive identification of a train driver calling the control centre is Network Rail's, and the more innovative digital GSM-R radio is used for general purposes such as communication by maintenance staff. (On Phase Two GSM-R will be used for both.) To make extra sure that Eurostars can be safe operating at TGV speeds, the route has double fencing along most of its length to prevent animals straying onto the line.

Whatever the political twists and turns along the way, the CTRL is an artery to be proud of. Any high-speed line would be an improvement on the congested switchback that London-bound international trains had to take for the nine years after the tunnel first opened, in marked contrast with the high speed, smooth ride and directness of the TGV route. Small wonder that French Eurostar customers were advised to treat the LGV-Nord and the tunnel as the flight, and the route through Kent as a protracted runway. But all that has changed, though the access to Waterloo from Swanley remains agonisingly slow. Indeed the CTRL resembles a Continental railway in most respects: French-style rail, sleepers and electric catenary are used, the loading gauge is the UIC B+ Continental standard which could accommodate TGV Duplex double-deck trains, and all CTRL line stations are being built to UIC dimensions with lower platforms to accommodate future types of European train that may use the tunnel, enabling TGVs to operate right into St Pancras.

The saga of the CTRL goes back to the early 1970s when the previous, abandoned, tunnel project was in the final stages of planning and BR's Southern Region concluded that there was no room on its network for high-speed international trains. As explained in Chapter One, a high-speed line was then proposed from the tunnel bypassing Ashford, following the existing line to Tonbridge, then continuing toward Redhill as far as Edenbridge where it would swing north on a new alignment almost to Clapham Junction before taking the West London Line to the White City terminal then proposed for international services. There was a bellow of protest from the Surrey commuter belt and the scheme was hastily dropped, ostensibly on grounds of cost.

When the tunnel project was revived a decade later, the 1987 Channel Tunnel Act was promoted and passed on the understanding that no high-speed link would be built and that trains would use the existing network. Yet even as the work of excavation began, the managements of Eurotunnel and the railways on both sides of the Channel - and the Department of Transport - concluded that for international rail traffic through the tunnel to take up the paths allocated to it, there was no alternative to building a high-speed line between the English portal and central London, whatever the political fallout. And the junior Transport Minister Michael Portillo was adamant that, as with the tunnel itself, the private sector must raise the lion's share of the cost.

On 15th July, 1988 BR reported that there was no alternative to building extra tracks to supplement additional routes to handle tunnel traffic or constructing a completely new alignment. Four options were suggested: (1) from Sidcup to the route of the CTRL as constructed near Detling, then on an alignment close to that eventually chosen to the tunnel with 'frontier sidings' at Westenhanger; (2) from a point near Farningham Road to route 1, then as above; (3) from the main line west of Swanley to slice through the picturesque Darenth Valley, running south-east to just north of Paddock Wood, then initially north of the Tonbridge-Ashford line before looping south of Ashford; and (4) an upgrading of the classic route through Sevenoaks and Ashford, but with a loop south of Tonbridge to ease congestion at the station and iron out the severe curve just north of it. BR's preparation of these options was amateurish, to put it mildly. At one point Routes 1 and 2 sliced through a housing estate that had been built since the Ordnance Survey map used in the exercise was printed, and cynics claimed that the planner in question had drawn it up on greaseproof paper on his kitchen table. While this may have been unfair, the upshot was an outburst of opposition as protest groups against not only the environmental impact of the proposed routes but also the inherent planning blight mushroomed right across Kent and South London.

Aghast at the outcry, which culminated in a demonstration in London by 10,000 residents of Kent, BR hired Saatchi and Saatchi at a reported £3 million to limit the damage and set up a Channel Tunnel Rail Link project group to redraw the plans. In August 1989 a clearer, single, route was proposed, following the M20 on an alignment close to that eventually chosen to Fawkham Junction (via Ashford, Detling, Upper Halling and Swanley) but then tunnelling under Foots Cray, Hither Green, Nunhead, Peckham, Walworth and Farringdon to a low-level terminal at Kings Cross. This station, accessed from a spectacular concourse between the Kings Cross and St Pancras trainsheds, would have had eight platforms: four for Eurostar and its regional services, two for Thameslink (replacing Kings Cross Thameslink station) and two for Kent commuter services over the CTRL. The associated development was designed to regenerate the vast and largely derelict railway lands north of Kings Cross.

This plan for the CTRL was far better thought out, but provoked a fresh wave of protest from dwellers near numerous parks and squares in inner South London where boreholes or air vents would be needed, and from some Kings Cross residents with a surprisingly rosy view of their current environment. It also triggered a campaign led by Newham Council for the CTRL to terminate at Stratford in east London which would eventually influence the routeing of the link, though not its final destination. One other point of controversy was BR's proposal for a Mid-Kent Parkway station in the narrow green strip between Maidstone and the Medway towns; useful as it would have been, it raised fears of fresh urban sprawl.

Some adjustments to the alignment were made to head off the greatest protests, and in November 1989 BR formed the Eurorail consortium with Trafalgar House and BICC to get the line built. It also promoted in Parliament a Kings Cross Railways Bill providing for the new terminal, a chord to divert Great Northern suburban services into St Pancras to free up station capacity, and links to the ECML, Midland Main Line and, by a new chord at West Hampstead, to the WCML.

Doubts quickly emerged over whether the link, with such a lengthy portion in tunnel, was the right option and whether it could be delivered at a price the private sector could afford, whatever inducements the Government might offer. On 14th June, 1990 Mrs Thatcher's final Transport Secretary, Cecil Parkinson, vetoed the BR/Eurorail scheme because it could not be delivered without a £3.5 billion call on the public purse. BR got to work again, and now proposed a shorter tunnel at the London end, between Hither Green and Kings Cross; Eurostars would also continue to serve Waterloo, but reach it overland, as now.

The consulting engineers Ove Arup were by now lobbying hard for an alternative, more easterly route, reaching Kings Cross by way of Dartford, Rainham, Barking and Stratford, with scope to operate a full international freight service and with a commuter station at Medway Parkway between Rochester and Maidstone. This routing eased the environmental problems of tunnelling or upgrading the line through the Kent suburbs, gave a new strategic link to the 'Thames Gateway' much desired by Michael Heseltine, who became Environment Secretary in John Major's Government in November 1990, and gave the Stratford campaigners much of what they wanted. Another group - TALIS - also wanted an eastern approach, but proposed to tunnel under the North Downs, and a fourth consortium, Rail Europe, wanted the line to run to the east of the Medway towns and across the Isle of Grain, crossing the Thames east of Tilbury. Had this been adopted, the logic of a new London airport at Cliffe Marshes beside its route, floated by the Government in 2002-03, would have been difficult to resist.

BR - despite a pro-Arup leak to the author from 'sources close to the Chairman' - did not want the Arup scheme, but having been told by Ministers to adjudicate between the rival plans on offer, felt unable to promote its own which had been refined into a much more sophisticated and bankable project. Dr John Prideaux, previously head of InterCity, was tasked by BR with the review and concluded that the logic of running a line in from the south that started east of London was 'rather shaky'. Prideaux's study recommended a change of alignment, and to the dismay of the BR Chairman Sir Bob Reid, the Arup route (minus Medway Parkway and the bulk of its proposed freight capacity) was formally adopted in October 1991 by Transport Secretary Malcolm Rifkind. There were some protests at the new routeing by way of Stratford to Kings Cross (particularly as BR toyed with running Eurostars along an upgraded North London Line until it discovered that tunnelling would cost little more), but also some relief - and concern from politicians in Kent that the tunnel was set to open without the link being ready to take trains from it.

This was just the first half of the Government's CTRL double whammy. BR's original route beneath south-east London having been torn up in favour of a higher-speed, higher-cost alternative in the name of regional policy, the Kings Cross Project (KXP to its highly committed staff, who still meet regularly to talk of what might have been) was also jettisoned in March 1993 after a Commons committee had spent a record two and a half years considering it. Following further friction within the BR Board, yet another Transport Secretary, John MacGregor, concluded a week after the first passenger stock had negotiated the Channel Tunnel that it would be far cheaper, less environmentally disruptive and operationally simpler to run Eurostars into the under-used trainshed at St Pancras instead of excavating next door an all-singing, all-dancing terminal with a spectacular new concourse. The decision - with BR allowed the figleaf of an independent study of the merits of the two terminals which reported in St Pancras' favour that October - meant that tunnel trains would enter the station from the north, leaving Thameslink trains from the south to use their original alignment . . . and a separate though connected new station at St Pancras Midland Road.

Together with his Kings Cross/St Pancras decision, Mr MacGregor announced a preferred route for the CTRL refined from Arup's (copies of local newspaper advertisements advising of the proposed route had been leaked by John Prescott the week before). He left open the question of where intermediate stations should be, and also whether the London portion of the route between Barking and St Pancras should be entirely sub-surface or only in tunnel between Stratford and Dalston. He tasked Union Railways, a BR subsidiary set up to form the vehicle for public/private construction of the CTRL, to consult on details of the route, and in January 1994 he published its final course. He opted for an alignment in inner London entirely in tunnel, two short extra sections of tunnel in Kent to limit environmental impact, and an intermediate stop for commuters at Ebbsfleet, on the North Kent Line between Dartford and Gravesend, rather than at Rainham, on the Essex bank of the Thames. A decision on whether Stratford merited a station was controversially left open, but provision was made for a freight connection there to Temple Mills yard. It was in this form that, on 24th November, 1994, the scheme was presented to Parliament in the Channel Tunnel Rail Link Bill, a measure which also provided for widening of a parallel section of the M2. Further adjustments to the route were announced in

September 1995 after a consultation process that included 1,700 meetings between Union Railways and local groups; short sections of tunnel beneath a residential area of Barking and at Harrietsham in Kent, a move away from a housing estate at Thurrock, and a lowering of the route near the picturesque Kentish village at Boxley into a cutting to reduce noise. These were incorporated into the Bill as it ground slowly through the Commons; its Select Committee stage took 320 hours in 70 sessions.

A consortium now had to be chosen to take over Union Railways and the shortly-to-commence operations of Eurostar, which Mr MacGregor optimistically assumed would 'provide a revenue stream' toward construction of the CTRL. Four consortia were short-listed in June 1994: EuroRail (BICC, Trafalgar House, GEC, Seeboard and the NatWest and HSBC banks); LCR (initially Ove Arup, Sir William Halcrow, Bechtel, the French construction consultants Sofrerail, National Express, Blue Circle and the bankers S.G. Warburg); the German construction group Hochtief with Costain, Nishimatsu, Siemens and Westinghouse; and John Mowlem and Taylor Woodrow with the German construction firm Philipp Holzmann and the consultants W.S. Atkins and Transurb.

On 29th February, 1996, after intense negotiations on how much public money the winning consortium would need, LCR was chosen ahead of Eurorail - having knocked £400 million off its bid at the last minute to make quite certain it won. By now the consortium comprised Arup (a 2% stake), Bechtel (18%), Halcrow (2%), London Electricity (12%), National Express (17%), Systra (14%), Virgin (17%) and S.G. Warburg (18%).

The package to which LCR signed up included firm commitments by the consortium to have the line open right through to St Pancras in March 2003. It also promised a through station at Stratford close to the important rail and underground interchange there, and a head-on connection outside St Pancras between the CTRL and lines to the WCML, allowing the then-projected Regional Eurostars for Manchester and Birmingham to make their London stop at Stratford only and offering the prospect of some domestic traffic. Neither of these schemes was provided for in the CTRL Bill, and separate public inquiries were duly held late in 1997.

In return for undertaking to construct the CTRL, LCR was given a 999-year lease on the line. Under a complicated subsidy package then claimed to be worth £1.4 billion (plus the writing-off of £1.3 billion in Eurostar debt), the company was gifted St Pancras station, much of the Kings Cross railway lands and land at Stratford, the profits from development to be split with the Government. The latter also put up a contribution toward Railtrack's Thameslink 2000 scheme, covering much of the cost of works at St Pancras in the expectation that a start on the project, still stalled today, was imminent, and there was further cash in recognition of the CTRL's likely value in eventually taking long-distance commuters from Kent off the Railtrack network.

LCR hit the ground running, taking over Eurostar and refining plans for the CTRL as the legislation passed through Parliament, being granted the Royal Assent on 18th December, 1996. However, it soon became evident that Eurostar would be a drain on LCR's resources rather than a source of income, and that even without the fire of November 1996, its market would grow 40 per cent less rapidly than had been predicted. In addition, the French management of the newly privatised Connex South Eastern was warning that commuter traffic from East Kent over the CTRL - income from which had been factored into the costings - was most unlikely to be economic. By the May 1997 election, the consortium's management had concluded that it would not be able to deliver the CTRL in the form promised without further Government funding, but left it just too late to approach Ministers before the poll.

As the position deteriorated, LCR first abandoned its plans to float that autumn on the stock market, then opened talks about some form of joint venture with Railtrack . . . whose new Chief Executive Gerald Corbett was in no hurry to add to that company's mounting burdens. Meanwhile the work of refining the plans for the CTRL - which continued to be costed at £3.4 billion - never faltered. Some preliminary works were begun and two tunnelling contracts awarded, but the target of a start on construction proper by the end of 1997 was quietly missed.

On 27th January, 1998, LCR imploded. Sir Derek Hornby - who later described the day as 'the worst in my business life' - and Adam Mills asked John Prescott for a further £1.2 billion to deliver the CTRL in return for a share of the eventual profits; to their surprise, if no-one else's, the Deputy Prime Minister flatly refused. The following evening Mr Prescott told MPs in an emergency statement that he had given LCR 30 days to come up with new proposals for funding the CTRL and supporting the operation of Eurostar, or the deal would collapse with BR taking back the flagship train service; his deadline was later extended to the end of June as a new way forward was negotiated. The alternative to setting such a deadline would have been to pull the plug instantly on LCR and come up with some completely new vehicle for financing and constructing the CTRL, delaying the project by a further couple of years.

On 3rd June, 1998 Mr Prescott approved an arrangement with Railtrack under which the CTRL would be delivered with only an extra £140 million contributed by the taxpayer - in return for a 35 per cent share in profits after 2020; the National Audit Office later queried whether the benefits were as great as Mr Prescott claimed - concluding in 2005 that the taxpayer might have to fund up to £400 million more than forecast - but the agreement did achieve its end of getting the link built. Under this Public-Private Partnership LCR remained in existence as a holding company to avoid legal complications, and with the length of the concessions for both the CTRL and Eurostar reduced from 999 years to 90, after which each would revert to the State. Operation of Eurostar was devolved to a new consortium of National Express, BA, SNCF and SNCB. Railtrack undertook to buy the Cheriton Junction-Fawkham Junction section of the CTRL on completion, with an option also to purchase the remaining portion from Southfleet to St Pancras which LCR was contractually bound to complete. In practice, however, Railtrack was now in the driving seat over construction of the CTRL, managing the project on LCR's behalf with Bechtel, and when three years later Railtrack's financial and management problems became acute, the company gave up its option over the second phase and Bechtel itself took charge of completing the line to St Pancras.

John Prescott's announcement marked the moment when a start, at least, on the CTRL was guaranteed. But he could not resist a backward look at the LCR fiasco. He said he had been 'appalled' on examining the deal for financing the CTRL concluded by the Conservative Government which had left its Labour successor 'seriously exposed'. Tory Ministers had taken, he said, 'the cheapest bid based on over-optimistic forecasts of Eurostar revenue' and as a consequence of their intention to conceal public subsidies for the Tunnel itself, 'Eurostar was hampered by the requirement to pay Eurotunnel for train paths it was not using'. Mr Prescott added that 'even this week, I was asked to find £100 million to pay for specially designed sleeper trains which don't work, have never been used and are now lying idle in a field'. This would not be the end of the financial juggling; under the agreement struck on 27th June, 2002 for Network Rail (NR) to replace Railtrack, Phase One of the CTRL was acquired by LCR for £295 million, offset by LCR's sale to NR for £80 million of the rights to operate, manage and maintain the entire CTRL and to manage St Pancras station.

On 5th October, 1998 LCR signed construction contracts worth over £350 million with Alfred McAlpine and AMEC for the first 10.8 km of route from Fawkham Junction to the river Medway, with Eurolink for the next 9.2 km including the Medway viaduct and North Downs tunnel, and with Kvaerner for the 14.4 km section of route through Ashford. And 10 days later John Prescott inaugurated work on the project in a ceremony beside the Medway.

Within months, a white scar began to stretch across the chalklands of Kent, turning to brown when the route veered away from the Downs, and a mottled concrete colour where it slices through the centre of Ashford. And before much longer, the formation of the new line was taking shape.

As Britain's first completely new main line for a century across a crowded region, the CTRL is a considerable feat of civil engineering. The 74 km (46 mile) Phase One alone involves 145 structures, 11 viaducts and half a dozen tunnels, while Phase Two - half the length of the initial section but 50 per cent more costly - will be in tunnel for more than half its length.

The most impressive structure on the first phase is the Medway viaduct, 1.25 km in length and crossing the river valley and two railways 80 metres upstream of the pre-existing M2 motorway bridge; a second viaduct for the M2 has also been built under the CTRL Act. The central bridge section of the railway viaduct is made up of two cantilevers cast on site, with a span of 152 metres, and one of its landward columns had to be sunk through a 20 metre layer of asbestos waste without any of the noxious material being released. But the greatest labour has gone into the 3.2 km North Downs tunnel, the first high-speed tunnel to be built in Britain, on which breakthrough was achieved on 8th June, 2000 after 14 months of tunnelling, and which was completed the following summer, five months ahead of schedule and £5 million under budget. The excavation by roadheader machines of the tunnel, 13 metres wide by 10 metres high, involved the removal of 500,000 cubic metres of chalk; the walls and roof were then shotcreted with a 30 cm thick mixture containing steel and artificial fibres to improve fire resistance in the aftermath of the Channel Tunnel fire. The tunnel is unusual in having walkways on either side and a central derailment barrier; there was room for this because of the need to provide in a single bore for the turbulence effects of two trains passing at a combined speed of over 600 kph.

Not all of the CTRL infrastructure is entirely new construction; the 5.9 km spur between Southfleet and Fawkham Junction, which may very well be mothballed once the line is open through to St Pancras, is laid mainly on the trackbed of the former Gravesend West branch, which had not seen a passenger train for half a century and was derelict and part-lifted by the time work began on the CTRL.

The most remarkable feature of work on Phase One, apart from the structures, was the development and operation of a gigantic infrastructure base at Beechbrook Farm, 5 km north-west of Ashford, which for 11 brief but crucial months served as a railway within a railway. Boasting 14.8 km of track in an extremely limited space with marshalling, reception and assembly areas, Beechbrook Farm was a nerve centre to almost rival the tunnel construction bases at Cheriton and Sangatte. Squeezed between the CTRL - to which a triangle gave access in both directions - and the Maidstone-Ashford line to which it was connected from the early autumn of 2001 till the start of 2003, it received deliveries of rail from Germany via the tunnel and ballast from Glensanda in the Hebrides, by rail from a 550,000-tonne stockpile at Grain. At Beechbrook Farm, 108-metre lengths of rail were welded into 324-metre lengths and loaded onto tracklaying trains, 1,100 metres of track having to be laid each day (the rail used at the Farm itself was second-hand from East Germany, delivered by road from Hoo Junction). Most of the gantries for the CTRL's electric catenary were also erected on site, then loaded onto trains for delivery. Two trainloads of ballast reached Beechbrook Farm each day from Grain; to maintain 'just in time' supply, two further ballast trains were kept on standby at the former Eurotunnel yard at Sevington where there was a reserve stockpile and supplies were also brought from 'virtual quarries' elsewhere in the South-East. At Beechbrook Farm the incoming trains of high-capacity hoppers - 175 of which were specially ordered by Railtrack - were remarshalled from 24 to 16 wagons for use on the route because of its steep gradients, with a locomotive at each end so that the trains could be split on site.

Beechbrook Farm also became home depot for four classes of construction locomotives - classes '08', '14', '20', and '66' - with its own stabling and fuelling point and an inspection pit for minor repairs. Ballast trains for the CTRL were hauled by Freightliner class '66/6s', which also brought in the deliveries, and EWS class '66s' also appeared on site. The locomotion for the wiring trains was more innovative: six ex-BR class '20s' from a variety of private owners, two of which (Nos. 20001 and 20148, now owned by the Class 20 Locomotive Society and the Midland Class 20 Association) had previously worked on construction of the Channel Tunnel itself. The class '20s' were backed up on occasion by two ex-BR class '14' 0-6-0 diesel hydraulics: No. 14029, hired by AMEC Spie from the Kent & East Sussex Railway as Beechbrook Farm's 'home shunter', and No. D9504. The class '14s' were not Railtrack registered but this did not matter as the CTRL until its completion was not connected to the network; they were preferred to the standard class '08' shunters because the latter lacked the power and speed needed to deputise for the class '20s' or to rescue heavy infrastructure trains. Two class '08s' did, however, also put in an appearance when No. 14029 had to be sent away for repairs. Work on the CTRL also required some impressive tamping machines which were based at Beechbrook Farm, and numerous road-railers.

Beechbrook Farm closed on 19th January, 2003 with its task officially completed, the last train working out onto the CTRL the following day. The chord to the CTRL was immediately severed, and the following month the Network Rail connection was also removed; remaining locomotives and stock had to be taken away by road. Some 70,000 tonnes of topsoil and other materials were moved in as work began on restoring the farm for agricultural use, and by August 2003 planting had been completed. (In the same spirit, construction work on Phase One of the CTRL was offset by the provision of 255 hectares of new woodland and 30 km of new hedgerows.)

On 21st January, 2003, a ceremony was held at Mersham, near Ashford, to mark the completion of civil engineering work with the Transport Minister John Spellar unveiling a commemorative plaque. The event was slightly premature: temporary sidings had to be laid beside the Lenham loops to accommodate infrastructure stock - including two class '20s' - evicted from Beechbrook Farm which had yet to complete their task, and other infrastructure trains briefly ran to sites along the CTRL from Dollands Moor; the last class '20' stayed on site until the end of June. The overhead catenary was energised in stages from 9th February, when the section between Sellindge and Detling went live. Signalling work continued into May 2003, after which Phase One of the CTRL was apparently ready for commissioning.

The first non-works trains to run on the CTRL operated as early as October 2002, when EWS class '66s' top-and-tailed the SNCF test car *Vulcain*; these runs continued until the following June. Test running proper began once civil engineering and signalling work was complete and the overhead wiring energised. On 23rd March, 2003, electro-diesel No. 73130 ran light on a video-recording trip to assist drivers' route learning. By early April an EWS class '66' was hauling a pantograph-fitted test train along the route. But the real breakthrough came on 13th April when 'North of London' Eurostar sets Nos. 373 313/4 ran at 20 mph between Ashford and Westenhanger to test clearances and overhead power supplies; quite apart from their greater availability, the shorter Eurostar sets offered greater acceleration, so could reach very high speeds more rapidly on the relatively short length of track being tested. The trial set also made the first run from the CTRL into Ashford International station on the night of 7th/8th June, and onto Network Rail metals at Fawkham Junction three nights later.

Speeds built up as the class '373s' tested out the route, mainly running at night; on 7th July the train reached the line speed of 300 kph (186 mph), comfortably exceeding the 259.5 kph (162.2 mph) record set in 1979 by the subsequently-abandoned Advanced Passenger Train, and the following day it set a further unofficial best of 330 kph (205 mph) near Lenham. In a possession on 13th July the CTRL and Eurotunnel signalling systems were finally meshed together, clearing the way for services to begin as anticipated on 28th September   - and for an official testing of the line's capacity.

Before driver training began on 3rd August, a public test run was staged on 30th July to set an official UK rail speed record and drum up business for the accelerated Eurostar service after a period when traffic had slumped. Nos. 373 313/4 left Waterloo International with driver Alan Pears of Staplehurst at the controls and with 80 railway managers and engineers aboard, including a test team from SNCF to monitor the interfaces with track and overhead. Running via Tonbridge to Ashford International, it then reversed onto the CTRL and ran to the Singlewell Freight Loop, at the 40 km mark from St Pancras, having touched 300 kph on the descent from North Downs tunnel. Reversing again, it ran past Ashford to Westenhanger at 270 kph, then on the return journey over 64 km between Westenhanger and Singlewell - running 'wrong line' - it touched 334.7 kph (208 mph) on the downhill section near Boxley tunnel. The train reached 200 kph within 2½ minutes and passed Ashford at 274 kph just five minutes after starting; kept down to 282 kph for the Tutt Hill curve, the train accelerated to its record-breaking speed, then twice touched 334.7 kph just north of the Crismill crossovers and in the Nashenden Valley before having to decelerate as the high-speed track ran out. This speed was only possible because the cab signalling had been disconnected to prevent the brakes being automatically applied on exceeding 330 kph; the train could have gone faster still, but safety inspectors had promised not to test the line's design speed of 350 kph - a limit still dwarfed by the TGV's best-ever 515 kph.

Phase One of the CTRL was formally handed over to Union Railways (South) by the Rail Link Engineering consortium - essentially the engineering shareholders of LCR who had forfeited their interest in operating Eurostar - at a ceremony on 22nd August, 2003; operation until 2086 devolved to Network Rail CTRL Ltd, a wholly owned subsidiary of Network Rail. Despite the appearance of on-time completion, it had in fact been a scramble to get the line ready for opening. A delay beyond the 28th September starting date was actively discussed with other operators until it became evident that this would cause chaos, as Connex would be introducing a completely reshaped timetable that day on the assumption that it would no longer have to contend with Eurostars on the routes through Tonbridge and Maidstone. As with the Channel Tunnel itself, the problem was not so much with late-running construction as with delays in delivery and installation of equipment – especially for signalling, with some issues still not resolved until well into August – disruptions in the power supply as late as the maximum-load power test on 27th August and a tardy commissioning process. Dynamic testing of the wheel/rail interface had slipped from March to June, and driver training could not begin until August; as two-thirds of Eurostar's 250 drivers are French and August is the month when working France is on holiday, not all had undergone training on the CTRL when full passenger services began.

With the loose ends of commissioning sorted out in the nick of time, the official opening of Phase One went ahead on 16th September. Prime Minister Tony Blair inaugurated the route at a ceremony at Waterloo International, commending Mr Prescott for rescuing the project in its early stages and saying of the day's slogan 'on time and on budget': 'We don't associate these phrases with civil engineering or railway projects in this country. This project gives optimism as to what we can do in the future'. The first civilian-carrying Eurostar – once again Nos. 373 313/4 – then made a high-speed transit of the CTRL from Fawkham Junction to a specially-constructed platform at Sandling, with Transport Secretary Alistair Darling and the massed ranks of the media aboard. Huge efforts were made this time to avoid the embarrassment of a breakdown: a Eurostar class '37' with match wagons looped at Kent House in case a rescue was necessary, a standby Eurostar in the loop at Singlewell and, at Sandling, a second North of London set, borrowed from GNER but in Eurostar livery. On the way back, the press train overtook at Peckham Rye Thameslink's No. 319 009 *Coquelles*, which a decade before had been the first passenger-carrying train through the Channel Tunnel.

The journey was flawless and the coverage positive, but as with the launch of Eurostar nine years before the success of the venture was overshadowed. This time the negatives were in no way Eurostar's responsibility: at 0700 that morning a GNER express to Glasgow derailed in the throat of Kings Cross station because a Jarvis maintenance team had removed a 5 ft section of rail and handed the line back for operation without informing the signal box. Given that the incident was a carbon-copy of two previous failures by Jarvis, at Potters Bar and Aldwarke, an avalanche of adverse publicity ensued, to the fury of Network Rail Chief Executive and Union Rail veteran John Armitt who, like the Prime Minister, had seen the CTRL opening as an opportunity to prove that the rail industry had turned the corner. Within a month, Jarvis had withdrawn from rail maintenance and Network Rail had announced that it was bringing all such work in-house.

On Saturday 27th September, 2003, a special train packed with celebrities, the media and competition prizewinners took advantage of the CTRL to set a new London-Paris record time of 2 hrs 18 min. 29 sec.; a second train reached Brussels in under two hours. The following day, with relatively little ceremony, the link between Fawkham Junction and Cheriton Junction came into commercial use, the first service train to transit it southbound being the 0801 Waterloo-Gare du Nord; as this train stopped at Ashford International, the first to use the full length of the new route was the 1007 non-stop service to Paris. Northbound the first train over the

An HGV shuttle train nears the tunnel's French portal. Note the club car and the loading wagon behind it. *Bob Sweet*

A busy time at Cheriton, with both types of Eurotunnel HGV shuttle stock in action: on the left, one of the original rakes of BREDA stock unloading, and to the right a train of the more open and recent Arbel wagons awaiting departure. *Bob Sweet*

White elephant: a seated carriage for the Nightstar service almost completed at Washwood Heath, Birmingham. *Bob Sweet*

The interior of a Nightstar seated carriage. The very high floor and consequent lack of headroom deterred potential users when the service was abandoned. *Bob Sweet*

The Eurostar 'flight deck' with comfortable driving position, modern controls and a surprisingly small window. *Eurostar*

Rebuilt shuttle locomotive No. 9825 at Coquelles prior to entering service in its new form, February 2004. *Eurotunnel*

A study in under-used power: No. 92028 emerges from the French portal with an international freight train.   *Bob Sweet*

Eurostars Nos. 373207/08 breast the tape at Waterloo International on 27th April, 2004 as they are named *Michel Hollard*.   *Bob Sweet*

Eurotunnel's other electric motive power - ex-SNCF 'Crocodile' No. 13044 at Coquelles.

Bob Sweet

Two of Eurotunnel's Krupp diesel-electric locomotives prepare to enter the tunnel at night with a works train. *Bob Sweet*

Winter in the Beussingue Trench: a Eurostar bound for SNCF metals leaves the French portal.
Bob Sweet

Activity at the French portal: a Tri-Bo banks in a car/coach shuttle train as a class '92' breaks cover with a freight.
Bob Sweet

The worst of the damage in the tunnel at the seat of the fire, just after removal of the train.

A close-up of the tedious process of removing and replacing the fire-damaged lining of the tunnel.

Patrick Ponsolle, Executive Chairman of Eurotunnel, unveils a plaque to mark the completion of repairs, May 1997.

Asylum seekers on the move in the yard at Fréthun - note the ones in the shadows checking freight wagons for a way in.   *EWS*

Farthest south (to date): the inaugural Eurostar reaches Avignon Centre, 2002.   *Eurostar*

Class '33/2' No. 33202 *Burma Star* is engaged on ballasting Waterloo International on 14th November, 1992, the first train into the new terminal. In the background class '60' No. 60040 *Brecon Beacons* and class '33/1' No. 33114 *Ashford 150* double-head as they depart from Waterloo with the 0930 'Mule and Otter Axeman' special for Okehampton and Meldon Quarry.

Brian Morrison

There are Eurostars in all five platforms at Waterloo International on 5th December, 2001. To the right class '159' No. 159105 slows as it enters Waterloo. *Brian Morrison*

The approaches to Waterloo. Commuter trains on the left, to the right an incoming Eurostar which has just passed Vauxhall. *Bob Sweet*

Class '373' No. 3101 stands outside North Pole depot on 9th December, 1993.

Brian Morrison

No. 3002 inside the depot at North Pole on 23rd June, 1993.   *Brian Morrison*

Class '373' units Nos. 3003 and 3004 on the 'classic route' between Dunton Green and Knockholt with the 1219 Paris Nord-Waterloo on 20th February, 2001. *Brian Morrison*

Ashford International: a class '373' pauses before the completion of the CTRL. Eurostars serving these platforms now travel 'under the wires'. *Eurostar*

International freight on the West Coast Main Line: EWS No. 92001 *Victor Hugo* hauls a train of containers well north of Wembley.   *EWS*

Dollands Moor yard from the west prior to the construction of the CTRL. A class '92' is in the maintenance shed, and a freight train bound for the Continent is just leaving the then main line for the exchange sidings.   *EWS*

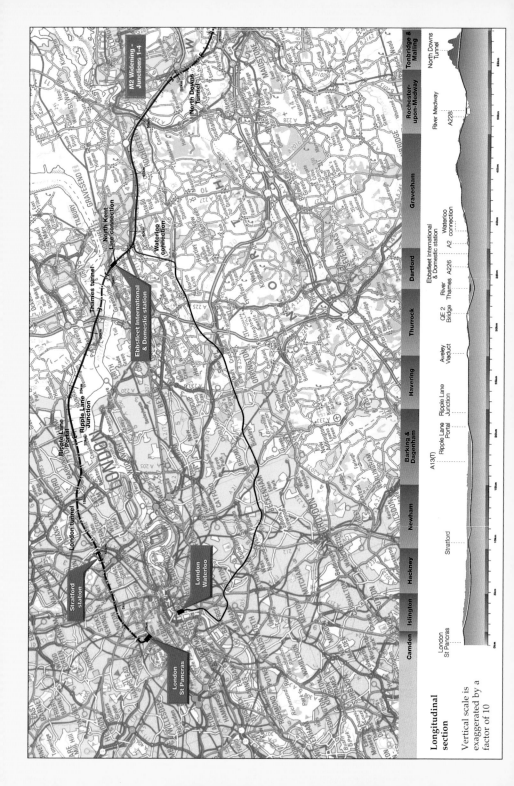

Longitudinal section

Vertical scale is exaggerated by a factor of 10

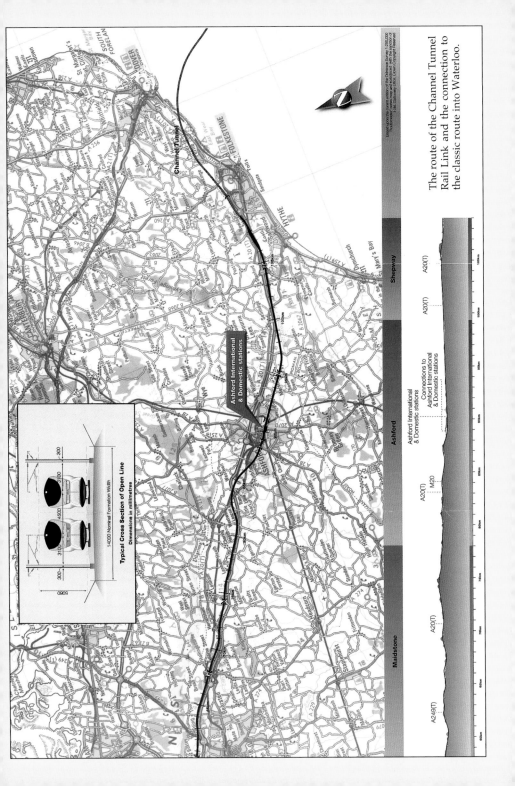

The route of the Channel Tunnel Rail Link and the connection to the classic route into Waterloo.

Typical Cross Section of Open Line
Dimensions in millimetres

14000 Nominal Formation Width

Maidstone

Ashford

Shepway

Ashford International & Domestic stations

Connections to Ashford International & Domestic stations

The Cheriton terminal looking towards London, on a quiet day at the turn of the century. The formation for the CTRL can be seen either side of the railway bisecting the site - the track has yet to be laid. Dollands Moor is just visible in the distance. *Eurotunnel*

CTRL was the 0756 Brussels-Waterloo; 10 minutes north of Ashford, it passed the 0801 at a combined speed exceeding 550 kph. The Channel Tunnel Rail Link was well and truly in business.

*   *   *   *   *

From the English Channel Tunnel portal to Waterloo International, by the classic route CTR1 was 114.1 km; the speediest trains took the best part of 80 minutes. Via the now-open section of the CTRL the journey is 110.9 km and the journey takes less than an hour; the record-breaking run on 27th September, 2003 covered the distance to Waterloo in 47 minutes. From the Cheriton portal to St Pancras the distance will be 111.6 km, and Eurostars will regularly do it in 32 minutes.

For trains arriving from the Continent, the CTRL begins 1.9 km to landward of the portal, where ownership switches from Eurotunnel to Network Rail. Originally Eurostars continued through the terminal site to link with the Folkestone line at Continental Junction after a further 1.8 km; that junction was disconnected in July 2002 and the connection with the Folkestone line moved 1.5 km westward to the present Saltwood Junction. Now, at a new Cheriton Junction some 600 m into Network Rail's territory, the CTRL diverges on either side from a 2.5 km double-track connection from the portal to the classic line from Dover toward London, which has been slewed a little to the south, parallel with the west end of Dollands Moor freight sidings; the new alignment takes this line close to Folkestone Rugby Club and a special fence has been erected to keep stray balls off the track. There is no facing connection at Cheriton between the CTRL and the Folkestone route.

Until the opening of the CTRL, Eurostars accelerated from the BR linespeed as they approached the tunnel; now they decelerate to the tunnel's maximum 160 kph, provided they have a clear path ahead. The fact that they are approaching the tunnel at higher speed than previously makes it more important ever that they arrive on time to secure their 'slot'; otherwise they face a severe check on the approach to Cheriton if a shuttle train ahead is proceeding on schedule; trains approaching the tunnel decelerate by stages through 300, 270, 240 and 200 kph to 160 kph to enter the tunnel. Equally, Eurostars emerging from the tunnel accelerate by stages to the line speed of 300 kph (186 mph).

The up line of the CTRL forks to the south of the connection with Network Rail parallel with the east end of the Cheriton terminal's loading platforms, running at first in parallel with that connection. The divergence of the CTRL's down line lies some 300 m to the west, level with the west end of the loading platforms. Soon after, the two lines of the CTRL diverge to run either side of the existing railway and Dollands Moor, the up line rising beside the yard onto the 320 m-long, 25 m-high Grange Alders viaduct to cross the Folkestone line and the down line falling to the same level as the sidings, from which there is a spur in either direction on a 1 in 40 gradient, quite a challenge for heavy freight trains making a standing start or braking as they come off the CTRL. As the domestic lines run into Saltwood tunnel, by now well above the level of Dollands Moor, the up CTRL is routed above it, slewing over to the north side of the Network Rail tracks to rejoin the down CTRL, which at this point is also in a short tunnel.

From there to Ashford, the CTRL runs on the north side of the existing railway, drawing close to it just west of Sandling station, rising and dipping alongside the domestic line (with very short tunnels at 104 km and 95 km from St Pancras) and passing unnervingly close to the down platform at Westenhanger station, close to which there is a pair of crossovers. Nine kilometres from the tunnel, around the 100 km mark, is the neutral section over which Eurostar drivers reset the height of their pantographs. Trains approaching the tunnel are generally coasting by this point, as their generous schedule out of Waterloo usually leaves them with time in hand to catch their 'slot' through the tunnel.

Approaching Ashford, the fan of sidings at Sevington, reached by a trailing connection from the Folkestone-Ashford line, can be seen on the seaward side, and soon after, on the town's eastern fringe, a pedestrian subway under the CTRL and the classic line replaces the celebrated Willesborough level crossing, the last manually-operated crossing on any British main line on its abolition in 2001. As the line enters the built-up area wooden baffles - preferred to the concrete ones used throughout the TGV system - shield residents from the worst of the noise. The section of line between Cheriton and Ashford was the last civil engineering contract to be let, because of problems of land acquisition, design and working so close to the existing railway. Unexpectedly wet conditions just below ground which resulted in a £50 million insurance claim led to sounder earth being transferred from the Dollands Moor area.

Into Ashford the London-bound CTRL rises onto a viaduct - not high but at 1.43 km the longest on Phase One - to take it over two branches of the River Stour and the Canterbury lines, slicing through the carriage sidings where the depot for the domestic CTRL stock will be located. At Ashford East Junction (92.7 km from St Pancras) two tracks branch off at ground level to serve Ashford International station, while the through CTRL runs past the platforms to the north on a decreasing elevation. In the station itself, four through platform lines have been dual-electrified on the third-rail and overhead systems - platforms 3 and 4 for use by international trains and 5 and 6 in reserve and eventually for domestic CTRL services - and Eurostars stopping at Ashford International - eight minutes from the Cheriton portal and 50 from Waterloo - switch from cab to lineside signalling through the station loop.

Eurostars not stopping at Ashford transit the town in a flash, and mostly underground. Commuters awaiting packed and snail-paced South-Eastern services for London were frustrated enough to watch Eurostars chugging through the station at less than 100 kph when the service began; now they can see them swooping across the viaduct only yards away at 270 kph before, in the case of those bound for London, plunging into a tunnel down a gradient roughly the length of the station's elongated platforms. The hope is, however, held out to them that by 2009 the CTRL will give them a better journey to work, though at a price. Commuter trains from St Pancras over the CTRL - up to four an hour at peak times and two off-peak - will take as little as 37 minutes to reach Ashford, 90.4 km from St Pancras. They will be able to access the domestic platforms, where temporary nosing – removable if TGVs ever start calling - extends the platforms to the width of Network Rail stock, and then continue to Canterbury or Folkestone/Dover. Similarly Eurostars routed over CTR1 and CTR2 because of engineering work on the Link will be able to rejoin the high-speed route over the Ashford station fan.

Originally the CTRL was planned to pass to the north of Ashford town centre, requiring the demolition of only four homes, but the borough council preferred a more central alignment despite the need for greater demolition and for a 1.65 km cut-and-cover tunnel under the west of the town. At the west end of Ashford station, the CTRL runs beneath the Maidstone line (CTR2) with an impressive pair of grade-separated junctions for the high-speed tracks serving the station; these continue beyond the tunnel's western portal to join the CTRL proper at Ashford West

Junction, 88.3 km from St Pancras. During construction of the CTRL through Ashford, a new Maidstone Relief Line was also built on a new formation around the CTRL 'box' to give access for trains to the north side of Ashford station from CTR2 without conflicting with international trains; this line came into use in September 2002.

For 30 km west of Ashford, the high-speed route runs roughly parallel with the Maidstone line and the M20 as far as Boxley, just north of Maidstone, though the motorway is more gently curved; one kink in the CTRL at Tutt Hill has required a 270 kph speed limit as its radius, at 4,000 m, falls well short of the standard 5,400 m minimum for French TGV routes which applies to the rest of the line. Even trains accelerating away from Ashford International overtake the traffic on the motorway at approaching thrice its speed; when the Ashford-Maidstone railway, the old CTR2, is reached, trains on it appear almost to be stationary. Past the site of Beechbrook Farm, 86 km from St Pancras, which has been restored to agricultural use, the line transits the 120 m tunnel at Leacon Lane (82.5 km) to reach the first of the two pairs of loops on Phase One (each of them 2 km long to accommodate two freight trains) at Lenham Heath (77-79 km).

On the London side of Lenham Eurostar passengers do not see much of the countryside; much of the line is in either chalk, grassy or baffle-lined cuttings and there are a further four short cut-and-cover tunnels, at Sandway (74 km), Harrietsham (71 km), Eyhorne (68 km) and Boxley itself, at the 60 km mark. These tunnels were constructed in a novel way; after excavation, concrete footings were built along each side of the line with a groove in their top surface. Into these, pre-cast concrete units were placed, each forming half of the tunnel's cross-section and joined where they met with a sealing strip. The opposing units were craned in in staggered formation, overlapping for half of their length to support subsequent units. Half-length sections were then installed to square off the tunnel portals. At Crismill (66 km), where the CTRL crosses the Ashford-Maidstone line to strike north, there is the first high-speed crossover since one close to the Channel Tunnel portal; lower-speed crossovers for freight and maintenance working are also provided at Westenhanger and either side of the Lenham loops. The following 15 km of line saw a new UK rail speed record of 334.7 kph set on a trial run on 30th July, 2003, but by the end of it service trains are reining back to 230 kph.

From Boxley the CTRL turns northward to transit North Downs tunnel (3.2 km in length), entering it 57.6 km from St Pancras and reaching a summit just inside the tunnel's northern end. Many passengers find the transit of this tunnel, though brief, even more dramatic than the journey beneath the Channel: Eurostars blast through it at full speed, passengers' ears 'pop' vigorously, you can feel the train passing over the hump that marks the summit and if you pass another train in the single bore the experience is remarkable. Out of the tunnel and now falling, the high-speed line joins the alignment of the M2, almost half-way from the Cheriton portal to St Pancras. Road and rail then run side by side, falling sharply, and at 51 km from its eventual London terminus, after further crossovers at Nashenden (52 km) the line crosses the Medway viaduct – from which the sea, as at Coquelles and Cheriton, is frustratingly not quite visible - passing over first the river, then the Maidstone-Strood line and, just beyond it, the Chatham-Victoria route which Eurostars for Waterloo will soon be joining at Fawkham Junction, in preparation for which they brake from their maximum speed after effortlessly outpacing motorway traffic over the river. Still hugging the M2 and later the A2, the line passes through a short tunnel at Halfpence Lane (45 km) and skirts the south of Gravesend, with a further pair of freight loops - their rails starting to rust through disuse - and a feeder station for the catenary at Singlewell, 42 km from St Pancras; between the Medway and Singlewell the line climbs steeply again from 44 metres (120 ft) above sea level to 107 metres (350 ft). Briefly near Singlewell there is a glimpse of the Thames Estuary, though once again it falls tantalisingly short of the sea itself.

Beyond Singlewell, with the line now falling, lies the grade-separated junction at Southfleet, 39.2 km out from Waterloo and 40.1 from St Pancras, which now marks the limit of high-speed working; it is preceded by a single crossover.

From Southfleet the 5.9 km double track connection to Fawkham Junction strikes sharply south-east at a flying junction over the route of the continuing CTRL; since mid-2005 the track has started snaking under the down line from Waterloo toward Ebbsfleet and St Pancras. Waterloo-bound trains are limited to 120 kph on the stiff curve at this point in preparation for the congested approaches to London, but in practice are running slower as they approach the neutral section. Between Southfleet and Fawkham Junction the switch from overhead to third-rail current and vice versa is made, a change often detectable from a momentary cut-off in the air conditioning, and trains progress gingerly in each direction; the catenary ends some 500 m short of the junction of the classic line from the Medway towns. The CTRL was planned on the understanding that it would open through to St Pancras from the start, so this connection was designed as a branch. But as the line was eventually built in two stages, the Fawkham connection will now carry all the CTRL's traffic - until 2007, though none thereafter.

From Fawkham, 1 km west of Longfield station, London-bound Eurostars run over the classic route to Waterloo, 34.6 km and 26 minutes away if all goes to plan. For the first 8 km they run on a section of double track previously unserved by international trains through Farningham Road to join CTR2, the present freight route to the tunnel, at Swanley, and thence to Waterloo as previously, with the Shortlands underpass making an on-time arrival more likely.

Westward of this viaduct, the line runs at ground level through an industrial area, re-crossing the Tilbury line west of Purfleet and then running just yards away from that route on its southern side as far as Dagenham Dock station. Soon after crossing the c2c route the CTRL runs onto the 750 m ground-level Aveley viaduct. In the spring of 2003 a 35 m-high piling rig – one of only three of its kind in the world – being used to move this viaduct forward toppled over onto the c2c lines when it met an underground obstruction; fortunately all trains were safely stopped. The CTRL next crosses Rainham Marshes; signs at Rainham station tell London-bound passengers to 'stand well back', but the 'whoosh' from the Eurostars just behind them will be far more unnerving than the passage of a class 357 'Electrostar' travelling at less than half the speed. This section of track has had to be heavily underpinned by piling because of the boggy ground beneath, so that it effectively runs on a ground-level viaduct; there is a 530 m viaduct proper across Rainham Creek.

As Dagenham Dock is approached, the CTRL threads its way between the c2c lines to the north and the huge Ford exchange sidings to Ripple Lane Junction, just at the London end of the station. Ripple Lane is of importance because it throws off the only link with the CTRL (the line into Dollands Moor yard apart) designed purely for freight. Although there will be a connection at Stratford for various uses, it will face away from the Channel Tunnel so Ripple Lane - where developers are now proposing an international freight facility - will be the prime, and possibly the sole, point for freight to join the route; indeed from this point no line speed for freight has been set. Ford's Dagenham plant is an important generator of traffic for the tunnel even after the end of car production; it will have effectively a private siding connection straight off the CTRL, so the connection to the Ripple Lane yards should prove of use. It will give access for international traffic not only to local freight objectives but, via Barking and the Tottenham and Hampstead line, to the East Coast and (more importantly) West Coast main lines. The freight chord would not enable through commuter services from St Pancras to Tilbury to operate, reviving an overground service that lingered into the 1960s for boat trains. There is, however, scope for CTRL trains unable to enter the London tunnels for any reason to access the exchange sidings; it is not clear what would happen after that. Heavy resiting work has been needed in the vicinity of Ripple Lane, including the slewing of one track of the Tilbury line, the relocation of some freight sidings, the reconstruction of three bridges over the route and the construction of a new one at Choats Manor Way. In addition, the up station buildings at Dagenham Dock, where a level crossing over the c2c route has been abolished, have had to be resited to squeeze in the CTRL.

Ripple Lane supplemented Kent Portal as the base for tracklaying, as the work moved nearer to St Pancras. In November 2004, class '14' No. D9504 was transferred north of the Thames to Ripple Lane to shunt infrastructure trains, and to handle them two new 'low emission' class '66/9s' from Freightliner were drafted in, Nos. 66951/52. These have hauled all tracklaying trains in the London tunnels, and also topped and tailed rakes of Autoballaster trains on the surface section - the only non-SNCF wagons used in the construction of Phase 2. In the tunnels on Phase 2, the track is put in place and then concreted in.

As the country portal of the CTRL's London tunnels, Ripple Lane is also the last place for 20 km where London-bound passengers will see daylight (save for a flicker in the Stratford station 'box'), and the first where those heading for Kent and beyond will come into the open; originally the line was to have stayed above ground for a few hundred metres closer to St Pancras, but protests from local residents led to a rethink. The CTRL's London tunnels, although constructed in several sections, have been built to a common specification. Reaching more than 30 metres below ground in places, they have twin bores, each 8.15 metres in external diameter with concrete linings 450 mm thick to give an internal diameter of 7.25 metres. Connecting cross-passages are provided roughly every 600 metres so that in the event of fire a smoke-free 'safe haven' for passengers can be created in the non-incident tunnel by large fans in the ventilation shafts which are provided every 3 km; these shafts are not designed for access or escape.

The first section of the 9.9 km East London tunnel heads north-west from Ripple Lane to Stratford. On a steady upgrade toward the city centre after the initial drop from ground level, it is was bored in two sections: 5.4 km from Dagenham to the ventilation shaft at Barrington Road, East Ham, and a further 4.5 km from there to Stratford, with two TBMs being used for each bore in each section. As far as Stratford, the line speed for Eurostars will be 230 kph, and for domestic trains 200 kph but in practice all trains will run at the same speed to prevent bunching. There will be paths for 16 trains an hour, two of them open-access to be offered to other operators. The two TBMs boring London-wards from Ripple Lane worked through to Barrington Road and were dismantled on site, their parts being removed via the ventilation shaft there and a second, temporary, shaft purely for this purpose. (There are smaller shafts halfway along this section, at Wayside between Ripple Lane and Barrington Road, and at Woodgrange between there and Stratford.) The tunnels between Ripple Lane and Barrington Road were bored in two years from June 2002 by the TBMS *Maysam* and *Judy*.

Two further TBMs – *Brunel* and *Hudson* - set out from the Stratford International station 'box' for Barrington Road toward the end of 2002, and safely negotiated a tricky opening section where the bores passed within 5 m of the Central Line underground tunnels. Then they hit trouble. They had got only as far as Lavender Street, close to Maryland station and well short of the Woodgrange ventilation shaft, when on 8th February, 2003 several back gardens disappeared into a large hole in the ground; homes were evacuated and work below ground suspended while 700 tonnes of liquid concrete were poured into the hole to stabilise buildings round it. One house was rendered uninhabitable and LCR purchased it. Locals claimed that warnings to project engineers that the area was honeycombed with 150-year-old wells had been ignored; one engineer told *The Times*: 'We knew of the wells, but we didn't expect them to interfere with the tunnel'. A re-examination of the area's soil structure was hurriedly undertaken, work resuming six months later; breakthrough at Barrington Road in this direction was achieved in December 2003.

Stratford International and Temple Mills

Stratford is the CTRL's secondary objective in London, but important nevertheless. Its pedigree as a railway interchange predates the Channel Tunnel by a century and a half, and by the Millennium it could boast the Anglia main line, the extensive network of Great Eastern suburban services, the eastern extension of London Underground's Central Line (running onto what were steam-operated suburban branches into the 1940s and beyond), the extended Jubilee Line, the Docklands Light Railway, Silverlink's Richmond-North Woolwich service via the North London line and a moribund West Anglia Great Northern (WAGN) service to the Lea Valley and

Stansted Airport. With a bus interchange offering services to most of East and North-East London, the City only 10 minutes away by rail or tube, a bustling local centre and a swathe of former railway land available for regeneration, it promises to attract considerable traffic for the CTRL on both international and domestic services. London's successful bid for the 2012 Olympic Games, with the principal stadium on former railway lands at Stratford, made considerable play of the CTRL's ability to bring in spectators.

The Stratford International station which CTRL trains will serve is 9.3 km or just 7 minutes from St Pancras. Over this section a 'Javelin' shuttle service will operate during the Olympics; to enable this, international services will not stop at Stratford for the duration of the Games. Stratford International has had to be sited slightly to the north of Stratford's existing two-level station complex where space simply could not be made for more platforms; appropriately it will be on the site of the former Great Eastern Railway locomotive works. The 500-metre transfer between stations would be irksome on foot, so Ministers specified a travelator - something LCR has resisted on grounds of cost and the surprising view that domestic routes serving Stratford will generate few Eurostar passengers. In addition a short northward extension of the DLR from Stratford to Stratford International has been authorised for completion late in 2008, after Stratford International has opened but before CTRL domestic services begin. Any extension to the existing DLR route from bay platform 4 of the present station - which itself has proved inadequate and is being replaced by two new platforms further south - would be impracticable without an expensive flyover or tunnel to cross all the high-level running lines, so the idea has evolved instead of handing over the Low Level platforms (and the line operated by Silverlink between there and Canning Town) to the DLR, with its trains running northward from those platforms to Stratford International, reinforced by a Stratford Low Level-Stratford International shuttle. Services to and from Richmond will be diverted into new platforms to the north of the main line.

Stratford International has been constructed below ground in a box 1 km long between the 9 km and 10 km marks, 50 metres wide and 25 metres deep which also served as the base for TBMs boring out toward Barrington Road and St Pancras, and back to which spoil from each bore was fed from the TBM head by conveyor belt (rather than by contractor's railway). The box was completed in 20 months from July 2001, during which time 800,000 cubic metres of spoil were removed from it. Just as work on the CTRL had uncovered Roman, Saxon and medieval artefacts of considerable charm and importance in the Kentish countryside, the Stratford box also yielded up relics of the past, but to the astonishment of the paleontologists who sifted through the spoil, the findings were of fossilised oysters, shark teeth and palm trees, indicating that 55 million years previously Stratford had been submerged under shallow sub-tropical waters. Maintaining the maritime theme, the station 'box' would accommodate the *Queen Mary* three times over . . . and would float on the groundwater beneath it but for six borehole pumps able to shift 43 cubic metres of water per hour.

Most CTRL domestic services will stop at Stratford, and perhaps half the Eurostars to and from St Pancras, it is possible the Stratford stops will be introduced some months after the switch from Waterloo to St Pancras. When 'North of London' services were planned, Stratford would have been the sole London stop for through trains between, say, Paris and Manchester. The possibility was also raised early on, and is now being mooted once more, that some West Coast Main Line trains could serve Stratford instead of Euston via the direct connection being installed north of St

Pancras. There will be two outer platforms for international trains and two in the centre, with a higher platform level, for domestic services operated by GoVia, the winner of the integrated South East and CTRL franchise. Not only will Eurostar passengers be segregated at Stratford International for customs and immigration; those awaiting trains for the Continent will only be admitted to the platform when their train is due, to guard against being swept off the platform by the blast from Eurostars passing through the confined space at 200 kph or more. The foundation stone for the new station was laid on 23rd March, 2004.

As the CTRL enters the Stratford International box from the east, a single track comes in from Temple Mills yard to the north, descending from ground to track level through the heart of the station and bisecting the central island platform in the process; it connects with each track of the CTRL at the portal of the tunnel for St Pancras. This chord will primarily be used by empty Eurostar stock running to and from the new Temple Mills depot.

The Eurostar rolling stock depot at Temple Mills was originally intended as a supplement to North Pole, not as replacement for it. Indeed the original contract advertised in the Official Journal of the European Communities in April 2004 was for a relatively modest depot, costed at £64 million. But a combination of increasing congestion on the North London line preventing stock moves between North Pole and St Pancras without further costly upgrades, and Eurostar's decision not to continue a limited service from Waterloo once the CTRL was completed, brought the further inevitable decision to base all Eurostar stock at the London end of the service at Temple Mills.

Thus it was that on 26th November, 2004, Transport Secretary Alistair Darling announced Government approval - and funding - for a £402 million depot at Temple Mills to house the entire Eurostar rolling stock operation 'in time for the commencement of Eurostar services on CTRL Section 2 in 2007', the headline figure to include the cost of relocation and of diverting the Stratford-Lea Bridge line a mile north of Stratford station to accommodate the now larger facility.

Temple Mills depot will be on a more generous scale than North Pole, partly because the site - on railway-owned land - is wider and partly because, in Eurostar's words, 'access to it will be to the larger European loading gauge so that, like the rest of CTRL, it can be used in the future by trains built to more generous European dimensions'. The main shed will have eight roads, and incorporate a servicing area, carriage wash and bogie drop together with offices and stores. The depot complex will include 11 miles of track with overhead electrification, and there will be facilities to test trains to mainland European voltages as well as the two UK systems. The depot will be protected by two miles of high steel fencing and £2 million worth of closed circuit television equipment. The transfer of operations and stock from North Pole to Stratford would involve a 12 hour shutdown of the service, with inbound Eurostars running empty for repositioning to Temple Mills.

To make way for the new depot, Network Rail has moved its major infrastructure yard at Temple Mills to a reconstructed Whitemoor yard at March. EWS has also had to re-site its Stratford diesel depot. But no room has been found to stable CTRL domestic stock; this will largely be stabled at Ashford. Space has also had to be found at Stratford during construction of the CTRL for an on-site factory for casting tunnel sections, and a sizeable stockpile of sections for when all four TBMs pushing away from the 'box' are working flat-out; this site is now ear-marked for the Olympic stadium.

Around Stratford International station, a huge redevelopment known as Stratford City is planned: 4,500 homes, 465,000 sq. metres of office space, two schools, a 50-storey hotel and 160,000 sq. metres of shopping space, most of this on former railway land, raised clear of the Lea Valley flood plain by spoil from the London tunnels.

Construction of Stratford International and its associated works has disrupted some train operations. The High Meads loop and Lea Curve were closed for a year in 2001-2, requiring the diversion of some freight trains via Stratford station which are normally able to avoid it, and of the Ipswich-Tilbury Freightliner via Cambridge. The then little-used Platforms 11 and 12 on the north side of the station which now host Stansted Airport trains were also severed, requiring WAGN's sole daily Cheshunt service (since increased) to use Platform 10a in the main station. But main line passenger services have largely been unaffected.

From the Stratford box, the CTRL runs almost due west in twin-tube tunnel for 7.5 km beneath the North London Line. Boring on this section by a Nishimatsu/Skanska joint venture began at Stratford on 29th August, 2002, when two 1,100-ton Kawasaki TBMs named *Annie* and *Bertha* by Islington schoolchildren got down to work with a target of 95 metres each per week; it had taken two months to crane the components into the box and assemble them. The principal ventilation shaft on this final section, at Graham Road, Hackney, is at 55 m in depth, the deepest in the world to have diaphragm walling; the first TBM reached this point from Stratford on 3rd June, 2003, and two months later *Annie* passed the 5 km mark, with the two TBMs between them having by then excavated a million tonnes of spoil, all of it fed back to Stratford by conveyor belt. *Annie* broke through at Kings Cross on 27th January, 2004, and *Bertha* on 11th March, completing the boring of the London tunnels. Concrete paving was laid along the tunnels, the final section on 22nd October, and that December tracklaying in the Stratford-Kings Cross tunnels began. One tunnel remained free of track just long enough for delegates from the International Olympic Committee to be whisked through it in Range Rovers on 17th February, 2005 to demonstrate the contribution the CTRL St Pancras connection could make to transport for the 2012 Games. The previous day there had been a press conference in the incomplete Stratford International station concourse. Transport was initially the London bid's Achilles' heel, but in the final outcome it was a strength.

For the final 5 km of tunnel, trains will be decelerating or accelerating sharply; smart control work will be needed on this section to keep services running on time and to capacity at peak periods. Clearances on this final section are tight; several surface railway lines crossing the route from north to south are being monitored for subsidence and interference to the electric overhead and signalling, and as the line rises toward the central London portal it must miss the bottom of the Fleet Sewer at Caledonian Road by 60 cm. There is one final ventilation shaft, at Corsica Street, before the line bursts out of twin portals at Gifford Street, 1,550 m from the St Pancras buffers, just in time to bridge York Way, which has been lowered to accommodate it, and then the East Coast Main Line (ECML) on the Kings Cross side of the North London tracks for the final approach. The structure carrying this final section of the CTRL looked striking in the early stages of construction, a conventional zig-zag of girders being encased in a rib-cage of curved steel members, but the ensemble is now less starkly encased in steel plating. The 2,065 tonne structure was assembled on the west side of the ECML, and slid into place over Christmas 2003. The reason for the plating is curious. Islington Council demanded that the CTRL remain under cover for its entire traverse of the borough, and the boundary is at the western end of the bridge. Tests have established, however, that the cladding will in fact amplify the noise, not reduce it.

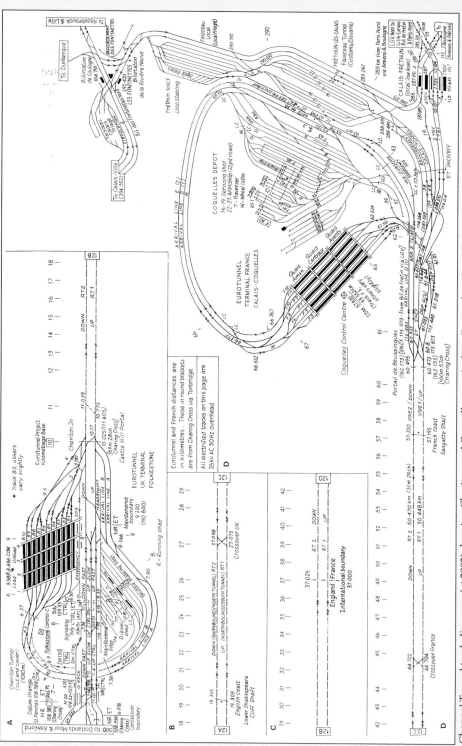

Channel Tunnel track diagrams (at 2002) showing Cheriton and Coquelles terminals.　　Extract from *Quail Railway Track Diagrams Book 5, courtesy TRACKmaps*

Having crossed the new Thameslink connection from the ECML to the resited station at St Pancras Midland Road as well as the tracks out of Kings Cross, the high-speed line curves sharply southward into the St Pancras station throat. Commuter trains from Kent curve most sharply, through a grade-separated junction, to their platforms on the east of the terminus. At the same time, the CTRL throws off a double-track connection continuing straight ahead for the West Coast Main Line, via the North London Line, which it joins almost immediately, and Primrose Hill or Hampstead Junction; this latter route would have enabled Eurostars to reach North Pole without crossing the WCML on the flat. Under original plans this link, which will cross all the lines north from Kings Cross and St Pancras on a viaduct, would have been used by Eurostars running direct from the Continent to the WCML, which would have made their London stop at Stratford. It now seems likely to see infrequent use.

The complex railway layout in the St Pancras station throat and the moonscape immediately to the north of Kings Cross has been completely reconfigured to make way for the CTRL, the opportunity being taken to provide several completely new and highly useful connections, including a better and less tortuous link from the ECML to the North London line, as well as to resite surviving freight facilities. From west to east across the throat there will be two tracks for Midland Main Line traffic, two for Eurostars and finally the two for CTRL domestic traffic. Connections are also provided to access the Eurostar platforms from the WCML (a single-line chord being the legacy of early plans for North-of-London Eurostars to reverse at St Pancras), the ECML and the MML. Beneath the throat, a bored tunnel will carry the two tracks from St Pancras Midland Road to the ECML; work on the 650-metre twin tunnels began in August 2003, a TBM named *Gertrude* by nurses from a local hospital doing the job single-handed. The CTRL contract, however, only covers the tunnels and formation; the track of this connection is to be added later. In this area, all but one of the gasholders that have been its dominant feature for over a century were demolished at an early stage, to be re-erected on a new site. The large volume of spoil from railway and other construction on the site immediately north of Kings Cross and St Pancras is being removed by train to the landfill site at Calvert, the present northern extremity of the former Great Central main line. The exercise also involved the disinterment and reburial at East Finchley of more than 5,000 bodies of people who had died between 1793 and 1854, and been removed from the old St Pancras churchyard to make way for the Victorian burials, only for the site of their second interment to be needed for the link. The reburials were completed at the end of 2004.

St Pancras

St Pancras station, with its majestic Gothic frontage and William Barlow's imposing 1869 trainshed, has arguably never had the rail services to match its splendour. Though it enjoyed greatness as the London terminal of the Midland Railway, it went into steady decline after the Grouping and in the 1960s was seriously considered for closure, with its main line services diverted into Euston. Now, however, the advent of all the Eurostars from Brussels, Paris and beyond and high-speed commuter trains from Kent is both giving St Pancras the range and intensity of train services it deserves and doubling the size of the station to 13 platforms with 21st-century terminal facilities, the entire operation costing £274 million. With the

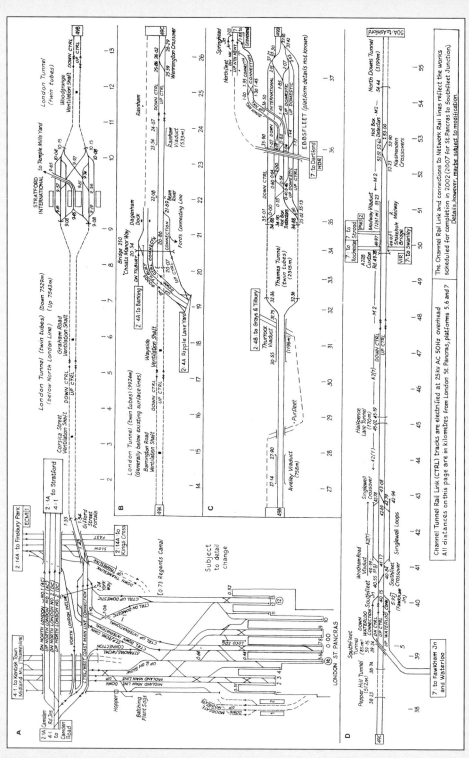

Channel Tunnel Rail Link, London-North Downs tunnel.

Extract from Quail Railway Track Diagrams Book 5, courtesy TRACKmaps

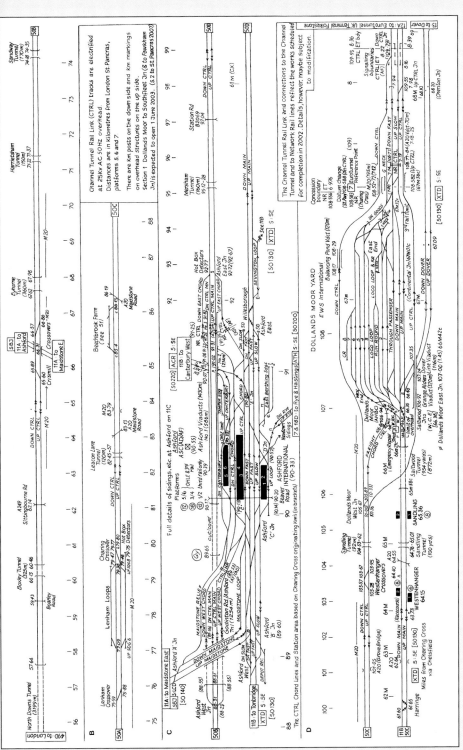

Channel Tunnel Rail Link, North Downs tunnel-Dollands Moor.

Extract from Quail Railway Track Diagrams Book 5, courtesy TRACKmaps

Digging the cutting at Newlands Road on the Channel Tunnel Rail Link. The digger stands where the 80 km post is now sited.   *Brian Stephenson*

Laying track panels beside the Maidstone East line at Tutt Hill on 3rd December, 2001.
Brian Stephenson

Class '20s' Nos. 20227 and 20189 on a concrete sleeper train at Beechbrook Farm in the company of 15 class '66s', nine EWS and six Freightliner, on 16th April, 2002. In the background is Kent & East Sussex Railway class '14' No. 48 (D9504).   *Brian Stephenson*

Class '66' No. 66531 leaves North Downs tunnel with an empty ballast train for Beechbrook Farm on 3rd May, 2002.   *Brian Stephenson*

Class '373s' Nos. 3209 and 3210 on the 0927 Waterloo International-Marne la Vallée service east of Ashford on 12th April, 2001. To the right construction on the CTRL viaduct is well advanced.
Brian Morrison

No. 373229 passes through Westenhanger on the 'Classic Route' with the 1022 Waterloo-Brussels service on 13th April, 2003. In the background No. 373313 is on test on the new line.
Brian Stephenson

A Eurostar train crosses the Medway viaduct parallel to the M2 motorway in January 2003.

Eurostar

The Medway viaduct from the air, looking towards London.

Eurostar

Entering one of the cut-and-cover tunnels on Phase 1 of the CTRL. Note the French style catenary and the block section marker (*left*).   *Eurostar*

A class 66-hauled works train which has just emerged from the Kent Portal (behind the camera) of the Thames Tunnel on the CTRL and now waits to enter Swanscombe yard on 11th October, 2005. Ebbsfleet International is just out of view.   *Kevin Wills*

Fenchurch St-Upminster line

CTRL

M25

A13

Fenchurch St-Tilbury line

QEII bridge

Upminster-Grays line

Thames tunnel

The CTRL snaking its way under the Thames, bisecting the lanes of the M25 and crossing the Essex marshes to Rainham *en route* for Stratford and St Pancras. This image was taken 430 miles above the Earth's surface by QinetiQ's TopSat satellite on 7th December, 2005.
QinetiQ

The Kent portal of the Thames tunnel on 26th February, 2005. All the activity is in the temporary yard.
Brian Stephenson

A low-emission class '66' stands in one of the East London tunnel bores between Dagenham and Stratford on 21st January, 2005. Fitting out is well advanced, but the catenary has yet to be installed.
Kevin Wills

The site of Stratford International station just before work began; the route of the CTRL is shown. The Stratford 'box' has been constructed in the centre; beyond the line into Stratford Low Level from Willesden which curves into the centre of the picture. The established Stratford station is on the right.

Fitting-out the Stratford 'box', 31st August, 2005. A platform canopy can be seen on the left; the class '66'-hauled works train is crossing the points at which the single line to Temple Mills depot diverges. A banner above and to the rear looks ahead to the 2012 London Olympics, the choice of Stratford for which was announced by the International Olympic Committee weeks before.   *Kevin Wills*

The Victorian train shed of the Midland Railway's St Pancras station forms the backdrop as we see the early stages of construction of the new terminal. *Brian Morrison*

St Pancras in 2005 after the completion of the Thameslink 'box'. *Brian Morrison*

A line up of Eurostars at Paris Gare du Nord in April 2004 with Nos. 3104, 3006 and 3221 on show.   *Brian Morrison*

Boarding the train at Gare du Nord, May 2004.   *Eurostar*

Lille-Europe station, dominated by the surreal L-shaped Crédit Lyonnais building.   *Eurostar*

A Waterloo-bound Eurostar arrives at Lille-Europe in January 2000. TGV and Thalys trains use the platforms to the left; the passenger concourse can just be seen above.   *Eurostar*

A Eurostar speeds through France on track shared with high speed services to Brussels and beyond. Note the similarities to the CTRL. *Eurostar*

Calais-Fréthun station in June 2002: the height of Gallic functionality. *Eurostar*

SNCB's smart new entrance to Brussels-Midi, the signage being more impressive than the entrance itself. *Author*

The Eurostar business lounge at Brussels-Midi in January 2003. *SNCB*

The Eurostar platforms on the west side of Brussels-Midi. An SNCB domestic service can just be seen on the left. *SNCB*

A London-bound Eurostar at speed through Belgium. *SNCB*

Charles Mackay, Chairman of Eurotunnel, prior to the ousting of his Board at the dramatic general meeting of 7th April, 2004. *Eurotunnel*

Jacques Gounon, who emerged as Chairman of Eurotunnel early in 2005 after a period of boardroom chaos and that June fought off a challenge from the previous Chief Executive Jean Louis Raymond. *Eurotunnel*

busy and prestigious Kings Cross station next door, the interchange of six London Underground lines beneath - which is also being extended to accommodate traffic from the new St Pancras - and a new Thameslink station in a box beside and beneath St Pancras, the capital's largest transport hub is being created. The possibility has been considered of numbering all the platforms within this complex - as many as 36 depending on how many suburban platforms at Kings Cross remain in operation - in one continuous series. But it is more likely that only the Thameslink platforms will be numbered with those of the St Pancras terminal.

From west to east, there will first be the new low-level Thameslink platforms, then above a new passenger concourse four platforms (1 to 4) for MML services at the height of the present station, then six Eurostar platforms (5 to 10) starting inside the shed but stretching 250 metres beyond it under a flat roof to accommodate all of the trains' 18 carriages, and finally three platforms for CTRL commuter trains (11 to 13) outside the shed's eastern wall but under that same flat roof. These last, like the MML platforms, start 50 metres or so north of the present concourse.

This layout is the result of a long and complex planning process during which a number of changes were made. When it began, Heathrow Express (HEx) was expecting to run services from platforms on the west side of the station to the airport via the Dudding Hill line; this idea fizzled out, as much as anything because of capacity constraints on the Great Western line through Ealing Broadway, but it is hard in any event to see how HEx services could have been squeezed into even an expanded St Pancras. Elimination of the Heathrow option meant that an extra platform could be carved out for MML, whose own inter-city business has been booming. It remains to be seen whether the balance between six platforms for Eurostar, with at most four departures in an hour - even with the diversion of all, rather than most, services from Waterloo - and three for the CTRL commuter service operating at double that frequency, is right.

The new St Pancras will come into full use between early 2007 and the commencement of CTRL domestic services in 2009. In the meantime a huge series of operations is being undertaken not only to construct the new platforms and the approach lines to them, but to keep existing services running across one of the busiest construction sites in Europe, with lines repeatedly having to be slewed and diverted. (One of the very earliest actions, in September 2001, was de-energisation of the overhead catenary, little used since the diversion of Thameslink trains underground in the late 1980s; at the same time an emergency turnback siding for MML and Thameslink trains was installed at Kentish Town).

One challenge has been to guarantee MML access to four platforms at St Pancras, the minimum necessary to maintain its 15-minute frequency. Outside the station, the Midland lines had to be slewed to accommodate an aggregates siding to replace one north of Kings Cross which was in turn relocated to make way for the Thameslink-ECML connection. Track was relaid on disused bridge decks to the west of the Midland tracks then in use, enabling platforms 6 and 7 to be severed in December 2002 for work to begin on the eastern extension to the structure of the terminal. In the winter of 2003-04 the MML was slewed back to the east, into an interim station on the new eastern deck extension, reminiscent of, though far more sophisticated than, the platform north of Broad Street into which North London Line trains were diverted in the dying months of that terminus. These interim MML platforms numbered 10 to 13, which came into use on 12th April, 2004, are due for further realignment to connect them with domestic services on the CTRL. Despite all this elaborate planning, MML's operations have inevitably been disrupted, and the company claimed compensation from London & Continental; LCR objected, but in April 2003 the Rail Regulator Tom Winsor ruled in favour of MML. LCR took Mr Winsor to court, but that November Mr Justice Moses ruled against the company, awarding MML up to £11 million in compensation.

The old St Pancras was seen off in style before the two day closedown to slew the MML tracks into the interim terminal. The last trains ran on 9th April, 2004 and the previous day MML ran a special train to Leicester and back hauled by 'Peak' No. 45112 *The Royal Army Ordnance Corps*, a type of locomotive that was a 'regular' on the route into the 1980s. The new platforms opened with the departure of the 0605 to Sheffield on Easter Monday 12th April. From the start of the blockade on 11th September, platforms 8 and 9 were added, for the use of Thameslink. When construction of the Thameslink 'box' (*see below*) was completed in May 2005 and through services resumed, the electric overhead was removed from the platform lines it had been using to facilitate the fitting-out of that part of the station for Eurostars.

While MML will continue to operate into St Pancras, save for the odd possession, Thameslink's Bedford-Brighton service was severed from September 2004 to May 2005 while the 'box' for its new St Pancras Midland Road station was constructed beneath the west side of the terminal and the grade-separated connections to the ECML north of the station are put in. Since a planning inquiry torpedoed the full Thameslink 2000 scheme, of which these new lines are a part, because of controversy over works in the Blackfriars-London Bridge area, Network Rail debated whether to go ahead during this interruption and fit out the new St Pancras Thameslink as a replacement for the present cramped platforms the other side of Kings Cross, but in the absence of Governement funding sadly decided against. In February 2006, Alistair Darling announced that work on fitting out the box could go ahead with a target of completion in December 2007.

When the box was first planned, the opportunity was also missed to create a four-platform station to increase capacity on the congested route, improve timekeeping and enable trains to pass. Work on the Thameslink 'box' which runs obliquely under the western side of the station was impeded by the refusal of Camden Council, supported in February 2004 by a planning inspector, to allow 24 hour working on the site; this made the blockade for installation of the box 10 weeks longer than had been intended. Even now, there will have to be a further blockade to put in the platforms, though the edges are now *in situ*.

London Underground's work beneath St Pancras is farthest advanced, because of the parallel needs to cater for the new Thameslink station and reduce overcrowding at Kings Cross. To this end a second ticket hall for the Kings Cross/St Pancras tube interchange is already being built beneath St Pancras which arriving Eurostar passengers will use, and a third, beneath the car park beside Kings Cross, will follow; this will service the CTRL domestic platforms and maybe Eurostar departures. There are also high hopes that Gilbert Scott's spectacular former Midland Hotel at St Pancras, restored by LCR in the hope of attracting an operator, will reopen under enterprising management when the station becomes London's gateway for the Continent. Camden Council gave planning permission early in 2005 to LCR and the Manhattan Loft Corporation for a 244-room hotel to be operated by Whitbread, and 68 apartments. The same applies to the former Great Northern Hotel between St Pancras and Kings Cross, which was forced to close when it became engulfed in a construction site.

The new St Pancras now slowly taking shape retains and accentuates the best of the old, and enhances it with contemporary and user-friendly facilities that benefit from being sited on a less confined space than that into which Waterloo International was squeezed. For a start, the principal entrance will not be, as before, at the front under the Midland Hotel building; instead, the main access is at the east end of a new glass-covered transept, 20 metres wide and more than 100 metres across, which runs across (but beneath) the existing station at ground level at the north end of Barlow's great trainshed; at the west end of the transept will be a further entrance and the descent to the new Thameslink platforms. The circulating area for passengers will be here, together with a shopping mall, and all the facilities for international departures will be on this level, with passengers getting up to their Eurostars by travelator halfway along the train; the international platforms, at existing platform level, will cross the transept at an elevation of 5.5 metres, so passengers using it will look up to the platformed Eurostars. North of the passenger area, also beneath the station extension, will be a coach station.

Barlow's roof span, 80 metres wide, 37 metres high and 197 metres long, is being restored and painted its original blue instead of the century-old dark brown. Beneath it at current platform level, a new concrete deck is being constructed; the horizontal beams below ground completing Barlow's structure have turned out to be life-expired so the deck will have its own separate support. Large slots are being cut in this deck on the site of the old Platform 4 to give greater light and new vistas to the circulating area below; to enable this the Eurostar platforms are offset to the eastern side of the train shed. Only Eurostars will operate into the trainshed; there is not room for all services, and as Eurostar's trains are far longer it made sense for them to take what were bound to be the longest platforms. This also enables arriving passengers to follow their instincts and walk to the front of the train and straight out of the original station building after passing through a bank of up to 30 customs and immigration desks.

For the extension necessary to house the 'country' end of the Eurostars and all other platforms, a vast new aluminium and glass roof on slim pillars, flat-looking but with aerofoil sections to let in more light and remove diesel fumes, is being constructed on the north side of the new transept, to cover all 13 platforms. Though designed in a radically different way from the Victorian train shed, the roof will run on for 200 metres from the 'windbreak girder' across the bottom of Barlow's arch, still well above the trains and passengers using it, so as to complement and not in anywhere obscure the dramatic lines of the original terminal. This less dominant but still stylish structure will be the port of arrival for MML and CTRL domestic travellers; for the latter there will be direct access to the new Underground ticket hall just to the side of Kings Cross station. This latter facility will not be ready until 2009. Alistair Darling ordered a halt to work on the ticket hall in January 2004 on learning that the cost had doubled to £250 million; a restart was permitted a year later. At that stage Mr Darling authorised further works that will transform the frontage of Kings Cross, removing the jumble of buildings erected in the 1970s to reveal Cubitt's Grade I listed facade, and substituting a glassy semi-circular concourse linking the west side of Kings Cross with the Great Northern Hotel.

In the short term, Underground facilities at Kings Cross St Pancras after the completion of the CTRL and even the start of domestic services will be pretty cramped. With some business passengers already uneasy at a longer Underground journey to the City than from Waterloo, there may be problems ahead.

Chapter Thirteen

Continental Links to the Tunnel

In France

The Channel Tunnel would have had little point as an artery for international passenger trains without France's construction of the 350 kph TGV-Nord Europe route connecting Paris with Lille, the tunnel and Brussels. In 1967 boat trains on the traditional route from the Gare du Nord to Calais via Amiens and Abbeville took some three hours to make the journey at an average 93 kph; with the high-speed line up and running a Eurostar can reach Calais-Fréthun in just 87 minutes, an average of 236 kph.

The TGV-Nord route had long been planned as an instrument of regional policy to bolster the depressed economy of Nord-Pas de Calais, but its viability depended on construction of the tunnel. Its initial alignment was approved in principle in October 1974, but the plan was abandoned when the British Government unilaterally halted work on the tunnel three months later, and was only revived in January 1986 when the tunnel project had become a near-certainty.

There were, however, other projects in France which have contributed to the success of tunnel rail services, notably the upgrading of the Gare du Nord in Paris, the new Lille-Europe station connecting Eurostar services with TGV routes all over France, the domestic and Eurostar station at Calais-Fréthun and the nearby SNCF freight yard, the Eurostar depot at Le Landy (Paris) and a variety of upgrading and electrification schemes on existing routes.

The TGV Nord-Europe route covers almost all the 326 km from the Gare du Nord to the tunnel portal. Only as Eurostar threads its way through Paris' northern suburbs on the route formerly taken by the Calais boat trains does it share tracks with conventional SNCF traffic. From the outset it was planned as a strategic route not just for TGVs and Eurostars but for PBKA (Paris-Brussels-Koln/Amsterdam), the international high-speed service eventually known as Thalys. As such, it was the first route of the European high-speed network unveiled in December 1990.

Construction of 333 km of route - including a short spur from Lille towards Belgium - to take ultra high-speed trains at a maximum line speed of 350 kph was a massive undertaking even though TGVs are expected to operate over tougher gradients than on a conventional main line. The final cost of the TGV Nord-Europe line and connected works (including new and upgraded stations) came to 18.5 billion francs (£1.85 bn) at 1992 prices, some way over budget. It involved the completion of 10 viaducts, 181 underbridges and 138 overbridges, and the moving of 51 million cubic metres of soil.

Of this total, 16 per cent went on environmental works to shield local communities from the sound of trains with 73 km of walls and banks, and to protect the teeming wildlife of the forests north of Paris and reserves near the coast; special bridges and culverts enabled deer, toads and other creatures to pass freely from one side of the tracks to the other. However, some animals did still stray onto the line once services had begun, at terrible risk to themselves. One North Pole-based Eurostar driver spotted a deer on the track as his train streaked through northern France. Having undergone a saturation course in railway

French, he alerted the signalling centre at Lille with the immortal words: 'I have just seen a horse with its pantograph up' (*un cheval lève-panto*). The French signallers knew exactly what he meant, and took the necessary action . . . then collapsed laughing.

Typically for a French prestige project, the TGV Nord-Europe line was conceived and constructed at a cracking pace. When the Transport Secretary Malcolm Rifkind asked a French counterpart how the project could be pushed through with minimal public consultation, he was told: 'In France, if we wish to drain the swamps, we do not ask the frogs'. Work began in the summer of 1989, and on 26th November, 1992 the completed new line was connected to track in the tunnel terminal site at Coquelles. On 23rd May, 1993 the first TGV ran between Paris and Arras, taking just 50 minutes, and on 26th September that year a full service was inaugurated over the entire route between Paris, Lille and Calais. Lille was now only an hour from Paris, Calais (Ville) 1 hr 50 mins, Dunkerque two hours and Roubaix 1 hr 40 mins.

The Tunnel was not yet open, though tantalisingly complete, when the TGVs started running, so the high-speed line carried no Eurostars for over a year after its inauguration. Nor was the Belgian high-speed line ready, though TGVs could now continue from the triangular grade-separated junction at Fretin, just south of Lille and 200 km from Paris, over a 12 km spur to the border before joining a route to Brussels that made BR's line through Kent feel quite rapid.

The rapid growth of TGV and Thalys services has, after a decade, brought traffic on the high-speed route between Paris and the triangular junction at Frétin, just south of Lille, close to capacity at times, with up to seven services an hour scheduled. Tentative talks have even begun about a duplicate high speed line between Paris and the Channel via Amiens. Eurostar services, a basic 14 (each way) a day at present, have to dovetail into these working arrangements, and this not only guarantees them a swift transit to fit in with other traffic but also means that Eurostar's progress over its entire route is dictated by the availability of paths at the French end. This, in turn, has impacted on the timing and operation of commuter services into Victoria and Charing Cross, plus Thameslink, which correspondingly have had to fit in with Eurostar timings at the London end. The heavy use of the LGV-Nord contrasts sharply with the initial load on the CTRL, with just 23 trains each way operated daily in the basic winter weekday service.

The Gare du Nord and Le Landy

The Gare du Nord, Paris' gateway to the Channel Tunnel, equates well to Waterloo, 494 km away, or St Pancras (495 km). In each case a well-established and renowned terminus had Eurostar facilities grafted onto it, but in this instance the project was less modernistic than either of its English equivalents, also offering - particularly to begin with - rather less for the passenger. SNCF could argue, however, that its hands were tied by both the formal layout of the pre-existing station and the volume of traffic it handles - at 500,000 passengers a day in 1,300 train movements from 28 platforms it is the busiest station in Europe - particularly as room also had to be found for SNCF's flagship Thalys service.

The Gare du Nord is roughly as old as Waterloo - the original station was opened in 1846 - but the present imposing building with its 180 m-long stone facade designed by Jacques Hittorff dates from 1864. Adaptations to take TGV traffic began in 1990, and four platforms dedicated to Eurostar (Nos. 3 to 6) were set apart on the west side of the station, with a passenger terminal - the Gare Londres - on a mezzanine floor inserted above, whose construction freed up valuable circulating space at ground level. The total improvements cost 750 million francs, almost half of this for an underground car park. The work took four years, and despite extensive trackworks and the installation of three new bridges on the station approaches they were carried out without the cancellation of a single train . . . though the station did have to be evacuated one night when 600 kg of explosives were used to blow up a blockhouse beneath the platforms with walls 1.5 metres thick.

Eurostar passengers from London and Ashford (plus Fréthun and Lille) leave the station at platform level with the minimum of ceremony, taking their chance in a lengthy taxi queue if they do not feel up to the Metro. Only departing passengers pass through the Eurostar terminal; it will be the same at St Pancras. Taking the escalator up from the concourse, they pass through ticket control, British then French passport controls, security - for which no provision was originally made - and customs into a rather clinical waiting area (expanded in 1998 but still cramped) where they wait until their trains are called. There is also a first-class lounge, refurbished by Philippe Starck in 2002 to provide a more comfortable waiting area for 154 passengers. When the train is called, travellers of all classes descend to their platforms by two sets of escalator and steps, both toward the rear of the train.

Shortly after your Eurostar leaves the Gare du Nord, it passes under the *Périphérique* ring road, and immediately afterward the depot at Le Landy can be seen, to the west (left, looking forward) of the running lines. After the TGV Nord-Europe, Lille-Europe and the Gare du Nord, SNCF's biggest investment in Channel Tunnel services - rolling stock apart - has been in Le Landy. By contrast with North Pole which is dedicated to Eurostar, Le Landy also services SNCF's TGV and Thalys fleets. The facility, like Caesar's Gaul, is in three parts: Le Landy Pleyel furthest from the station which mainly handles TGV coaches, Le Landy Centre which maintains all types of high-speed stock and includes a three-track 400m-long shed for Eurostars, and Le Landy Sud where routine examinations and train preparation are carried out. Le Landy dates back to 1878, but was heavily rebuilt for TGV and Eurostar services and extended to cover 30 hectares. At first 16 Eurostar rakes were based there, but this number was reduced when demand expanded less rapidly than expected and some stock was diverted to other uses; in the autumn of 2003 the 13 sets still used on London services were transferred to North Pole for all but the most major overhauls - *Visite Générale* and *Grande Visite Générale* - because the capacity was needed for domestic TGV-Est stock. Le Landy remains, however, the principal maintenance point for Eurostar brake gear and bogies.

Eurostars could, in the medium term, be squeezed out not only of Le Landy but of the Gare du Nord itself. The terminal is already heavily overcrowded, and the surge in Eurostar traffic now the CTRL is in use could break the camel's back. In October 2001 David Azéma, Eurostar's Chairman, floated the idea of a completely new Eurostar terminal in Paris, but a far more likely prospect is that Eurostars would be diverted into the Gare de l'Est, with a convenient stop at Charles de Gaulle airport *en route*. SNCF is planning a direct line into the Gare de l'Est from the airport, but lack of capacity at the station throat could rule it out for Eurostars without further investment. Another idea being floated is for a cross-Paris TGV connection from the Gare du Nord to République and the Gare de Lyon.

To Lille and the Tunnel

Beyond Le Landy, London-bound Eurostars thread their way north along the classic Nord route through St-Denis, crowded with double-deck suburban stock as well as TGVs, to Gonesse, 15 km out, where the LGV-Nord bears away to the right and the speed begins to notch up. Gonesse, sadly, is best known for the moment on 25th July, 2000 when an Air France Concorde crashed onto a hotel close to the line, killing 117 people, after suffering damage on take-off from Charles de Gaulle airport which is visible from the train.

France's airport 'hub' is served direct by a TGV station on La Jonction, the 56 km high-speed line that skirts Paris to the east, linking in turn the LGV-Nord, the LGV-Est and the high-speed route to the South that becomes the LGV-Méditeranée. Eurostars for Disneyland Paris, Avignon and the Alps pass through Charles de Gaulle station without stopping, but Eurostar has give some consideration to operating regular business services between London and Charles de Gaulle as an alternative or supplement to flights between Heathrow and Charles de Gaulle; the journey time would be 20 minutes less than to the Gare du Nord. Air France, indeed, has been thinking of withdrawing from the London-Paris route once the CTRL is open in its entirety (the Gatwick route has already gone), reckoning that centre-to-centre timings will no longer be competitive for air, with Eurostars operating as 'feeders' to its long-haul flights.

Shortly beyond the airport on La Jonction the proposed connection to the Gare de l'Est would branch off, and further along, due east of Paris, lies its other station: Chessy Marne-la Vallée, adjoining Disneyland Europe, served daily by trains from Waterloo during the holiday season and occasionally used for crew and servicing purposes by Eurostars for further south; there is a connection here to the Paris RER system.

La Jonction connects with the LGV-Nord at a triangular junction at Vemars (also known as Moussy), a little way north of Gonesse. Paris-London Eurostars transit the north-western side of the junction close to top speed, connecting with La Jonction 29.5 km from the Gare du Nord; Eurostars to and from Disneyland Paris and beyond use its eastern side without an appreciable slowing, and high-speed services between the Gare du Nord and the airport take the tighter curve on the west side.

The high-speed route to the Channel turns steadily from north-east to north and at Verberie, 45 km from Paris, stands the most dramatic structure on the route, where the line emerges from a tunnel onto a viaduct 70 m high and 500 m long to cross the river Oise, three main roads, a gas pipeline, an overhead power line and the conventional railway to Brussels between Creil and Compiégne.

From here the LGV-Nord parallels the A1 autoroute to its east for 130 km, TGVs and Eurostars comfortably outpacing even the fastest vehicles on the road. This stretch of line crosses some of the most bitterly contested battlefields of World War I, and small, well-kept cemeteries can be seen. The legacy of war remains a problem for SNCF in this area because of the number of unmapped tunnels dug by sappers during years of trench warfare, over which the LGV-Nord was constructed; in the summer of 2001 serious subsidence affected the line around milepost 94 (Roye, in the Somme Valley), and an 80 kph emergency speed restriction was imposed while the formation was strengthened. More durable restrictions of 170 kph were imposed over 31 km of track between the 85 km and 144 km markers.

The route of the line through Picardy was the subject of intense controversy, for the very opposite reason to the uproar in rural Kent. For while the CTRL in its various guises was the subject of vehement environmental protests for a quarter of a century, rival communities actively fought to attract the LGV-Nord. The city of Amiens, traditionally the principal stopping-point between Paris and the Channel ports, waged a desperate campaign for the high-speed line to serve it, before the decision was taken in October 1987 that it should be bypassed to the east. SNCF championed a routeing via Lille as the most direct alignment possible, offering a 20-minute saving on the journey time to London and simplifying the planning and construction process by running parallel to the A1. What was more, Lille lay on the SNCF's preferred direct route for Brussels and beyond, which was at least as important commercially and politically as the rail connection with Britain. Even so, the original plan was for the line to avoid the centre of Lille, with a station on a greenfield site outside the city limits; this proposal was stamped on firmly by Lille's influential mayor, Pierre Mauroy, and a route through the city itself substituted.

The people of Amiens feared that the routeing the LGV-Nord into the heart of the more populous and politically heavyweight city of Lille would damage their local economy. Protesters bought land in the path of the preferred route and sold it in metre-square patches to passers-by in Amiens in an effort to frustrate the plan, but in the end their city did not even gain a spur from the TGV route as was awarded to Arras, further north. As a consolation prize, Amiens and Saint-Quentin to its east were awarded a TGV stop (not served by Eurostar) at Haute-Picardie, halfway between the two but a good 50 km from each. Situated in bleak countryside near the village of Ablaincourt-Pressoir, 126.5 km from the Gare du Nord and 369.3 km from St Pancras, it was christened 'Gare Beetroot' after the local crop. In common with other intermediate stations on the TGV network, Haut-Picardie, opened after the line itself in 1994, consists of two long, low platforms with minimal shelters; little patronised to begin with, it now boasts a healthily used car park.

Stations apart, the route is also provided with permanent way sidings at regular intervals. To the British observer, a remarkable feature is how many secondary lines have survived not only to pass under the high-speed route, but to have physical connections to it which for the most part appear to see regular traffic; one such is the short spur for TGVs for Arras, which diverges westward onto the classic Amiens-Arras route halfway between Haute-Picardie and Lille. Shortly after passing Arras, the LGV-Nord parts company with the A1, close to where it makes a T-junction with the A26 bound from eastern France to the tunnel at Coquelles.

The high-speed route through Picardy passes through a landscape generally featureless until spoil heaps from old coal workings start to be visible, mainly just to the west of the line. That said, the longest viaduct on the LGV-Nord, at 1,827 metres, is at Haute-Colme on the Paris-Lille stretch of line.

There is no serious urbanisation between the Paris conurbation and the outskirts of the booming city of Lille. Just as these are reached, at 217 km from the Gare du Nord, is sited the grade-separated Frétin triangular junction; here TGV and Thalys expresses for Brussels and beyond bear round to the east at a maximum 300 kph, while the line to Lille and the tunnel curves sharply from north-east to north-west with a 220 kph limit; Eurostars between Lille and Brussels take the northern curve, reined back to 160 kph. Almost immediately after the junction, northbound

Eurostars and TGVs burrow into the centre of Lille, whether or not they are scheduled to stop there.

The futuristic interchange at Lille-Europe, 225.4 km from the Gare du Nord, 105.8 km from Brussels, 269.6 km from St Pancras and 103 minutes from Waterloo, is the jewel among the TGV Nord-Europe's stations. Costing 252 million francs and hailed by its designers as 'a cocktail of glass and steel', Lille-Europe is the centrepiece of Euralille, the city's new business centre. Topped by three tower blocks of offices, it is situated 450 m east of Lille-Flandres, the city's pre-existing main station which now handles local traffic and is the terminus for TGVs from Paris. Its four 480 m platforms (two island platforms for TGVs, Thalys and Eurostar, bisected by two through tracks) are a hub of the TGV system and the most convenient connecting point for Eurostar passengers from Britain travelling to the regions of France: TGVs from there bypass Paris (via La Jonction) to serve destinations including Lyon (in three hours), Montpellier, Marseille, Nice, Nantes, Rennes, Quimper, Bordeaux, Dijon, Avignon, Poitiers and Tours. President Mitterrand underlined the station's importance by opening it *en route* to the inauguration of the Channel Tunnel itself on 6th May, 1994, arriving on the first TGV journey from Brussels; scheduled services operated from 29th May.

Lille-Europe is built on three levels, with the tracks at the lowest. Road access is at the top (the station has parking for 1,500 cars), with a road bridge on semi-circular supports slicing straight through the structure, above which overhangs an asymmetrical modernistic office building. At mid-level is a long if narrow concourse, 270 by 8 metres, connected by modernistic walkways to the VAL metro system and the TGV platforms and by escalators to the Euralille centre. The island platforms served by Eurostars - more London-Brussels trains stop at Lille than London-Paris ones - because the former have more spare seats - are reached, appropriately, by wooden walkways and stairs reminiscent of the gangways of a ferry; they are numbered 43 and 45 for northbound Eurostars and 44/46 for those heading south. Non-stopping Eurostars shoot past at up to 200 kph on through tracks in between the two sets of platform roads, partly shielded by concrete walls and pillars.

Eurostar passengers arriving at Lille-Europe walk straight out of the station without customs or immigration checks. They have to be careful to take the exit facing Euralille; take the wrong one and they will think they have missed the city altogether. But if they do the latter, a brisk right turn will bring them to a boulevard skirting Euralille to the south which takes you over the throat of Lille-Flandres station. From this vantage point the station with its pitched roof, neat parallel tracks and elderly electric locomotives push-pulling 1950s SNCF railcars looks like something out of a post-war train set. Exit Lille-Europe through the Euralille centre and you will find a very different aspect of Lille-Flandres: the smart, modernised concourse and a range of contemporary emus, *Corail* stock and the occasional TGV.

Passengers boarding Eurostars at Lille-Europe purchase their tickets - if they do not already have them - at a dedicated counter in the SNCF booking office in the station concourse, and are processed at the concourse's north end. Because the traffic is limited - perhaps 80 people for a busy train - there is only a 10-minute cut-off before each departure; passengers are quickly processed through ticket and custom control, but spend rather longer in the baggage security check. They then have use of a large if Spartan waiting room before going down for their train. One word of warning: passengers for high-numbered carriages at the rear of London-bound trains must trek the entire length of the platform to be in position.

Lille is also the home of Eurostar's French control centre, the CCV (*Centre de Contrôle Voyageurs*). Sited behind Lille-Flandres, it keeps in touch with drivers, signal boxes and stations to keep Eurostars to time and make sure stock is in place for each service. The CCV is closely linked to the larger and more complex TGV control centre close by.

Beyond Lille, the LGV-Nord heads straight for the Channel across the Pas de Calais, a handful of daily TGVs still accompanying the now-predominant Eurostar traffic; these trains peel off to serve first Dunkerque and finally Calais and Boulogne. To enable these local TGV services and also tunnel freight trains to run, the SNCF lines from Calais to Boulogne and to Hazebrouck and St-Omer were electrified when the LGV-Nord was constructed. The former route, on which local services continued to be diesel-operated, was also realigned just south of Calais to serve the new Calais-Fréthun station and pass by the exchange sidings used in construction of the tunnel and the Coquelles terminal; the original formation (an embankment and a bridge) to the south-east of the present metals can be seen from the Eurostar tracks just north of Calais-Fréthun. In addition SNCF fitted the track between Fréthun and Calais-Ville with British AWS magnets so that class '92s' could operate sleeping-car trains bound for Brussels and beyond into a major station for a change of locomotive.

One other major work near the tunnel portal was the Fréthun freight yard, to which materials and rolling stock were delivered in the later stages of construction and which became the French equivalent of Dollands Moor as a transit and locomotive change point for international freight trains. From the Fréthun yard, beside the existing Calais-Boulogne route at its intersection with the TGV route and close to the tunnel portal, tunnel freight trains move to the core SNCF network via Hazebrouck, Lille and Somain. Services using the yard *en route* for Britain had to run the gauntlet of asylum-seekers from Sangatte until SNCF belatedly installed security fencing in 2002.

As trains from the south approach the station at Calais-Fréthun, they are already braking for the tunnel even if they are not scheduled to stop. In the reverse direction they are accelerating to TGV speed, a task hampered by a neutral section just south of the station at the foot of a challenging gradient.

The ascetic station at Calais-Fréthun, sited almost within sight of the tunnel portal 3.4 km away and to the south of the freight yard, was opened to TGV passengers on 24th May, 1994 having cost 27 million francs or £2.7 million, roughly the amount Network Rail now quotes for a simple new station for a housing estate. It has two high-level platforms (and four running lines) accessible only by Eurostars, and two below served by TGVs and Calais-Boulogne local services; there is a single-track connection from these to the main line for the tunnel as it enters the Beussingue Trench. Calais-Fréthun is the two-thirds point on the journey from Paris to London, 326.2 km from the Gare du Nord and 159.8 km from St Pancras. It is served by just three Eurostars a day (four southbound); business with Waterloo and Ashford is light, but some 70 domestic passengers use each train to and from Paris and, as with the purely local Haute-Picardie, the car park is filling up. Once through Calais-Fréthun, and with trains that have stopped there still accelerating, Waterloo-bound Eurostars quickly pass onto Eurotunnel metals after 315 km of high-speed running, and then down the Beussingue Trench into the tunnel.

In Belgium

For Belgium's state railway the SNCB, with the smallest national stake in Eurostar, a limited volume of tunnel-bound freight and no Channel Tunnel portal, there was less urgency to upgrade its network for services to and from Britain; the prospect of TGV and eventually Thalys traffic from France was a far greater stimulus. Yet the expected advent of Eurostar and cross-Channel night services either bound for Belgian destinations or crossing the country was a factor in Belgium's decision to build a high-speed line as well as providing up-to-date terminal and servicing facilities in Brussels. To provide for continuity, a decision was taken to electrify the new line at 25kv AC, in common with the TGV route and Eurotunnel, instead of on the Belgian domestic 3kv DC system, though all SNCF and Eurostar high-speed stock entering Belgium is equipped to operate on both. However, the system of electrification, and Belgium's less aggressive pursuit of high railway speeds than its French neighbour, led to the maximum line speed being set at 220 kph instead of TGV Nord-Europe's 350 kph.

The Belgian high-speed route as constructed extends for some 90 km, from a head-on triangular junction with the TGV Nord-Europe at Frétin, just inside the French border, to the southern approach to Brussels-Midi. The only sign that the route has crossed into Belgium at Wannhein is a deceleration to a maximum 220 kph, and different pillars and supports for the overhead catenary. For the first 71 km the alignment is new, and includes a strange zig-zag either side of Mons; on the further brief stretch from Tubize, two new tracks have been added beside the pre-existing Paris-Mons-Brussels conventional route. There is a connection with SNCB's Route 94 line at Le Coucou, 5 km east of Ath; with international trains not taking up the high-speed route's full capacity, there have been moves to switch the hourly domestic service from Brussels to Tournai and Mouscron from the slow and jolting Route 94 to the high-speed line between Brussels and Le Coucou.

For over 18 months after London-Brussels services began running in November 1994, Eurostars had to use that same Route 94 through Tournai and Ath; this kept the average speed for the 376 km journey down to little over 100 kph. But once tracklaying began on 3rd October, 1995, the Belgian high-speed project was swiftly brought to completion. The first section, 20 km from the French system to Antoing, opened in June 1996; here there is a connection to the important Tournai-Mons line. Another 55 km to Lembeek, in the Brussels suburbs, opened in June 1997 and a further short stretch partly on viaduct to Forest (Vorst), close to the heart of Brussels, that 14th December. From then Eurostar services were intensified and accelerated with a best London-Brussels time of 2 hr 36 min., and a new Thalys timetable inaugurated with 15 trains each way between Paris and Brussels (and in most cases beyond) with a best time of 80 minutes. All that remained for completion was a further viaduct just to the south of Brussels-Midi segregating Thalys and Eurostar services from domestic and slower international traffic, the first part of which was first used by inbound trains only on 25th June, 2001. An additional stretch of viaduct to reduce conflicts further is not used by Eurostars. New signalling equipment installed by Alstom in 2002 enabled the line speed for Eurostars on all but the final approach to Brussels-Midi to be raised from 160 kph to 220 kph.

For Brussels-Midi (South), the advent of Eurostar was just one of several developments that turned the station into a major international hub; Thalys services between Paris, Amsterdam and Cologne and the extension of the German

ICE network to Brussels completed the picture. For all these reasons a complete upgrading of the station - which like the Gare du Nord first opened in 1846, but had been heavily rebuilt after World War II to accommodate the new direct link with Brussels Nord - was necessary. Work began in December 1992 on the new international section of Brussels Midi: segregated terminal platforms 1 and 2 for Eurostar on the west side of the station, completed in 1994, and through platforms 3 to 6 for Thalys. As at Waterloo and the Gare du Nord, passengers join and leave the trains by separate routes. Those departing use the main station concourse beneath these platforms, on which level ticket and security checks are also carried out. The Brussels Eurostar terminal is less striking than Waterloo's but smarter than that at the Gare du Nord; its first-class lounge is comfortable and admits a wider range of passengers, and while the terminal has little in the way of catering and retail facilities for the general public there are plenty on the concourse, though a shortage of seats. The original exit from the Eurostar platforms, down an escalator and straight out into the station concourse, was not ideal but could cope with the initial low levels of traffic. But as patronage of the Brussels service surged after completion of the first phase of CTRL, the facilities for arriving passengers were improved; since August 2004 a large 'meet-and-greet' area has been provided at platform level, and more capacious exits now enable an entire trainload to leave the station in 10 minutes, at the price of being shunted out of a side exit. Strangely, however, the near-direct escalator connection between the Eurostar and Thalys platforms were closed at the end of 2004, worsening the interchange just as demand was picking up.

The gleaming terminal initially contrasted with the scruffy neighbourhood outside the station, which lies just south of the city centre, but redevelopment of the entire area is now almost complete. Brussels Central, the next stop to the north, would have been a more convenient destination for Eurostar and other international passengers, but the six-track spine route through the capital to Brussels Nord simply could not handle any more traffic once Thalys trains to Amsterdam and Cologne were accommodated. Indeed by 2000 SNCB was urging local politicians to let it build a new TGV terminal at Schaerbeek, just north of the city centre, and divert TGVs (and probably Eurostars too) away from Midi to Schaerbeek over an existing suburban line which branches off north of Halle, 14 km out, to skirt the city centre to the west, running to Nord by way of the small Gare de l'Ouest.

In the decade since Eurostars began to serve Brussels-Midi, times through the station to destinations in Germany and the Netherlands have steadily improved, even if the connections have not always been well publicised and the trains have not been co-ordinated to make the best use of faster line speeds. Poor connections at Brussels-Midi have been one factor behind Eurostar's interest in eventually extending services to Amsterdam; correspondingly they have depressed loadings to date and made it harder to prove a business case for the through services. One notable improvement came on 15th December, 2002, when the opening of SNCB's Leuven-Liége high-speed line brought German ICE3 trains into Brussels and brought Cologne comfortably within 6 hours of Waterloo; from the summer of 2003 three such trains a day have been operating, in competition with seven Thalys journeys.

One early difficulty experienced at Brussels-Midi stemmed from the insistence of the Belgian authorities on rigorous immigration checks for all Eurostar passengers, despite the UK being a member of the European Union. Belgium took the view that only nationals of countries that signed the Schengen agreement abolishing frontier controls (which the UK has not) were exempt, and the fact that all trains from London had already halted at Lille (in 'Schengenland') counted for little. The effect was twofold: the lengthy checks faced by arriving Eurostar passengers caused many to miss ongoing Thalys connections, and passengers inadvertently arriving without their passports, including on one occasion Eurostar's then Chairman Sir Derek Hornby, were sent straight home. One 94-year-old woman in a wheelchair was even kept in the cells before being put on a train back to Waterloo. It took several years for a more relaxed regime to come into operation, with most passengers just nodded through. By that time illegal migration to the UK via Belgium was starting to become a problem; from September 2002 British immigration officials were able to board Eurostars in Brussels to check passengers' travel documents and since the summer of 2004 passengers bound for London have had to go through UK passport control.

Just as the upgrading of Brussels-Midi was a joint project for Eurostar and Thalys, so was the creation of a dedicated depot and servicing facility at Forest, to the east of the running lines on the southern approaches to Brussels-Midi. Until 1990 Forest was the site of an SNCB depot for electric multiple units, but in preparation for high-speed international services this function was moved and a four-track shed 420 m long constructed for routine maintenance, safety inspection and cleaning of the new generation of trains, Thalys using one side and Eurostar the other. Enough capacity was provided to service five Eurostar rakes per night, but as at Le Landy this level of operation has not so far been reached; it has, however, come to specialise in maintaining the air conditioning systems of all Eurostar trains. Two smaller sheds cater for heavier repairs and maintenance as required. The remodelling of the station throat in 2000/2001 created the opportunity to add three more sidings on the eastern side of the depot, and to give easier rail access to it.

Chapter Fourteen

A New Start for Eurotunnel?

Eurotunnel at the end of 2003 appeared in no worse a plight than at any other time in the decade since completion of the project. Its financial position might be 'desperate rather than serious', in the immortal words of one Irish Prime Minister, but that was nothing new. Serious challenges lay ahead, but the management appeared to be addressing them. With cross-Channel truck traffic buoyant even if car shuttles were less full, rail freight slowly reviving and the first phase of the CTRL open, veteran Eurotunnel-watchers expected the company to stagger on from crisis to crisis without collapsing into the arms of its creditors, who had no wish to take over a debt-laden transport operation, and gradually reduce its debts.

When the maverick right-wing French politician Nicholas Miguet and Joseph Gouranton of the small shareholders' association Adacte demanded changes to the Eurotunnel Board at the company's annual meeting that May, their initiative appeared as unlikely to succeed as the decade-long campaign to prosecute Sir Alastair Morton and André Benard for having allegedly misled stockholders into thinking profits were round the corner. Certainly Eurotunnel's Chairman and Chief Executive, Charles Mackay and Richard Shirrefs, regarded M. Miguet as no more than an irritant; the company contested in the French courts his claim to represent the 5 per cent of shareholders necessary to call a further special meeting of shareholders, and Mr Shirrefs secured €10,000 in damages for defamation in another French court against M. Miguet, whom he and Mr Mackay termed 'a financial journalist with a criminal record'.

M. Miguet's recipe for reversing the company's fortunes did indeed look far-fetched. Under it Eurotunnel would refuse to repay 80 per cent of its debt, with the British and French Governments taking over part of it (this would require a change to the Treaty of Canterbury), the company would triple its revenues under new management, London-Paris journey times on Eurostar would be slashed and the railways would pay higher access fees than those they were already contesting.

Unfortunately for the predominantly British management, M. Miguet launched his campaign just as Eurotunnel was starting to face the crunch, with revenues for 2003 down 5 per cent year-on-year to £566 million because of a price war with the ferries and budget airlines, and the deficit up from £148 million to £1.33 billion after a writedown due to traffic falling short of estimates. Lorry shuttle traffic was up 4.5 per cent to 1.28 million and railfreight by 19 per cent to a still risible 1.74 million tonnes, but car shuttle traffic was down 2 per cent to 2.28 million and Eurostar passengers by 4 per cent to 6,314,795, despite a 15 per cent surge in the final quarter due to the first benefits of the CTRL. Furthermore two ominous deadlines for the company were looming at the end of 2006: the point when Eurotunnel would have to start repaying its £6.4 billion debt and the date when it would cease to receive minimum access payments from its rail customers, principally Eurostar, which in 2002 accounted for £77 million of its £232 million rail revenues.

The company faced this challenge with a radical programme it branded 'Project Galaxie', asserting that this was the 'only reasonable hope' of easing the plight of the investors. It proposed to cut the access charges, which Mr Shirrefs said were 'strangling' railway use of the tunnel, by up to 75 per cent in the case of freight users, and refinance the business by buying back part of its debt at 50p in the pound; City analysts described the idea as 'woolly', but it was only one of several. Eurotunnel was also pressing ahead with its own plan to operate rail freight services from France, Germany, Switzerland and Italy to a £7 million multi-modal terminal on spare land at Cheriton. The company also proposed to the UK Government that it take over London & Continental Railways and with it ownership of the CTRL, creating a single-owner rail corridor from St Pancras to Coquelles . . . and looked to a surge in commuting to Kent and even London from the Nord Pas-de-Calais once the CTRL was up and running.

M. Miguet was not as impressed by these arguments as by the fact that he had lost almost £2 million in trading on Eurotunnel shares during 2003, when the price rose from 23½p to 70¼p in six months as his share-tipping line urged investors to 'empty your savings accounts, go right now to your bank and use your money to buy shares', then fell back to 37½p. His activities had led Eurotunnel in October 2003 to accuse 'certain shareholders' of 'the dissemination of false and misleading information and manipulation of the Eurotunnel share price'. Two months later, crucially, France's commercial court ruled that he did indeed represent 5 per cent of shareholders – four-fifths of whom by now were French – and ordered Eurotunnel to hold a special general meeting by 15th April, 2004.

In advance of the meeting, set for 7th April, the Eurotunnel Board belatedly took steps to redress the national balance of the company, nominating Philippe Bourguignon, the experienced and well-connected former chief executive of Club Méditéranée and EuroDisney, to join it with a view to succeeding Mr Mackay as Chairman that autumn and leading the negotiations over Project Galaxie. But it was a case of too little too late. M. Miguet had made his dispositions, writing to shareholders on the eve of the vote: 'This is a historic day, without precedent in the history of world capitalism. We are the defenders of good, and opposite us are the defenders of evil'. He went on to urge his supporters to behave in a 'dignified' way and not to use the occasion to promote his ambitions for the Presidency of the Republic.

On the day, thousands of shareholders crammed into a conference centre near Charles de Gaulle Airport to applaud wildly as Mr Mackay announced that the Board had been ousted and the annual report rejected; although the meeting was of Eurotunnel's French company, the British Board also quit in consequence. The ousted Chairman told the meeting: 'We did not get enough votes', then handed over to Mr Shirrefs, who told an unbelieving audience that Project Galaxie was in their best interests, then defended himself against bitter questioning over his £381,901 salary including a £62,000 bonus. Mr Shirrefs, who was also voted out with a £310,000 payoff, courageously told his ousters that while Mrs Thatcher's insistence that the Tunnel received no public money was 'probably not a good idea', there was no hope of the British and French Governments bailing out the shareholders. A jubilant M. Miguet successfully proposed Jacques Maillot, the founder of the tour group *Nouvelles Frontières*, as Eurotunnel's new Chairman; reporters noted that M. Bourguignon had left the building. Jean-Louis Raymond, a marketing executive, took over as Chief Executive.

Mr Mackay later conceded that the Board had been wrong not to rebut M. Miguet's criticisms from the outset, saying: 'In the early months we felt we should not dignify his attacks by responding publicly.' He also accused the French establishment of not taking the threat from M. Miguet seriously, and claimed the coup had been pulled off with the votes of fewer than 30,000 investors, representing 18 per cent of the stock by value. Senior members of the ousted management also claimed they had been maybe only a week away from doing a deal based on Project Galaxie with the UK and French Governments, but this appears unlikely.

The following day Hervé Huas, deputy Chief Executive under the new regime, made his debut in London before a less hubristic meeting of 200 British shareholders. Diplomatically he declared that it was 'time to bring an end to the rancour', and contrived, in the view of one reporter present, 'to agree with almost every proposition from the floor'. Reminded from the floor that if the new Board failed to get a grip or made matters worse the creditors, led by Crédit Agricole, HSBC, the US financial services giant MBIA, the European Investment Bank and Soros Asset Management, might take over the company and wipe out the value of its shares, M. Huas said: 'We are neither fools nor heroes. We are not going to do things that will put anything on jeopardy for the shareholders'. Yet he caused some alarm by saying the new Board would 'take time to really understand the Galaxie plan' . . . the plan M. Miguet and his supporters had comprehensively rubbished prior to ousting the previous management.

The victors promised four early British appointments to the Board, and action to implement their other pledges. To this end they held an early meeting with M. Sarkozy, now Finance Minister; while they categorised the talks as 'constructive' and said the French Government had undertaken to 'bring its technical expertise in financial matters' to bear, there was no promise of public money. The same message was conveyed more publicly by the Transport Minister, Gilles de Robien, who flatly ruled out any change to the Treaty. On the day the new management met M. Sarkozy, Roger Burge, Eurotunnel's finance Director who had been with the company since 1992 and worked up Project Galaxie with Richard Shirrefs, announced his departure for 'personal reasons'. M. Huas took on Mr Burge's responsibilities, having promised that all senior executives under the new dispensation would draw half their predecessors' salaries. M. Miguet was barred from serving on the Eurotunnel Board – or any other - because of a conviction in 1999 for 'bankruptcy, fraud and forgery' which cost him four weeks in preventitive detention. He was also, according to Le Monde, under a French police investigation over the 132 per cent increase in Eurotunnel's share price in the five months from 19th May, 2003.

The scale of Eurotunnel's problems was underlined by the results for the first quarter of 2004, which showed a 13 per cent drop in car shuttle traffic and a 17 per cent fall year-on-year in coaches carried by shuttle. HGV shuttle business was up 7 per cent, Eurostar by 19 per cent as the CTRL caught on and rail freight by 7 per cent, but this meant no extra income for the company as access payments were still guaranteed, and overall revenue was down 3½ per cent. Against this stark background, Eurotunnel staff put a brave face on the 10th anniversary celebrations of the opening of the tunnel, held in an appropriately low key on 6th May, 2004.

The new management team had promised to produce a recovery plan within 90 days, but this was put back to October as the scale of the problems facing the company, and the limited room for manoeuvre, became clearer. Assertions from M. Raymond that Eurotunnel could raise €100 million a year from internal savings and revisions to its 'incoherent' fare structure did not over-impress the markets. Nor did the figures for the first half of 2004, which sent the share price down to an all-time low of 20¼p: operating profits down, costs up, shuttle revenues down 6 per cent and car traffic down 14 per cent . . . plus the £1.8 million cost of staging April's special meeting. M. Raymond left the briefing for City analysts to M. Huas, and took a much-needed holiday in Corsica.

Chickens were also coming home to roost from M. Miguet's campaign against the previous Board; angered by comments levelled against them, some of Eurotunnel's 200 creditor banks now got their own back by refusing to finance its plan for the intermodal terminal at Cheriton, thus aborting the through freight service from the Continent which the new management had changed their mind about and agreed to press ahead with as an easy way of building the business. Left hanging in the air when Eurotunnel shelved the project – temporarily, it hoped - in July was its order for three Alstom Prima tri-voltage electric locomotives for the service, with an option on a further two. One unusual traffic that did use the tunnel in 2004/05 was two gigantic high output ballast cleaners ordered by Network Rail from Plasser & Theurer in Switzerland. These 16-axle behemoths were an exotic chnage from the regular rakes of new Desiro electric units from Siemens.

The new Eurotunnel Board was learning the art of diplomacy, however, and its statements and actions became more conciliatory. By late summer, indeed, there was speculation that Project Galaxie would be dusted down and implemented in some form having proved the only game in town, as Mr Mackay had insisted less than a year before. Certainly action was needed, as Eurotunnel was seeing a reduction both in traffic levels and in its share of the cross-Channel market. For the third quarter of 2004, the company reported a 5 per cent fall in passenger shuttle traffic – now running 25 per cent below its peak in 2000 before the end of duty-free - a 4 per cent drop in HGVs and a 13 per cent slump in coaches; the loss of HGV traffic was particularly worrying as the market actually increased by 8 per cent during the same period. M. Raymond placed the blame at the door of the ousted Board, saying: 'The results are obviously not satisfactory. These figures demonstrate that Eurotunnel's previous strategy was not adjusted to market trends in terms of capacity and pricing'. M. Huas blamed the fall in car shuttle traffic on 'aggressive pricing' by SpeedFerries, a newcomer to the route, and on Eurotunnel's 'very complex pricing structure', with 60 different fares. Simplified fares for car and HGV shuttles alike would take effect early in 2005, with the aim 'not volume or yield, but profitability'.

With Eurotunnel in ferment, Eurostar decided to limit its own reorganization. A single commercial management structure was established, as foreshadowed in 'Project Jupiter', but the plan to form a single company to run the high-speed passenger service was dropped; National Express reiterated its intention to sell its stake, but SNCB, despite its misgivings, stayed in. One other change further reduced Eurostar's attraction to illegal migrants: the summer of 2004 saw an extension of UK immigration controls to its terminal at Brussels-Midi, in line with an agreement that April between the Home Secretary, David Blunkett, and his Belgian opposite number Patrick Dewael. The arrangement, similar to that which had already applied for three years at the Gare du Nord, involves British immigration officers refusing to let passengers with false, stolen or inadequate documents board the train, with suspects handed over to the Belgian police for questioning.

On the track, Eurostar continued to notch up milestones; on 30th April the 10,000th service ran over the CTRL, with punctuality over the entire route running at 88.4 per cent and rising, against 75.7 per cent for the final services over the 'classic' route; in the week from 12th July, 97.3 per cent punctuality was recorded. In the first half of 2004, Eurostar carried 3.4 million passengers, up 10 per cent on the year before, with revenue 16 per cent higher. While Eurotunnel's market share was falling back, Eurostar's was forging ahead: on the London-Brussels route up from 43 per cent a year before to a mould-breaking 63 per cent in August, and on the Paris run from 60 per cent to 68 per cent. Eurostar's dominance in this market impacted both on the ferry services and on Eurotunnel's car shuttle business, but the main damage was done to the airlines: Ryanair took off its London-Brussels Charleroi service early in 2004, Easyjet reduced its Luton-Paris flights from five to three a day, and at the end of October British Airways withdrew its Gatwick-Paris service; London's second airport now offered no flights to Paris for the first time in over 40 years, and only two to Brussels. October 2004 was Eurostar's best ever month, with 641,957 passengers carried, and the ski trains for the February 2005 half-term sold out so quickly that, three months beforehand, an extra daytime service was organised, out from Waterloo on Sunday 13th February and back the following Sunday, making three trains in all on those weekends. Against this background, Eurostar's 10th birthday celebration on 15th November, 2004 – delayed a week because of a crash on a level crossing in Berkshire between a Great Western express and a car whose driver was apparently intent on suicide which left seven people dead - was noticeably more upbeat than Eurotunnel's had been. To mark the carriage of 59 million passengers in a decade and an annual loss down to £42 million and falling, parties were held at Waterloo - with a 2.5 metre long cake in the shape of a train - and in Paris, Lille and Brussels, and a Eurostar power car was floated down the Thames on a barge.

Just 48 hours after the festivities at Waterloo, which promoted reams of press coverage about the benefits the completed CTRL would bring, Eurostar and Transport Secretary Alistair Darling came up with a double whammy. Eurostar announced that it had abandoned on economic and operational grounds its plan to continue operating some services from Waterloo International once the new St Pancras terminal was ready in 2007. Then Mr Darling announced – surprisingly to some observers given Ministerial efforts to tighten rail's purse strings - that the Government would find £402 million to enable Eurostar not merely to build its promised rolling stock depot at Temple Mills, but to transfer there at the same time as the exit from Waterloo all the stock and operations now based at North Pole. Waterloo International's five extra-long platforms and the train paths to them would now be available for domestic main line and commuter services, though South West Trains initially baulked at the expense; North Pole would be offered to other train operators and rolling stock companies. A third announcement had just predated Eurostar's anniversary: Mr Darling's naming of Hitachi as preferred bidder to contrast the high-speed commuter stock for domestic services over the CTRL, and his disclosure that the first domestic services between St Pancras and destinations in Kent would not commence until well into 2009, two years after the opening of the new terminal. As work on a third London Underground ticket hall for Kings Cross/St Pancras which would serve the commuter platforms had earlier been halted by Mr Darling on grounds of runaway cost (it was resumed after a year), this delay was probably just as well.

At the close of 2004, Eurostar was able to announce a better year: 7.27 million passengers carried - 15 per cent more than the year before - and income up by a similar degree, and 89.2 per cent punctuality. International freight traffic, meanwhile, was still recovering with agonising slowness from its slump during the asylum crisis. EWS' new Canadian boss, Keith Heller, saw volume for 2004 climb back over the 2 million tonne mark, still well below the previous best and far short of rail's potential share of a 60 million tonne market; he mused aloud that EWS was 'exploring a more significant presence on the Continent'. The year saw a resumption of direct trains between Mossend and Continental destinations after over three years during which Scottish traffic was transferred to and from feeder trains at Daventry,

Wembley and other locations. Throughout 2004 awareness grew that the crunch was approaching over the future of the Minimum Usage Charges paid to Eurotunnel for passenger and freight trains to transit it, those for EWS - £26 million a year - being met by the British Government through the vestigial successor of British Rail and Eurostar's by the operator itself, amounting to 60 per cent of its revenue. The existing agreements were soon to terminate, and the Government's liability to cover the charge for EWS ended in November 2006. The Rail Freight group was warning, to EWS' irritation, that through freight traffic might halt if the burden of continuing charges fell on EWS, Eurostar was lobbying for a reduction, and the new Board of Eurotunnel was hoping to negotiate an increase.

The 1st September, 2004 was a sad day for everyone connected with the realisation of the Channel Tunnel project, with the death aged 66 of Sir Alastair Morton. He had been in poor health for some time, and his final berth as Chairman of the Strategic Rail Authority had not been a happy one; having been appointed to 'grow the railway', he found himself after the Hatfield disaster lacking the wherewithal to do so. But in the words of one associate quoted in his obituary, 'God created Alastair to supervise the Eurotunnel project', and while he lived just long enough to see the successor to his own management structure collapse, none of the hundreds who packed Southwark Cathedral for his memorial service on 23rd November had the slightest doubt that the Channel Tunnel was here to stay, and would prove a fitting memorial.

Sir Alastair would have allowed himself a wry chuckle when on 29th October, 2004 the new regime at Eurotunnel unveiled 'Project DARE', its strategy for keeping the company afloat and avoiding default on its debt. By increasing revenues - which were still on the slide - and reducing costs, the Board aimed to increase Eurotunnel's operating margin by £70 million in 2007, and to open talks with its apprehensive banks, led by HSBC and the French investment bank Calyon, on what M. Raymond called 'solutions that will allow us to reach a sustainable level of debt'. It announced an end to overcapacity on shuttle services, excessive operating costs, and the 'permanent cycle of promotional activity' indulged in to meet them. This would be achieved by cutbacks in both passenger and HGV shuttle services, with some shuttle stock being mothballed. There would also be staff cuts, and savings on procurement by buying components 'off the peg' instead of ordering custom-made products.

To raise yield by 8-10 per cent in 2005, the Board announced an overhaul of pricing for HGVs, with high-volume hauliers encouraged to book ahead on an annual basis and steep increases for individual drivers switching to the tunnel when bad weather halted the cheaper ferries. It also undertook to renegotiate access contracts with Eurostar and the freight operators to maintain its income after the expiry of the Minimum Usage Charges. It still hoped, as well, to go ahead with its own rail freight service, Europorte 2 having received its safety certificate from the French Ministry of Transport the previous week. Overall the targets set were challenging, but M. Raymond warned that this would only be the beginning of hauling Eurotunnel out of the financial mire.

Within weeks, Project DARE had run into trouble. The hauliers Eurotunnel wanted to sign up to year-long contracts baulked at a tariff which meant paying a competitive £200 a trip if they stuck to their forecasts, but up to £750 if they dispatched too many or too few trucks through the tunnel. In this way the company hoped to carry virtually the same level of HGV traffic while running 60,000 shuttle trains a year instead of the previous 71,000. As 2005 opened and the new system took effect, many of Britain's deeply individualistic haulage community were threatening to vote with their feet rather than sign up to future service patterns which depended entirely on unpredictable levels of business.

There was trouble in the boardroom, too. After more than six months M. Huas and his associates had been unable to recruit a single British Director; there was speculation that Dame Pauline Neville-Jones, a former senior diplomat who had advised Mrs Thatcher in her negotiations with the French prior to the Treaty of Canterbury, would come on board, but at the end of October 2004 she declined. Then, at the end of November, Pierre Cardo, a non-executive director of Eurotunnel and a deputy from President Chirac's UMP party, left, impatient at the failure of colleagues on the company's new Board to take the drastic action to sort out its finances that they had promised when they ousted the previous management. As M. Cardo departed, attacking what he termed the Board's refusal to face up to the need to restructure Eurotunnel's balance sheet, the company returned to a process used to sort out its financial disputes during construction of the tunnel and nominated the French lawyer Regis Valliot as *mandataire ad hoc* to mediate between the parties while project DARE was implemented. Eurotunnel strongly denied that the appointment was linked to an 'insolvency procedure'.

Eurotunnel's results for 2004 showed a loss of £570 million compared to £1.3 billion the year before, and an operating profit up 2 per cent to £171 million; the auditors hesitated before certifying that the company was a going concern. M. Raymond attributed a 4 per cent overall fall in sales to £548 million to the increasing impact of the budget airlines and the strategies of the previous Board. Shuttle revenues were down 7 per cent at £285 million, with HGV traffic static at 1,281,027, car traffic down 8 per cent at 2.1 million and coaches down 12 per cent to 63,467, and rail revenues up 2 per cent at £234 million, £67 million represented by the Minimum User Charge from the British and French Governments which would expire in November 2006. Eurostar reported a 15 per cent increase in passenger numbers - to 7,276,675 - and revenue as the full effect of CTRL Phase One was felt. The company also attributed the surge in bookings to the global success of Dan Brown's novel *The Da Vinci Code*, which posited that Paris was the hiding place of artefacts detailing the true nature of Christ.

The year 2005 nearly opened with a bang - or rather two bangs - as far as the Channel Tunnel was concerned. On 25th January a British businessman caused a bomb alert at Coquelles when he tried to carry onto a shuttle train a live World War I mortar shell he had found by the roadside in northern France; the train was evacuated and detained for 3½ hours while French experts carried out a controlled explosion. Then, on 28th January, security staff at Cheriton found unexploded munitions from the two World Wars on a car about to be driven onto a shuttle train. The terminal was evacuated and the tunnel closed for 3½ hours as the bomb squad was called in; many trains were halted or delayed and those that had recently entered the tunnel from the French end were ordered to reverse to Coquelles. Eurostar services were severely disrupted that day, but not as badly as they had been on 22nd January when the return overnight ski train was prevented from leaving Bourg St-Maurice because of a landslide, eventually departing over 24 hours late.

Eurostar's passenger base was growing steadily more varied. Early in May 2005, 300 French surgeons, striking against low pay, long hours and soaring insurance premiums chartered a Eurostar from the Gare du Nord to Ashford to conduct a seminar in the surreal environment of Pontin's holiday camp at Camber Sands. The previous month the actress and singer Grace Jones was escorted off a train at

Ashford by police after allegedly attacking a train manager during an argument over a ticket upgrade, having sworn at her in French and English. And more seriously, the absence of outgoing UK passport checks at Waterloo led to Hussain Osman, one of the suspects for the abortive suicide bombings on the London Underground on 21st July, 2005, evading intense security (and a French passport check) five days later to escape by Eurostar to Rome. Immediate orders were given to close the loophole, but Eurostar's revenues over the next few days were boosted by a series of television and newspaper reporters who managed to buy tickets and board trains at Waterloo with false identities. Eurostar management had already been taking other precautions; during the winter of 2004/05 first class passengers were issued with plastic rather than metal cutlery in an attempt to prevent hijackings, though where the trains could have been hijacked to was never explained.

Buoyed by the refurbishment of more than half its fleet, Eurostar was now polishing up its offering to passengers. Ending a decade of absurdity, it entered an alliance with Thalys and DB to offer connections and through ticketing beyond Brussels to Germany, offering fares starting from £69 return and best journey times of 4 hr 23 min. to Aachen and 5 hr 2 min. to Koln. Then, from 1st September, 2005, it set out to win more business traffic from the airlines by replacing its premium and first class brandings with 'Business Premier' and 'Leisure Select'. The former offered a 10 minute fast track check-in, lounge access, at-seat meal and drink service, power sockets and on board newspapers and magazines, with a chauffeur service available at extra cost. Leisure Select offered 30 minute check-in, at-seat meals and drinks, power-sockets and on-board reading matter, thus preserving the sanctity of Eurostar's business lounges. Ticket prices were based on how far in advance tickets were booked and the level of flexibility required.

Eurotunnel made more radical changes to its fare structure in the summer of 2005, using the model so successful for the budget airlines by cutting prices to fill its car shuttles. From 7th June, standard fares were based on a one-way crossing and no longer determined by length of stay, regardless of whether travel was at peak times or off-peak. The single fare for a car and five occupants came down to just £49 if booked for an off-peak time or far enough in advance, and a new 'Flexi-plus' package allowed dedicated check-in, priority boarding and access to a passenger lounge with complimentary light meals, drinks and newspapers. For breaks of up to five days a new 'Short Stay Saver' ticket gave discounts of up to 50 per cent on standard fares, while 'Day Trip' fares, for up to 48 hours, started at £30. Greater scope was also offered to amend bookings already made.

This positive thinking did not reflect calm in the all-French boardroom, however. M. Maillot quit as Chairman in February in the wake of disappointing traffic figures and criticism from M. Cardo over his perceived failure to address the problem of the company's debt mountain. His place was taken by Jacques Gounon, one of the non-executive directors and former French country president of Alstom, and on 5th April representatives of 69 per cent of Eurotunnel's junior debt agreed to waive default clauses and open talks on debt restructuring. However M. Huas and M. Miguet were already voicing discontent, the strains intensified and on 13th June, a week before Eurotunnel's annual general meeting, M. Raymond resigned as Chief Executive, accusing M. Gounon of publicly criticising the company for 'purely political reasons'. While M. Gounon was seeking a write-off of most of Eurotunnel's debt, which now stood at £6.3 billion, M. Raymond considered this unrealistic given that the creditors were pressing for a debt-for-equity deal which would dilute the shareholders' already devalued stake in the company. M. Raymond launched a campaign to supplant M. Gounon, with the support of M. Huas and M. Miguet - who had cheekily billed Eurotunnel for the €400,000 (£276,000) cost of staging the 2004 shareholders' meeting - who claimed that everything achieved prior to M. Gounon's arrival as Chairman had been undone. The stage seemed set for a second putsch in just 14 months.

This time, however, the challenge was illusory. The 600 shareholders who packed the hall at Coquelles on 17th June, 2005 were not after blood, believing M. Gounon's claim that he could reduce the company's debts without further devaluing their shares; M. Miguet sensed this and switched sides, M. Raymond threw in the towel and M. Gounon was re-elected with 98 per cent of the votes cast, 82,000 shareholders having responded to a last-minute plea for support with free shuttle rides for 1,000 of them as an incentive. M. Raymond observed: 'Good old Joe Stalin didn't have an election as easy as that'.

M. Gounon was able to report income of £268 million for the first half of 2005, up 2 per cent, with savings of £20 million a year identified and a programme of up to 400 voluntary redundancies due to start the following month (French trade unionists protested with flares outside the hall). HGV and passenger shuttle revenues were up £9 million at £146 million; M. Gounon credited the new charging structure for a 9 per cent increase in HGVs carried to 703,363, but a series of disruptions at Calais early in the year when a ferry berth was out of action was the principal reason for this and a 1 per cent rise in car shuttle traffic to 951,561. The one clear win after a disappointing 2004 was a 34 per cent upsurge in coach traffic to 39,381. Railway revenues were steady at £117 million; Eurostar traffic continued to forge ahead - by 8 per cent to 3.68 million for the half-year with sales up 14 per cent - but EWS/SNCF freight traffic slumped by 13 per cent to a woeful 847,716 tonnes despite the resumption of automotive traffic from Corby to Paris.

On 14th July, 2005, with the rest of France celebrating Bastille Day, M. Gounon, now acting Chief Executive, met the owners of Eurotunnel's £4 billion in junior debt, represented by the European Investment Bank, MBIA and two American mutual funds, in Paris to present his first detailed proposals for debt restructuring. Using a business plan stretching to the end of Eurotunnel's concession in 2086, he argued that the company could support no more than £2.24 billion (€3.3 billion) of debt if it were to remain a going concern. Eurotunnel was keen to reach a deal before the end of 2005 when the waiver allowing it to pay part of its interest in notes convertible into shares expired. However M. Gounon's task was complicated by the emergence of a second creditors' committee, understood to be centred on funds managed by the financier George Soros. But unless the debt were reduced, M. Gounon told the *Sunday Telegraph*, 'bankruptcy is clearly scheduled for January 2007', the point at which the company was due to start repaying its borrowings, with at least £274 million due to be returned to creditors by 2009.

M. Gounon now hired Jean-Pierre Trotignon, former operator of the port of Dunkerque, to run Eurotunnel's transport operation while he negotiated the company's rescue. An early product was the opening on 12th December of 24 automatic check-in lanes at the Cheriton and Coquelles terminals. The cross-Channel climate was getting tougher, and not just for Eurotunnel; P&O reported a 13 per cent drop in its ferry traffic for the summer quarter of 2005. M. Gounon's medicine was harsh: the announcement that October of 900 redundancies, over a quarter of Eurotunnel's workforce and 450 of them at Cheriton. He told shareholders that 800 staff had already volunteered to go. A week later he announced 'promising progress' in the talks with creditor, though these were still not concluded when, in the first days of 2006, Eurotunnel's stock price in Paris shot up, then stalled to the accompaniment of leaks of internal figures to the press. M. Miguet had resumed his share punting activities, and there were demands for an official inquiry.

Eurostar came out of 2005 in confident mood, having finally concluded a marketing partnership with Thalys, seen the resumption of the fast connection between Brighton and Ashford International and reported traffic up again marginally to 7.5 million. With business custom surging, a tenth daily service to Brussels was announced for February 2006. But on the rail freight side the moment of truth was looming. Faced with the prospect of having to pay the £26 million Minimum Usage Charge on its small and shrinking business, EWS served notice on the British Government at the end of 2005 that it would halt all international freight traffic from the end of 2006, up to which point Transport Secretary Alistair Darling had agreed to meet the charge, unless it was drastically reduced; the Department for Transport passed the ball to Eurotunnel and a negotiating cliffhanger to rival Eurotunnel's own seemed in prospect. Yet EWS continue to plan ahead. Continental services from early 2006 were expected from a new freight terminal at Raithes Farm, Aberdeen and, more significantly, EWS now launched its much-heralded freight service from and within France: Euro Cargo Rail (ECR), awarded its French safety certificate on 26th October, 2005. Having dispatched a class '66', No. 66215 to France for trials, ECR hired four 87.3 ton Vossloh G1206BB diesel locomotives rated at 1,500KW and took delivery of the first – No. FB1544, hired from Angel Trains - on 2nd December, when it hauled a freight from Somain to Fréthun. The first ECR service proper ran on 20th December when the first Vossloh hauled aggregates from Caffiera quarry to Calais, a class '92' taking it forward to Dollands Moor *en route* for Sevington.

EWS was not the only freight operator planning operations away from its home base involving the tunnel. Eurotunnel's Europorte 2 was still on the table, and had now been granted a French open access licence. Plans by rail4chem, Germany's largest private freight operator, to operate from Mannheim and Dusseldorf to Dollands Moor from early 2005 did not materialise. But on 16th December, 2005, Fret SNCF announced that it was applying for a safety certificate to operate in Britain, using its nine virtually unused class '92's to take trains through to London. SNCF made plain the service would only begin if there were a satisfactory outcome on setting tunnel user charges.

With the CTRL nearing completion without severe overruns, the future prospects of LCR with its guaranteed flow of revenue from train access charges and its St Pancras and Stratford property portfolios began to interest financial markets. On 14th February, 2006 Alistair Darling told MPs that a consortium led by Sir Adrian Montague, the merchant banker who had advised the Government on the economics of Crossrail, had approached his department about a possible bid for the company. Under the rescue negotiated by John Prescott in 1998, 95 per cent of LCR's equity in Union Railways South, which built Phase 1, was converted into preference shares gaining 7 per cent in value each year but which shareholders - with Bechtel and the investment bank UBS the largest with 22.4 per cent each - could only redeem after the opening of Phase 2. The *Financial Times* reported that it was these preference shares that made LCR particularly attractive for a bidder.

Chapter Fifteen

The Future

With the Channel Tunnel now firmly established as a transport artery and traffic through it well established if still unspectacular, Eurotunnel's priority remains the operation of a safe and convenient system. Yet at the same time the tunnel's operating company, the railway companies that run services through it and other interests are constantly considering new services and projects to enhance the usefulness of the tunnel and impact on transport systems on both sides of the Channel.

The first and most spectacular of these is the possibility of a second Channel Tunnel to duplicate the original. Given the cost and time overruns arising from the construction of the first which nearly bankrupted Eurotunnel, one might have thought such a prospect far-fetched. Yet Eurotunnel was obliged to present a feasibility study for a second fixed link to the British and French Governments by the end of 1999 as a condition of its concession, and duly did so. As a company spokesman observed, 'In satisfying its contractual obligations Eurotunnel preserves an exclusive option to construct a second tunnel without any need to take a decision for some years yet'.

The study for a second tunnel was written into Eurotunnel's original contract for two reasons: the hope that within a decade or so capacity on the existing system would be exhausted, and the belief of Mrs Thatcher and, indeed, many other Britons that what was really needed was a drive-through tunnel obviating the need for shuttle trains. If the funds could be raised for a second tunnel and the project embarked upon without bringing Eurotunnel financially to its knees once again, either a road tunnel or a second rail tunnel would be a possibility, but there are question marks against both.

A drive-through tunnel would be enormously attractive to motorists and lorry drivers, but there are three big disadvantages: the difficulty of extracting exhaust fumes from a tunnel whose midway point would be almost 25 km from land, the risk of fire - far greater in free-moving traffic than in vehicles carried on trains - and driver boredom. Each of these may be surmountable, but nowhere else has a road tunnel of this length been contemplated. Eurotunnel's proposed road tunnel would be a double-deck affair running parallel to the rail tunnels, with one gigantic bore linked to a new service tunnel. In an emergency, passengers would use stairways to the other deck where buses would rescue them.

A second rail tunnel, for which Eurotunnel has also produced plans although none were required under the concession, is harder to justify on grounds of demand; until the present tunnels are booked to capacity, which the company does not expect to happen before 2025, who would use it? And could rail traffic alone, even including car and HGV shuttles, ever reach the level where a second rail tunnel would be economic? There are times, even now, when almost every train path through the tunnel is taken, but the timetable expert Barry Doe calculated in September 2003 that over the year 52 per cent of the paths available for traffic remain spare - and that was before Eurotunnel scaled back the number of HGV shuttles on economy grounds. Would any finance house back a project costing a good £10 billion and required only for through international freight trains, the least successful of the four services now being operated through the tunnel, and only at the very heaviest period of demand? The jury is likely to be out for some time, and Eurotunnel has until 2010 to take a final decision.

One project whose backers claim would transform the economics of the Channel Tunnel is Central Railway (CR), the much-publicised scheme for a primarily freight railway, electrified throughout and to TGV loading gauge, from the tunnel to the Midlands and North via the old Great Central route, which was built to Continental clearances but largely closed in the late 1960s and since lifted between Calvert, north of Aylesbury, and Leicester North. The original route proposed in the early 1990s would have run via Redhill and an upgraded West London line as far as Leicester with passenger stations at Croydon, Kensington, West Wycombe, Brackley, Woodford Halse, Rugby and Lutterworth and freight terminals in West London and on the M1/M6 near Lutterworth. This proposal generated immense opposition despite its laudable objective of taking entire lorryloads of freight off the motorway network, and Central Railway appeared a lost cause when in July 1996 MPs refused by 172 votes to 7 to order a public inquiry under the Transport And Works Act. The main reason for this decisive vote was anger in the Croydon area over planning blight caused by an ill-defined route. This was not the only section of the alignment to cause difficulty; on the approach to Cheriton where it would have paralleled both the traditional railway and the CTRL, Central Railway as then planned overlapped the formation marked out for the CTRL, running 15ft higher. The economics were also suspect; LCR's forecasters estimated that the line would only be viable, even on Central Railway's tight estimates of cost, if more traffic were generated than the entire capacity of the Channel Tunnel. Moreover, no Government financial support of any kind was envisaged.

After their defeat in 1996, Central Railway's promoters licked their wounds and regrouped. The scheme they came back with stretched not just from the tunnel to Leicester but from Lille to Liverpool, and instead of cutting through west London would skirt the capital parallel to the M25, tapping Heathrow and joining the Chiltern route near Denham, and like the original route crossing to the GC alignment by reconstructing the grade-separated Ashendon Junction, between Haddenham and Bicester. This route was better thought out, and seemed to answer the prayers of Railtrack, the Strategic Rail Authority and Transport for London for a way of getting freight traffic off increasingly congested passenger routes. Moreover, SNCF took an interest in Central Railway; in November 2000 Thierry Mignauw, a senior SNCF executive, joined the company's Board describing its dedicated lorries-on-trains concept as 'revolutionary'. It must also have been in his mind that Central Railway - unlike the CTRL and the lines connecting to it - offered clearances generous enough for full-scale TGVs to run through from France to the English regions.

Yet again, however, Central Railway ran into opposition: from residents of the Surrey commuter belt who find the M25 quite enough to tolerate and were concerned about CR's proposal for a seven-mile tunnel under the Downs in the Leatherhead area, and from Chiltern commuters worried that fitting in extra tracks beside their line would wipe out most of their station car parking spaces. By the autumn of 2000 Chiltern itself had proposed reopening of the Great Central from Calvert to Leicester to passenger traffic under its successful franchise renewal bid, and was assuring passengers and residents that it was in no way connected with the more ambitious Central Railway. The Government and the Strategic Rail Authority remained unconvinced of the business case for the line, Transport Minister John Spellar asking Central in 2002 for more detailed information before deciding whether to support a Hybrid Bill.

The response, when it came from Mr Spellar's successor Kim Howells on 25th March, 2004, was negative. Dr Howells told MPs that while CR could make a contibution to getting freight off the roads and onto rail, the promoters of the line had 'not substantiated the financing of the proposals'; the Government had concerns about operational effects on the existing rail network 'and on the capacity of the construction and financial markets, and the mitigation of the adverse financial impacts'. But Ministers' prime concern was that, despite CR's assurances, it might not raise the cash to build the line and that, having promoted the Bill, the Government 'could not escape intense pressure to intervene'. This produced a bitter reaction from CR's Chairman Andrew Gritten, who described the rejection of a scheme that had taken 14 years to work up and which he insisted was fully financed as 'unacceptable'. Central Railway vowed to fight on, but Mr Gritten's sudden death in December 2004 was a further body-blow to the project.

Central Railway's strength is also its greatest operational drawback: the jumbo loading gauge it needs to get lorries on board. This makes it a highly effective means of getting freight traffic off the roads, but equally makes it incompatible with any other British railway operation; the width of its passenger trains would be such as to prevent any domestic operator's rolling stock reaching the station platforms! Thus the network benefits it would offer would be limited. Nevertheless something like Central Railway may have a future - and if it does, a second rail-only Channel Tunnel might eventually prove necessary.

Late in 2000, however, Sir Alastair Morton, then Chairman of the SRA, made it plain that his preferred rail freight route round London involved a river crossing to the east - and intriguingly his view was mirrored in the launch of a rival project, Direct Route North, by a pressure group with unquantified backing early in 2001. This would be a 'new spinal rail system, with curves suited for high speed passenger trains, gradients suited to freight and clearances adequate for Continental sized rolling stock' running north from the Channel Tunnel, by way of a tunnel under the Thames east of London, then up the east side of Britain to central Scotland with branches towards Birmingham, Manchester and the North West and South Wales; cities would be avoided, and trains would instead serve 25 out-of-town 'Railports'. The project sounds like pie in the sky, particularly with so many other demands for an improved rail infrastructure, but the CTRL and proposed high-speed line to the North, originally proposed by Virgin in its bid for the East Coast franchise and subsequently taken up on a more westerly alignment by the SRA, could form elements of it.

Apart from sheer financial survival, the greatest challenge to Eurotunnel comes from ferries. The company had long imagined that if overcapacity and near-suicidal price-cutting on the cross-Channel ferry routes were abolished, most of its problems would disappear. However, the price-cutting has proved more damaging to the Tunnel than the ferries, and whenever the ferry operators have rationalised to create an 'orderly market', a newcomer with rock-bottom costs has appeared on the scene and driven prices even lower.

Eurotunnel thus needs to look elsewhere for its salvation. Recognising that its revenues will plunge when its Minimum Usage Charge - the UK and French Government guarantees of set levels of through rail traffic - expires late in 2006, the company has been exploring a 'lorries-on-trains' proposal of its own. The original idea was for longer shuttle journey than simply through the tunnel, though one that would only ease congestion within the UK on 18 km of the M20 between Cheriton and Ashford. The tunnel operator first envisaged turning the Sevington freight yard used in constructing first the tunnel and subsequently the CTRL into an intermodal terminal. HGV shuttle trains less generously proportioned than those now operating, and with a new generation of locomotives unless class '92s' could be harnessed, could then be run from a starting point well inside France - relieving congestion on the autoroutes - straight through to Sevington, where there is 45 hectares of space for a terminal; the lorries on board would transfer back to road. The loading gauge between Dollands Moor and Sevington would have to be raised at least to standard Continental clearances and the tracks probably set further apart, the main expense being the reboring of Saltwood tunnel; Eurotunnel missed the opportunity to have this work done in conjunction with construction of the CTRL, and the original target date of 2004 has been put back some years. This plan has considerable attractions for Eurotunnel, particularly as its terminals will be hard pressed to handle further increases in HGV shuttle traffic beyond the doubling of original capacity completed in 2003. But it alarmed EWS, which saw it as a direct threat to its own operations through the tunnel.

When the EU opened up rail freight markets in February 2003 Eurotunnel responded by applying to run trains between points in France and Britain, Eurotunnel Chief Executive Richard Shirrefs envisaged a high-frequency container shuttle initially linking Dourge yard at Lille with Daventry. The company claimed both that this was not a challenge to EWS and, just as surprisingly, that it could operate the service without Eurostar's surplus class '92' locomotives; one alternative considered was using Belgian crew and locomotives and starting from a Belgian transfer point to avoid the frequent railway strikes in France. By September 2003 Eurotunnel was envisaging in the longer-term a through service to Dagenham over the CTRL (despite its unsuitability for heavy freight) and eventually to Daventry should a Continental-gauge line be constructed alongside the West Coast Main Line. But Mr Shirrefs set the immediate goal of an intermodal service from the Continent to a new transhipment terminal within the Eurotunnel complex at Cheriton, to commence operations early in 2005; studies on the new infrastructure needed were completed in October 2003. Eurotunnel's aim was to increase the number of freight trains to 300 a week by the end of 2007; this compared with 100 in the spring of 2003 and 180 at the peak in 1998. As we have seen, the Europorte 2 plan, although it gained endorsement from both Governments, fell victim to the shareholders' coup at Eurotunnel. Yet of all the schemes on the drawing board, it must still have one of the best chances of coming to fruition.

The expansion of direct rail freight through the tunnel to something like the levels forecast before its opening remains the fervent wish of all involved, but while the crisis over asylum seekers has been overcome, too many problems remain for a clear and lasting upward trend to be predicted with any confidence. EWS has struggled to make its international services competitive to shippers, and the concessions granted to British hauliers after the fuel protests of September 2000 which paralysed the country, coupled with a further increase in the maximum HGV axle load, have made the challenge for rail even tougher. Dover Harbour Board was both reflecting shippers' frustrations and identifying a business opportunity when early in 2002 it floated the idea of resuming train ferry operation, using the ferry *Nord Pas de Calais*, which still has rails in its deck. Subsequently, Finesse, a consortium of ports and regional authorities in Britain, France and Belgium, backed by the European regional development Fund, started investigating the reintroduction of pilot services between Dover and a French and a Belgian port. A final report is due in December 2005, backed by a €500,000 EU grant for a feasibility study and two pilot schemes.

While EWS has overcome the worst of its own service delivery problems and the most bureaucratic UK customs clearance procedures have been eased, major problems with rail freight still remain on the Continent. For rail to take off as a serious trans-European competitor for road, bottlenecks at borders and locomotive changes born of habit rather than necessity still have to be tackled, and some Continental railways need to regard freight as a priority and their own services as part of a greater European whole. At the time of writing, it is too early to say whether the trans-European rail freight corridors pioneered by Neil Kinnock in the late 1990s will make enough of a difference. Shippers speak highly of the wagonload service between Wembley and Gremberg, in Germany, which began in December 1998 and which by special agreement runs through France and Belgium without intermediate marshalling, and there are high hopes for the freight corridor to Hungary. But one swallow does not make a summer.

With Eurotunnel's aspirations to operate through freight traffic from the Continent on hold, it has been left to EWS, Fret SNCF and potentially other operators to grow this business. The start of operations through the tunnel by the EWS subsidiary Euro Cargo Rail late in 2005 could turn out to have been the start of a revolution - or a damp squib.

The prospect for through rail passenger services is hopefully more promising, and certainly highly interesting, the motors being the impending completion of high-speed lines on both sides of the Channel. The opening of the TGV-Mediteranéé south from Valence to Marseille in June 2001 was followed the next year by a weekly Eurostar service as far as Avignon, its most popular destination beyond Paris. The opening of the Dutch and German high-speed lines for Thalys by 2005 has led Eurostar to consider operating some direct services from London beyond Brussels to Cologne, or more locally, Amsterdam – with chief executive Richard Brown seeing eight million passengers to this latter destination on a 3 hr 30 min. timing as 'up for grabs' once the CTRL and the high-speed line between Antwerp and Amsterdam are completed.

With this in mind, Eurostar in the summer of 2004 opened negotiations with the High Speed Alliance, a consortium of KLM and NS, which will be responsible for passenger servics on the new Brussels-Amsterdam high speed line which is due to open at the same time as Phase 2 of the CTRL. SNCB, incidentally, discovered in the summer of 2003 that it had miscalculated how long the Brussels-Amsterdam journey would take. The Belgian operator upped its estimate from 93 minutes to 110; after a bitter reaction from the Dutch Government this was nudged down to 108 minutes, with the promise of a four minute reduction later on, but the Belgians will forfeit the previously-agreed €148 million annual user charge the High Speed Alliance had agreed to pay until the 93 minute timing is met. This made Eurostar's hopes for a 3 hours 30 minutes headline time from St Pancras to Amsterdam unrealistic; with even only a five minute station stop at Brussels, Eurostars will be lucky to do the trip in much under 3 hours 50 minutes, though this is still pretty attractive. In the euphoria of Eurostar's shattering of the UK rail speed record in July 2003, Frankfurt and even Strasbourg were mooted as potential Eurostar destinations; we shall see. Better journey times could equally be achieved by better connections with Thalys at Brussels and promotion of Eurostar and Thalys as an integrated service, which SNCF for reasons of its own has steadfastly resisted. There remains a pressing need for interavailability of tickets between Eurostar and Thalys, but it will probably take Eurostar operations into Amsterdam to achieve this. Eurostar's agreement on connections and through ticketing with Thalys and DB from April 2005 was a step in the right direction.

Eurostar is cautious about any expansion of its services after having its fingers burned so badly over the abandoned Nightstar and North of London services. Moreover, current Eurostar stock would require costly conversion for it to operate beyond the SNCF and SNCB networks. It is possible that the idea of operating locomotive-hauled services will resurface, though special rolling stock would be needed for operation through the tunnel; there have been rumours that clearance for this route has been sought for the carriages of the Royal Train. For the longer term, there is the prospect of a successor train to the Eurostar. The company's Chief Executive Richard Brown has already speculated that the logical choice would be the TGV 'duplex' double-deck train, cheaper and less complex than the present stock as the trains will not be constrained by third-rail operation and the British loading gauge. But all these possibilities are some way off.

Completion of the CTRL, apart from making train travel from London to Paris and Brussels even more competitive, could create a fresh political head of steam, and even passenger demand, for through services extending beyond London. Given the economics of the issue which have now been heavily explored, the most likely possibility would seem occasional Eurostars starting off from Watford Junction (or even Birmingham) to connect with WCML services, bypassing St Pancras and stopping instead at Stratford. Indeed Watford Junction might be a better generator of traffic than the now-cancelled residual service from Waterloo. As mentioned in the context of Central Railway, there is also the possibility of TGVs from the French domestic high-speed network serving English destinations if a route with generous enough clearances ever were constructed. However, the blast of publicity surrounding Eurostar's 10th birthday heavily emphasised the greatly improved connectional times for the Midlands and North that the switch to St Pancras would offer. Specimen times quoted by Eurostar were Peterborough to Paris 3 hr 42 min., to Brussels 3 hr 20 min.; Grantham to Paris 3 hr 59 min., to Brussels 3 hr 37 min.; Leicester to Paris 4 hr 13 min., to Brussels 3 hr 41 min.; Ipswich to Paris 3 hr 44 min., to Brussels 3 hr 22 min.; York to Paris 4 hr 44 min, to Brussels 4 hr 22 min.; Sheffield to Paris 4 hr 58 min., to Brussels 4 hr 36 min.; Nottingham to Paris 4 hr 40 min., to Brussels 4 hr 18 min.. In every case (except Nottingham-Paris) the train would be quicker than a budget airline, and according to Eurostar cheaper in every case as well.

Finally, the tunnel could also play host to local services between towns in Kent and centres just across the Channel. Antoine Hurel, the head of Connex, told the author in 1997 that if his company were to order high-speed dual voltage stock for commuter services over the CTRL, these trains could be used outside peak hours to operate through the tunnel itself between, say, the Thanet towns or Canterbury and Lille. Nothing more has been heard of this idea – and not much of Connex which was stripped of its franchise in 2003 - and the economics of domestic train operation over the CTRL remain shaky, but it is a brave concept and one that could eventually come to fruition.

Other new generators of traffic could, however, emerge. Responding to John Prescott's proposal to site many of the 800,000 new homes needed in the South-East in Kent, Eurotunnel and Kent County Council proposed in April 2003 that more than 10,000 people, many of them commuters, move to the Calais area and commute through the tunnel. Sandy Bruce-Lockhart, leader of the county council, said that such a move, once the CTRL had brought Calais within an hour of London, would also 'encourage a flow of business people and tourists across the Channel by dramatically reducing fares'. Estate agents warned, however, that fully one-third of the Britons who bought second homes in northern France when the tunnel first opened had sold up when regular cross-Channel travel proved a strain.

Less exotic and eminently sensible, unless you are trying to attract business to airlines flying out of Heathrow, is Air France's suggestion that once the CTRL is complete, Eurostars instead of flights from London's airports could act as 'feeders' to the French flag carrier's long-haul services out of Charles de Gaulle. When in 2003 the British Government called for submissions for an aviation White Paper, Eurostar suggested that its capacity to run up to six trains an hour from London to Paris and Brussels would make short-haul flights on those routes unnecessary. It suggested that congestion at Heathrow, which had led to calls for controversial new runways there, could be eased by using Charles de Gaulle as a 'relief' London airport and using the existing rail infrastructure - and the tunnel - to operate Eurostar feeder services. Up to six trains a day could be operated direct from St Pancras to Charles de Gaulle, with passengers on the UK rail network being able to purchase joint rail and air tickets for flights to destinations not served from UK airports. Eurostar also held out the carrot of its fares being reduced if these services proved a success.

Proposals of this kind are at the margin, however, where operation of the Channel Tunnel itself is concerned. At the close of its first decade it has settled well into its role as a tried, tested and vital transport system; by early 2005, over 100 million car, coach and lorry users had passed through it and over 60 million had made the transit by Eurostar. Despite the cost overruns that very nearly drove Eurotunnel to the wall, one seldom hears anyone question the wisdom of constructing the tunnel; rather, they ask: 'How on earth did we manage without it?' HGV shuttle traffic has proved to be the backbone of the tunnel's business, even if Eurotunnel's expansion of shuttle capacity was followed by cutbacks in service. Tourist shuttle traffic has been a little slower to build than had been hoped, but here too the trend is generally upward. Eurostar, despite falling far short of its promoters' projections, has nevertheless expanded the cross-Channel travel market impressively and again looks set for steady expansion. And while through rail freight traffic has been frankly disappointing, in the long term the only way for it to go is up. So provided Eurotunnel can provide the capacity and continue to run its services with efficiency and safety, the future for the tunnel is bright.

Yet the Channel Tunnel is not just an increasingly indispensible strategic transport link; it is also, despite its mundane appearance to travellers using it, one of the wonders of the modern world. In 1999 the tunnel was named by a panel of American architects as the construction project of the 20th century, outranking the now-destroyed World Trade Centre in New York, the Panama Canal, San Francisco's Golden Gate Bridge, the Sydney Opera House and Hong Kong's Chek Lap Kok airport. That is both a fitting memorial to the men who perished during the hazardous task of constructing it, and a source of pride to everyone involved in bringing it successfully to fruition. As the tunnel plays an ever more vital part in the Europe of the 21st century, let us never take that achievement for granted.

Index